Explor

C000092054

Scottish Garde
open for charity

Contents

Sponsored by

⊕ Investec

Welcome

It's an enormous pleasure to introduce my first Scotland's Gardens Scheme Guidebook as Chairman of this great charity and I'd like to take the opportunity to thank everyone who makes our programme of charity open days happen each year.

Our wonderful Garden Openers and our network of District Teams who work so hard throughout the year – planning, promoting, paying charities, baking – and above all, gardening! And by sharing their gardens, time and enthusiasm so generously, bring such great enjoyment to so many throughout the year and raise vital funds for over 200 charities each year, including our core beneficiary charities, the Queen's Nursing Institute Scotland, Perennial and Maggie's.

We want to spread the word about open gardens so please, tell a friend about Scotland's Gardens Scheme and encourage them to come along to an open garden and share in this truly special experience – all while raising funds for charity.

Dougal Philip
Scotland's Gardens Scheme Chairman

If you've enjoyed an open garden, why not get involved yourself?
Donate – to Scotland's Gardens Scheme to support our work
Join in – get involved in your local District Team
Open your garden – we welcome gardens of all shapes, sizes and styles

Front cover image: Glassmount, Fife © Ray Cox
rcoxgardenphotos.co.uk

Back cover image: Broadwoodside © Jane Valentine

Artwork: Matt Armstrong – Serious Artworker, Daria Piskorz-Pronobis, Hazel Reid

Maps: Alan Palfreyman Graphics

Contains OS Data © Crown Copyright and Database 2022

Printed by Belmont Press
ISBN13: 9780901549389

MIX
Paper from responsible sources
FSC® C015185

Scotland's Gardens Scheme Head Office
2nd Floor, 23 Castle Street, Edinburgh EH2 3DN
T: 0131 226 3714   E: info@scotlandsgardens.org
W: scotlandsgardens.org

Charity no: SC049866

Staff:
Liz Stewart – Chief Executive
Daria Piskorz-Pronobis – Marketing Manager
Hazel Reid – Office Manager
Marianne Spence – Volunteer Support Officer

Read about our Trustees here:
scotlandsgardens.org/our-trustees/

Tips & key to symbols

Top tips

By Arrangement

This is a great way to see a garden when it's quiet and Garden Owners will be delighted to hear from you to book a visit. Many gardens welcome visits from larger groups or clubs such as horticultural societies, as well as individuals or couples. Do get in touch.

Photography

Most of our gardens are privately owned so any photographs taken must be for private use only. The Garden Owner's permission must be sought if images are to be included in publications. Our Volunteer Photographers may take photos on the open day. Please notify them if you don't wish to appear in our promotional materials.

Gardening Advice

Our Garden Openers love to chat about their gardens. If there's a bit of advice you're after, do ask!

Extra Assistance

Carers are offered free entry to our gardens and Assistance Dogs are always welcome.

Children & Families

Children are welcome with an accompanying adult, unless otherwise stated, but must be supervised at all times. Some openings offer children's activities – look for the children's activities symbol.

Group Visits

Many of our gardens are pleased to have groups visiting. Get in touch with the garden or contact the local District Organiser for more information.

Toilets

Private gardens do not normally have outside toilets. For security reasons, our Openers have been advised not to admit visitors into their homes.

Cancellations

All cancellations will be posted on our website, scotlandsgardens.org, under the garden listing.

Key to symbols

 Gardens open for the first time, or after a long break

 Dogs on leads welcome

 Full or partial wheelchair accessibility

 Locally grown plants for sale

 Children's activities, varying from quizzes, identification exercises to hands-on projects

 Snowdrops & Winter Walks

 Details of public transport access can be found either in the directions section or with a map navigation app

 Champion Trees, from the UK Tree Register

 National Plant Collection®, from Plant Heritage

 Gardens and Designed Landscapes by Historic Environment Scotland (links on our website)

 Basic teas

 Cream teas

 Homemade teas

Refreshments

Accommodation available at the garden; visit the garden website for details

Always check our website before setting out, for any cancellations, last-minute changes to opening details or booking arrangements.

Our impact

Scotland's Gardens Scheme exists to raise funds for a host of good causes and we are proud to have supported over 220 charities in 2022. However, the impact of what we do is so much more. Our roots are deep, our relationships are longstanding, and we are proud of our loyal and established community of garden openers and volunteers – across Scotland and across generations!

Grow

- Scotland's Gardens Scheme enables people to come together, share unique and memorable experiences and have a positive impact within and beyond their communities.
- People reap the benefits of spending time in nature and the wellbeing gained through connecting with others.

Give

- Together, we enable funds to be raised for many charities and causes, close to the hearts of our garden owners.

Inspire

- We are open to all, welcoming both seasoned gardeners and the next generation of gardeners, sharing good gardening practice and inspiration along the way.

We are also proud to support our three amazing core beneficiaries again in 2023 and the important work they do to support wellbeing.

In 2022

Nearly **500** gardens opened their gates – welcoming and inspiring visitors.

Over **1200** volunteers supported open days – sharing their time, skills and passion for gardens.

We estimate that over **70,000** people visited our gardens.

Over **220** charities, large and small, received funding through garden open days.

Garden Openers nominated causes

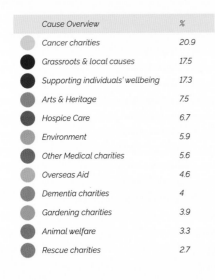

Cause Overview	%
Cancer charities	20.9
Grassroots & local causes	17.5
Supporting individuals' wellbeing	17.3
Arts & Heritage	7.5
Hospice Care	6.7
Environment	5.9
Other Medical charities	5.6
Overseas Aid	4.6
Dementia charities	4
Gardening charities	3.9
Animal welfare	3.3
Rescue charities	2.7

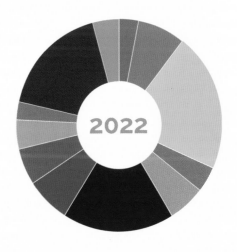

2022

First-time garden opener Tatyana Aplin in her garden at Broomhill Villa

Join in

Scotland's Gardens Scheme is powered by hundreds of volunteers and garden owners and there are plenty of opportunities to get involved and raise money for hundreds of charities each year.

Volunteer with us

We have wonderful District teams working together around the whole of Scotland to share gardens with visitors. Use your skills to help organise open days, source gardens and advise garden owners, bake and help with gardening in the run up to the big day; be a social media volunteer or share your photography skills. Best of all, you will meet lots of lovely, like-minded people as part of the Scotland's Gardens family.

Find out how you can get involved
scotlandsgardens.org/join-in/

Open your garden with Scotland's Gardens Scheme

We welcome gardens of all shapes, sizes and styles, from cottages to castles and urban to rural. Persuade your friends and neighbours to join in as a group or village or go it alone! If you have a garden that you'd like to share, we'd love to hear from you.

THE QUEEN'S NURSING INSTITUTE SCOTLAND

Scotland's Gardens Scheme was founded in 1931 to raise money for the Queen's Nursing Institute Scotland. The Institute has been generously supported by garden owners and visitors in Scotland's communities ever since.

Thank you.

Today, funding from Scotland's Gardens Scheme goes directly to supporting Scotland's community nurses so they can be agents for health improvement and catalysts for social change.

Together, we can drive positive action. Two charities working together to make Scotland's communities -

Healthier, Kinder, Fairer & Greener.

Email: office@qnis.org.uk

Web: www.qnis.org.uk

Phone: +44 (0)131 229 2333

Diana Macnab Award
for outstanding service

Once again, we are proud to make special mention of not one, but two Volunteers who are wonderful examples of what makes Scotland's Gardens Scheme such a special charity. Both have been nominated by their peers and we would like to take this opportunity to say thank you and celebrate their contribution as SGS stalwarts.

Julia Young, District Organiser, Fife

Julia has given many years of dedicated service to SGS both as a Garden Owner and as a District Organiser. Julia is an excellent plantswoman and brings that to the fore when co-ordinating the famous Fife Autumn Plant Sale, which she has organised for many years. She is a wonderful ambassador for the charity and is always so helpful and knowledgeable, and her immense enthusiasm and good humour is always infectious. She makes everyone feel very welcome, both to her lovely garden at South Flisk and also to the many garden open days she supports through the year.

Joan Johnson, District Organiser, East Lothian

Just over the water from Fife, is Joan Johnson, our District Organiser for East Lothian. During her tenure, Joan has made great improvements to the smooth running of SGS openings in East Lothian, such as streamlining the distribution of signs and posters around the county, working hard to encourage new gardens to open and to pilot creative combinations of garden opening arrangements. In addition to her work within the district, she has been a great support to the Head Office team, providing advice and support on a number of topics. She has also been a regular fixture in the office, helping to produce thousands of posters and fliers to promote gardens around the country.

Thank you to all our Scotland's Gardens Scheme Volunteers!

Find your way through cancer

Come to Maggie's

Maggie's offers the best possible psychological and emotional support for free to anyone with cancer and their families.

Built in the grounds of NHS hospitals, our centres are warm and welcoming places, with professional staff on hand to offer the support you need to find your way through cancer.

Our centres are open Monday to Friday, 9am – 5pm, and no referral is required. We are also online at maggies.org.

Maggie's centres across Scotland receive vital funds from every garden opening. Our heartfelt thanks go to everyone who supports Scotland's Gardens Scheme by opening their garden, volunteering or visiting a garden.

Scotland's
GARDENS
Scheme
OPEN FOR CHARITY

maggies.org

Maggie Keswick Jencks Cancer Caring Centres Trust (Maggie's) is a registered charity, no. SC024414

MAGGIE'S
Everyone's home of cancer care

Pass on your love of gardens
with a gift in your will

Leaving a gift to Scotland's Gardens Scheme will help us to continue to share the joy of garden visits into the future.

As a charity that receives no statutory financial support, we rely on visitors, volunteers and supporters like you to be able to carry out our annual programmes of garden openings. Your support will help us to keep sharing beautiful gardens and inspiring a love of gardens in future generations.

To find out more, call us on 0131 226 3714, email info@scotlandsgardens.org or visit scotlandsgardens.org/gift-in-will/

Scan for more information

Photo © David Blatchford

How Perennial Helps

Perennial is the UK's only charity helping people working with plants, trees, flowers and grass build and live better lives. But we can't provide our support without your help. There are lots of ways to get involved. To find out more visit **perennial.org.uk**.

"Our wellbeing benefits from gorgeous gardens. However, all of us working in horticulture need more than nature's support. Please spread the word that Perennial is here, helping those in need bloom again."

Carole Baxter,
Perennial Trustee and presenter of BBC Scotland Beechgrove TV programme.

How we helped Coleen*

A diagnosis of severe osteoporosis left Coleen, an employed gardener in Scotland, unable to work and with no idea how she was going to manage. Through the support and advice offered by her Perennial caseworker, Coleen received the help she needed with benefit claims, obtaining mobility aids to maintain independence, gaining confidence in computing and financial matters, and building a support network. By working with her caseworker, Coleen was able to find a manageable path to move forward.

"I appreciated your call last week and I feel you understood how difficult things are for me. You made me feel like I am not alone."

 Find out more
perennial.org.uk

 Helping people
in horticulture
Perennial

Our Ambassadors

We're delighted to welcome two new Ambassadors to Scotland's Gardens Scheme for 2023.

photo © Malcolm Ross

Brian Cunningham

Scotland's 'Ginger Gairdner' will be familiar to many screens around Scotland on *Beechgrove* and also well-kent as the Head Gardener of Scone Palace Gardens.

"I'm always leafing through the yellow book or keeping an eye on the website for gardens to visit and as a plantaholic myself, it's always good to meet the garden owners to share a bit of plant chat. We're also looking forward to hosting our own snowdrop open day at Scone Palace for Scotland's Gardens Scheme in February for the first time, so hope to meet lots of SGS visitors then."

The Schofield Family

Lizzie Schofield and her lovely family are opening their garden in Moray for the third time this year, having been crowned the *Gardeners' World* Magazine People's Choice winner in 2020. Lizzie also appears on *Beechgrove* and is a star on Instagram sharing her creative garden adventures @cuthbertsbrae_garden.

"It's a real privilege to be SGS Ambassadors! Our family love to open our garden each year. There is an eagerness and excitement leading up to the weekend that brings our friends and family together, everyone gets involved. Talking to people about gardening is one of my favourite things to do so having a whole weekend to talk and inspire people about coastal gardens is an opportunity I relish."

Be your own Ambassador for Scotland's Gardens Scheme – share your garden visits on social media, tag us and use the hashtag **#lovescotlandsgardens**

Find us and follow!

Facebook @scotlandsgardens
Twitter @scotgardens
Instagram @scotlandgardenscheme
YouTube @ScotlandsGardensScheme
TikTok @scotlandsgardens

At Queen Victoria Park
one's visitors always get a royal welcome.

Queen Victoria Park is an exclusive residential neighbourhood for the over 55s within a 100-acre garden paradise at Inchmarlo Retirement Village near Banchory in Aberdeenshire on Royal Deeside.

Queen Victoria Park is next to Inchmarlo Golf Centre and the River Dee, and comprises an active community of like-minded people with round-the-clock security and support services.

- 1 bed apartments with balconies from £79,500
- 2 bed apartments with balconies from £90,000

To find out more or to arrange viewings: please call Fenella Scott on 01330 824981 or email fenella.scott@inchmarlo-retirement.co.uk

INCHMARLO
RETIREMENT VILLAGE

Where Gracious Living
Comes Naturally

inchmarlo-retirement.co.uk

Discover how Queen Victoria Park might be just your type of place.

Exclusively yours...
for the day

Willowhill © Julianne Robertson

Did you know that we have hundreds of gardens that are open to visitors by arrangement with the garden owner? This is your chance to arrange an exclusive visit!

Benefits of arranging a visit

Flexibility – arrange a time to suit you and the garden owner and last-minute bookings are often available.

Privacy – see a garden away from the crowds.

Enjoy a guided tour or freedom to wander.

Small groups/couples or bigger groups welcome – just ask the owner or check the listing.

How to arrange your visit

Browse the guidebook or website and look for 'by arrangement' gardens in the opening details for each listing.

Contact the garden owner to arrange a time – contact details or booking links will be in the book/on the website listing.

Eas Mhor © Maurice Wilkins

Scan the code to find out more about 'by arrangement' visits.

Mozolowski & Murray
Garden Rooms

To find out more call us on

0345 050 5440

Visit our design centre
or request a brochure.

Mozolowski & Murray
Design Centre
57 Comiston Road Edinburgh EH10 6AG
Open 6 days, Monday to Saturday 10am to 4pm
with Saturday by appointment.
www.mozmurray.co.uk

Judges' Choice Award – **Maggie Wormald**, 2 Durnamuck, Little Loch Broom

2022 Photography Competition winners

Congratulations to our Photography Competition winners! Thank you to all participants, and the voting audience.

The Judges' verdict: "We were very impressed with the photographs submitted to the competition and it was hard to initially narrow the choice down to five. However, there was one photograph that stood out for all of us, and it was Maggie Wormald's shot of 2 Durnamuck. The picture caught our attention right away, it has mountains in the background and blue sky, grasses and colourful flowers. It is an archetypically Scottish Highland scene. If I had that border in that setting, I'd pat myself on the back. You can look at this picture for half an hour and still see interesting things. The composition is great, all elements add up to its beauty. We would like to congratulate all the contestants, it was a pleasure to review your photographs that were full of creativity, colour with wonderful stories behind."

Judges: Brian Cunningham, Scone Palace Head Gardener & SGS Ambassador; Lizzie Schofield, SGS Ambassador & Garden Owner; Richard Bath, Editor of *Scottish Field* Magazine.

Audience Award – **Sophie Blanchard**, Quoy of Houton, Orkney

The perfect gift for those who love all things Scottish

SCOTTISH FIELD

SCOTLAND'S QUALITY LIFESTYLE MAGAZINE

FREE

Subscribe to Scottish Field and save over 20% on the cover price, only £11.50 per quarter delivered direct to your door and receive a free bottle of Gin Bothy Gunshot, Original Gin or Raspberry Liqueur*.

Call **01778 392014** and quote **gdn2** or visit **scottishfield.co.uk/subscriptions**

Country news   Interiors   Field sports   Heritage   Gardens   Wildlife   Interviews   Whisky

Scottish Gardens
open for charity

Welcome to our gardens

We hope you have a fabulous season ahead exploring the gardens on the following pages.

Don't forget to:

- **Plan ahead**

  Things can change so do check the website for any cancellations, changes to timing or new garden openings being added.

- **Book a visit**

  Did you know that many gardens are open by arrangement? Contact the garden owner to plan a visit; just call or email using the contact details in the garden listing – they will be delighted to hear from you!

- **Share your visit**

  Tell a friend about Scotland's Gardens Scheme or share your pictures on social media and tag us **#lovescotlandsgardens**. Or why not complete our short visitor survey **scotlandsgardens.org/visitor-survey/**

Enjoy your visits and we look forward to seeing you in the garden.

Visit four Botanic Gardens to see one of the richest plant collections on Earth

Edinburgh
Arboretum Place and Inverleith Row,
Edinburgh EH3 5LR
Tel 0131 248 2909 | rbge.org.uk
Open every day from 10 am (except 1 January
and 25 December)
Garden entry is free

Logan
Port Logan, Stranraer,
Dumfries and Galloway DG9 9ND
Tel 01776 860231 | rbge.org.uk/logan
Open daily 1 March to 15 November
(open weekends in February)
Admission charge applies

Benmore
Dunoon, Argyll PA23 8QU
Tel 01369 706261 | rbge.org.uk/benmore
Open daily 1 March to 31 October
Admission charge applies

Dawyck
Stobo, Scottish Borders EH45 9JU
Tel 01721 760254 | rbge.org.uk/dawyck
Open daily 1 February to 30 November
Admission charge applies

Become a Friend and help us to explore, conserve
and explain the world of plants for a better future.
Call **07917 837821** or visit **rbge.org.uk/membership**

Royal
Botanic Garden
Edinburgh

Snowdrops & winter walks

Start the garden visiting season in style with a visit to a snowdrop garden. These gardens are listed below and full details can be found in the listing page and on our website.

For more places to visit as part of the Scottish Snowdrop Festival, visit **discoverscottishgardens.org**.

Aberdeenshire

· Bruckhills Croft
· Laundry Cottage

Angus and Dundee

· Kinblethmont House
· Lawton House

Dumfriesshire

· Craig

Dunbartonshire

· Stuckenduff

East Lothian

· Shepherd House

Fife

· Dunimarle Castle
· Lindores House
· Millfield Garden

Inverness, Ross, Cromarty & Skye

· Abriachan Garden Nursery
· Dunvegan Castle

Kincardine & Deeside

· Ecclesgreig Castle

Kirkcudbrightshire

· Barholm Castle
· Brooklands
· Danevale Park

Lanarkshire

· Cleghorn

Moray & Nairn

· 10 Pilmuir Road West

Peeblesshire & Tweeddale

· Garvald West Linton Gardens
· Kailzie Gardens
· Kirkton Manor House

Perth & Kinross

· Braco Castle
· Cloan
· Fingask Castle
· Princeland House
· Scone Palace Garden

Stirlingshire

· Gargunnock House Garden
· Kilbryde Castle
· Thorntree

Wigtownshire

· Craichlaw
· Logan Botanic Garden

RHS
Membership

Get closer to the world you *love*

BECOME AN RHS MEMBER TODAY

Your membership supports our work as a charity

rhs.org.uk/join

Plant sales & special events

Our District Teams proudly present a range of special events including bumper plant sales and family fun days. Keep an eye on our website for additional events and updated details through the season.

As well as our major SGS Plant Sales where you can stock up on locally grown goodies, we have a number of special events through the year. More details online or on the garden page. Sign up to the SGS e-newsletter on the website for further news.

Angus & Dundee
Ashbrook Nursery Tours (part of Letham Grange Gardens Open Day)
Letham Grange, DD11 4QA
10 June, 1 – 5pm

Angus Plant Sale
Logie Walled Garden, DD8 5PN
1 July, 2 – 5pm

Dunbartonshire
James Street Community Garden Plant Sale
Helensburgh, G84 8EY
2 September, 12 – 3pm

East Lothian
Winton Castle Open Day
Pencaitland, EH34 5AT
26 March, 12 – 4.30pm

Edinburgh, Midlothian & West Lothian
Redcroft Open Garden & Bumper Plant Sale
23 Murrayfield Road, Edinburgh EH12 6EP
13 & 14 May, 2 – 5pm

Fife
St Andrews Botanic Garden Spring Fair
St Andrews, KY16 8RT
8 April, 10am – 4pm

Cambo Spring Plant & Garden Market
Kingsbarns, KY16 8QD
15 April, 11am – 4pm

SGS Plant Sale at St Andrews Botanic Garden
St Andrews, KY16 8RT
8 October, 12 – 3pm

Kincardine & Deeside
Douneside Summer Fair
Tarland, AB34 4UD
9 July, 12 - 4pm

Kirkcudbrightshire
Threave Open Day
Castle Douglas DG7 1RX
1 May, 10 - 5pm

Peeblesshire & Tweeddale
Lamancha Community Hub Plant Sale
Lamancha, EH46 7BD
11 June, 10am – 1pm

Perthshire
Scone Palace Garden Fair*
Perth, PH2 6BD
2 & 3 June (see the garden's website for details)
*Event not organised by SGS but we will be attending.

Drummond Castle Open Day
Muthill, Crieff PH7 4HN
6 August, 1 - 5pm

Renfrewshire
Kilmacolm Plant Sale
Kilmacolm Library, PA13 4LE
22 April, 10 – 12noon

Mclaren's Nursery Tours
Uplawmoor, G78 4DN
Dates to be confirmed

Stirlingshire
Kilbryde Castle Plant Fair
Dunblane, FK15 9NF
4 June, 11am - 5pm

New gardens for 2023 NEW

Welcome to our new (and returning) gardens this year! We're delighted to share a wonderful collection of new gardens, all generously opening their garden gates for charity. Please do come along and show your support and appreciation.

Angus & Dundee: Braidestone Farm

Orkney: Kierfiold House

Peeblesshire & Tweeddale: Beechwood

Dumfriesshire: Arkleton Walled Garden
© Polly Armstrong-Wilson

Perth & Kinross: The Abercairny Garden

East Lothian: The Gardens at Archerfield Walled Garden

Moray & Nairn: Carestown Steading

Angus & Dundee: Kinblethmont House

Ayrshire: The Pines

Fife: Dunimarle Castle

Moray and Nairn: Glenernie © Robert Laing

Kincardine & Deeside: Hopewell

New gardens by district

Aberdeenshire

- Kemplemyres Farmhouse
- Westfield Lodge*

Angus & Dundee

- 6 Minto Place
- Braidestone Farm
- Inverbrothock School Sensory Garden and Forest Garden
- Kinblethmont House

Argyll & Lochaber

- Baravalla Garden

Ayrshire & Arran

- Burnhouse
- Dalhowan Farm
- The Pines

Berwickshire

- The Moorhouse

Caithness, Sutherland, Orkney & Shetland

- 11 Lyron
- 16 Mulla
- 19 Burnside
- Annie's Place
- Castlehill B&B
- Finya
- Kierfiold House
- Linfirlea
- Round House
- Westlea

Dumfriesshire

- Arkleton Walled Garden (Trio of Langholm Gardens)
- Tinnisburn

Dunbartonshire

- Stuckenduff*

Returning after a break of over five years

East Lothian

- Bowerhouse*
- Papple Steading
- The Gardens at Archerfield Walled Garden
- West Bank

Edinburgh, Midlothian & West Lothian

- Falcon Bowling & Tennis Club
- Maggie's Edinburgh
- Suntrap Garden*

Fife

- 20 Brucehaven Crescent
- Dunimarle Castle
- Harthill
- Kenlygreen House*
- Swallows Rest
- The Garden with the Dragon

Kincardine & Deeside

- Arbuthnott House Gardens
- Hopewell

Moray and Nairn

- Carestown Steading*
- Easter Laggan
- Glenernie

Peeblesshire & Tweeddale

- Beechwood
- Garvald West Linton Gardens

Perth & Kinross

- 7 Craigend Cottages
- Scone Palace Garden*
- The Abercairny Garden*

Renfrewshire

- The Bishop's House

Roxburghshire

- Larch House
- Old Coach House

Groups & villages

Group and village open days are amongst our most popular events, giving visitors the chance to explore gardens great and small, of all different styles, all on the same day.

Aberdeenshire

- Two Gardens in Banchory Devenick (New)

Angus & Dundee

- Braidestone Farm and The Doocot (New)
- Brechin Gardens in Summer
- Edzell Village Gardens (New)
- Letham Grange Gardens & Ashbrook Nursery Tours (New)
- Montrose Gardens
- Westgate & Windyridge

Argyll & Lochaber

- Ardverikie with Aberarder

Berwickshire

- Duns Open Gardens

Dumfriesshire

- Craigieburn House with Waterside Garden
- Dalswinton House with Gardens Cottage (NEW)
- Langholm Gardens Day Trail (New)

Dunbartonshire

- 18 Duchess Park with Westburn

East Lothian

- Eastfield and Redcliff Gardens
- Gifford Village & Broadwoodside
- Tyninghame House and The Walled Garden

Edinburgh

- Dean Gardens
- Eskbank Village Gardens
- Moray Place and Bank Gardens
- Stockbridge Gardens

Fife

- Crail: Gardens in the Burgh
- Kincardine's Gardens – Great and Small (New)
- Newburgh – Hidden Gardens

Glasgow & District

- Kilsyth Gardens
- The Gardens of Milton of Campsie

Inverness, Ross, Cromarty & Skye

- Kiltarlity Gardens

Lanarkshire

- Biggar Open Gardens

Moray & Nairn

- A Trio of Gardens near Rafford (New)

Peeblesshire & Tweeddale

- Gattonside Village Gardens
- Macbiehill Gardens (New)
- West Linton Village Gardens

Perth & Kinross

- Muckhart Open Gardens

Stirlingshire

- Bridge of Allan Gardens
- Dunblane Gardens
- Killearn Village Gardens (New)

Our districts

SHETLAND

ORKNEY

North of Scotland
& Islands

CAITHNESS,
SUTHERLAND,

INVERNESS, ROSS,
& CROMARTY

SKYE

MORAY
& NAIRN

ABERDEENSHIRE

KINCARDINE
& DEESIDE

East of
Scotland

ARGYLL & LOCHABER

ANGUS & DUNDEE

PERTH
& KINROSS

STIRLINGSHIRE

FIFE

West & Central
Scotland

DUNBARTONSHIRE

GLASGOW
& DISTRICT

EAST
LOTHIAN

South East
Scotland

RENFREWSHIRE

EDINBURGH, MIDLOTHIAN
& WEST LOTHIAN

BERWICKSHIRE

ARRAN

AYRSHIRE &

LANARKSHIRE

PEEBLESSHIRE
& TWEEDDALE

ROXBURGHSHIRE

KIRKCUDBRIGHTSHIRE

DUMFRIESSHIRE

WIGTOWNSHIRE

South West Scotland

Map by **The Port Creative**

Aberdeenshire

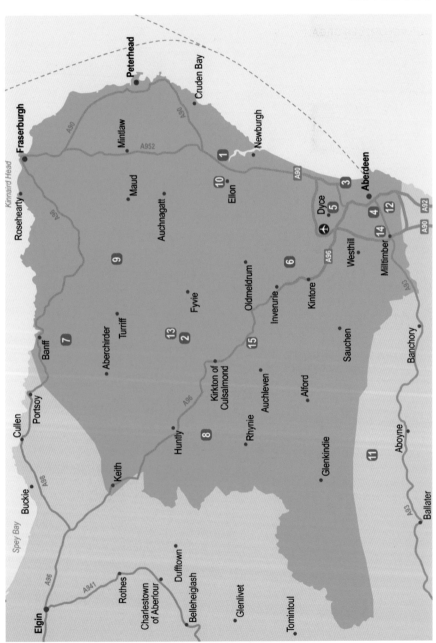

Aberdeenshire

OUR VOLUNTEER ORGANISERS

District Organisers:	Verity Walters	Tillychetly, Alford AB33 8HQ E: info@scotlandsgardens.org
Area Organisers:	Gill Cook	
	Anne Fettes	
	Jennie Gibson	6 The Chanonry, Old Aberdeen AB24 1RP
	Denise Jones	Smiddy House, Glenkindie, Alford AB33 8SS
	Anne Lawson	Asloun, Alford AB33 8NR
	Helen Rushton	Bruckhills Croft, Rothienorman, Inverurie AB51 8YB
	Madeleine Fraser	
District Photographer:	Andy Leonard	Parkvilla, 47 Schoolhill, Ellon AB41 9AJ
Treasurer:	Ann Doyle	South Cottage, Fisherford, Inverurie AB51 8YS

GARDENS OPEN ON A SPECIFIC DATE

Auchmacoy, Ellon	Sunday, 9 April
Westhall Castle, Oyne, Inverurie	Sunday, 16 April
Two Gardens in Banchory Devenick, Aberdeen	Fri/Sat/Sun, 9/10/11 June
Heatherwick Farm, Kintore, Inverurie	Sunday, 25 June
Bruckhills Croft, Rothienorman, Inverurie	Sunday, 2 July
Parkvilla, 47 Schoolhill, Ellon	Saturday/Sunday, 8/9 July
Garden House, 5 Woodlands Gardens, Cults, Aberdeen	Sunday, 9 July
Two Gardens in Banchory Devenick, Aberdeen	Fri/Sat/Sun, 21/22/23 July
Tarland Community Garden, Tarland, Aboyne	Saturday, 12 August

GARDENS OPEN BY ARRANGEMENT – BOOK A VISIT WITH THE GARDEN OWNER

Laundry Cottage, Culdrain, Gartly, Huntly	1 January - 31 December
Bruckhills Croft, Rothienorman, Inverurie	25 January - 11 March
Chaplains' Court, 20 The Chanonry, Old Aberdeen, Aberdeen	1 March - 30 September
Grandhome, Danestone, Aberdeen	1 April - 31 October
Upper Third Croft, Rothienorman, Inverurie	1 June - 31 August
Middle Cairncake, Cuminestown, Turriff	1 June - 31 August
Two Gardens in Banchory Devenick, Aberdeen	1 June - 31 July
Westfield Lodge, Contlaw Road, Milltimber, Aberdeen	26 June - 23 July
Kemplemyres Farmhouse, Alvah, Banff	1 - 3, 8 - 10, 15 - 17, 22 - 24 & 29 - 31 July

Aberdeenshire

1 AUCHMACOY
Ellon AB41 8RB
Mr and Mrs Charles Buchan
E: sharon@buchan.co.uk

Auchmacoy House's attractive policies feature spectacular displays of thousands of daffodils.

Open: Sunday 9 April, 1pm - 4pm, admission £4.00, children free. Please, NO dogs.

Directions: A90 from Aberdeen. Turn right to Auchmacoy/Collieston.

Opening for: The Royal British Legion: Ellon Branch

2 BRUCKHILLS CROFT
Rothienorman, Inverurie AB51 8YB
Paul and Helen Rushton
T: 01651 821596 E: helenrushton1@aol.com

An informal country cottage garden extending to three-quarters of an acre with a further acre as wildflower meadow and pond. There are several distinct areas which include a white border, a butterfly alley, kitchen garden with polytunnel, greenhouse and fruit cage, an orchard, and a blue and yellow border. Relax on one of the many seats in the garden and soak up the atmosphere. Awarded National Collection status for *Galanthus* (snowdrops) in 2021. National Plant Collection: *Galanthus.*

Open: by arrangement 25 January - 11 March for Snowdrops and Winter Walks. Also open Sunday 2 July, noon - 5pm. Admission £5.00, children free.

Directions: From Rothienorman take the B9001 north for two-and-a-half miles. On the S-bend turn left. Take the second left (*Bruckhills* sign). At the farmyard turn sharp right (opposite farmhouse), and the croft is at the end of the lane.

Opening for: Befriend A Child Ltd & SGS Beneficiaries

3 CHAPLAINS' COURT
20 The Chanonry, Old Aberdeen, Aberdeen AB24 1RQ
Irene Wischik
T: 01224 491675 E: irene@wischik.com

This historic walled garden has a long, well-stocked herbaceous border offering a succession of vivid colour from early spring to winter. It is divided by an ornamental pergola, a perfect place to sit and enjoy the garden. Large trees of ash, beech, horse chestnut, oak and sycamore give this garden a mature feel. A specimen Camperdown elm sits in the centre of the lawn, which in spring is covered in a carpet of crocuses, snowdrops and *Scilla*. Vegetables and herbs produce plentiful crops, together with newly planted espalier and fan-trained apple and pear trees.

Open: by arrangement 1 March - 30 September, admission £5.00, children free.

Directions: Bus 1 or 2 from Aberdeen city centre to St Machar Drive, and head towards St Machar Cathedral. Or drive down St Machar Drive, turn into The Chanonry and drive down until the junction with Don Street.

Opening for: SSAFA Forces Help

Aberdeenshire

 4 GARDEN HOUSE
5 Woodlands Gardens, Cults, Aberdeen AB15 9DU
Keith Thornton

A two-thirds of an acre plot planted out in 2008 and specialising in more unusual trees and shrubs. The collection of magnolia trees has reached flowering size, and includes *Sprengeri* 'Diva', *Sargentiana* 'Star Wars' and *Michelia doltsopa*. The rhododendron borders include early flowers, scented species and scented azaleas. Old roses feature with a collection of scented heritage French varieties, including *centifolia de peintre*, 'cabbage' roses and Pemberton musk roses. There is a small orchard of apple, pear and plum trees, and a large outdoor peach in the courtyard garden. Soft fruit and vegetable plots are laid out.

Open: Sunday 9 July, noon - 5pm, admission £5.00, children free.

Directions: From the A90, take Milltimber junction A93 to Cults. At lights turn left up Kirk Brae, then right to Friarsfield Road. At top of hill, turn right into Woodlands housing estate, first left then first left again into Woodlands Gardens. From the A92 take the A93 to Braemar, after 200m turn right to Craigton Road, follow this for one mile, then Woodlands estate is on the left. The nearest bus stop is *Baird's Brae* on routes 19 or 201, then about 18-minute walk.

Opening for: Scottish SPCA, The New Arc & Annie's Trust

 5 GRANDHOME
Danestone, Aberdeen AB22 8AR
Mrs WJB Paton
T: 01224 722202 E: admin@grandhome.co.uk

Eighteenth-century walled garden incorporating a rose garden and policies with daffodils, tulips, rhododendrons, azaleas, mature trees and shrubs.

Open: by arrangement 1 April - 31 October, admission £5.00, children free. Please, no dogs.

Directions: From the north end of North Anderson Drive, continue on the A90 over Persley Bridge, turning left at the Tesco roundabout. After one-and-three-quarter miles, turn left through the pillars on a left-hand bend.

Opening for: SGS and Beneficiaries

Chaplains' Court

Aberdeenshire

 6 HEATHERWICK FARM
Kintore, Inverurie AB51 0UQ
Lucy Narducci

Come and enjoy a wander round the spacious lawns which connect the various areas of the garden. Densely planted perennial borders dominate in the front, while a more evergreen, winter-friendly area occupies the back for viewing from the kitchen windows. Explore the busy herb and vegetable garden, designed to be pretty as well as productive; the new apple orchard; and lastly, take in the farmland views, along with some peace and serenity while you stroll the paths of the wild paddock. With its open nature and many seats, the garden is accessible to all.

Open: Sunday 25 June, 1pm - 5pm, admission £5.00, children free.

Directions: Please use postcode AB51 0RQ for SatNav and the location as per the map on Scotland's Gardens Scheme's webpage. From Inverurie centre, take the B9001 southwards. At the corner of St Mary's Place and St James's Place follow signs for *Keithhall*. Then follow signs for *Balbithan*. Heatherwick is signposted and on the left after Hogholm Stables. It is three miles from the centre of Inverurie.

Opening for: Myeloma UK

 7 KEMPLEMYRES FARMHOUSE
Alvah, Banff AB45 3UR
Jane Duffield
T: 07778 083759 E: janeduffield@hotmail.co.uk

A large wildlife garden, still in the making. Starting from a completely blank canvas 15 years ago, we wanted the garden to blend sympathetically in to the wider, natural landscape. We're constantly learning how to garden creatively, in order to live harmoniously alongside the visiting deer and badgers! Areas of interest include a rose garden, stone circle garden, dell garden, two wildlife ponds, mixed shrub beds and our current project, a small walled kitchen garden.

Open: by arrangement, Saturdays, Sundays and Mondays in July, admission £5.00, children free.

Directions: From Turriff, take the B9025, signposted to *Aberchirder*. Approximately five miles out of Turriff, turn right, on to the B9121, signposted *Banff* and *Whitehills*. After approximately two miles, take the right hand turn, signposted *Alvah*. The road passes farm buildings on your left. Just past these, at the bottom of the hill, take the left hand turn, signposted *Kirktown of Alvah*. The road dips down to a small bridge over a burn, with a short, steep climb up the other side. Our drive is on the right-hand side, by the big beech tree, with double wooden gates, signposted *Kemplemyres Farmhouse and the Bothy*.

Opening for: Parkinsons UK

Aberdeenshire

8 LAUNDRY COTTAGE

Culdrain, Gartly, Huntly AB54 4PY
Judith McPhun
T: 01466 720768 E: judithmcphun@icloud.com

An informal cottage-style garden of about one and a half acres by the River Bogie. Two contrasting steep slopes make up the wilder parts. The more intensively gardened area around the cottage includes a wide variety of herbaceous plants, shrubs and trees, an orchard area and fruit and vegetable plots, making a garden of year-round interest.

Open: by arrangement 1 January - 31 December, admission £5.00, children free. Snowdrops during February and March.

Directions: Four miles south of Huntly on the A97.

Opening for: Amnesty International UK Section Charitable Trust

Laundry Cottage © Andy Leonard

9 MIDDLE CAIRNCAKE

Cuminestown, Turriff AB53 5YS
Nick and Penny Orpwood
T: 01888 544432 E: orpwood@hotmail.com

The garden at Middle Cairncake is a good example of what can be achieved using ordinary and everyday plants; many visitors have returned to tell us that they felt inspired to try ideas in their own gardens. The garden is traditionally planned and is now, with small changes, becoming easier to manage without compromising our high standards of sustainability and self-sufficiency. We offer visitors an enjoyable tour showing a productive kitchen garden, roses, herbaceous annuals and perennials. Visitors can end their visit with a homemade tea in our winter garden. Group visits are welcome.

Open: by arrangement 1 June - 31 August, admission £5.00, children free. Homemade teas £5.00 for SGS and Parkinsons UK.

Directions: Middle Cairncake is on the A9170 between New Deer and Cuminestown. It is clearly signposted.

Opening for: Parkinsons UK

Aberdeenshire

10 PARKVILLA

47 Schoolhill, Ellon AB41 9AJ
Andy and Kim Leonard
T: 07786 748296 E: andy.leonard@btinternet.com

A south-facing Victorian walled garden, lovingly developed from a design started in 1990 to give colour and interest all year. Enjoy densely planted herbaceous borders, pause under the pergola clothed in clematis, honeysuckle and rambling roses, continue on to the bottom of the garden where three ponds and wildflower beds reflect a strong focus on wildlife. This is a hidden gem of a garden that has won awards including *Ellon Best Garden* and with plants rarely seen in north-east Scotland.

Open: Saturday/Sunday, 8/9 July, 2pm - 5pm, admission £5.00, children free. Please, NO dogs.

Directions: From centre of Ellon head north towards Auchnagatt. Schoolhill is third left. From Auchnagatt head into Ellon along Golf Road, Schoolhill is first right after the golf course. Limited on-street parking, car parks in Ellon (five minutes walk) and Caroline's Well Wood. Public toilets in Ellon town centre.

Opening for: St Mary On The Rock Episcopal Church Ellon, Alzheimer Scotland & Ellon Men's Shed

Parkvilla © Andy Leonard

Aberdeenshire

11 **TARLAND COMMUNITY GARDEN**
Tarland, Aboyne AB34 4ZQ
The Gardeners of Tarland

Tarland Community Garden opened in 2013 and is a Tarland Development Group project. It provides an inclusive and accessible community growing space for local residents. It has indoor (polytunnel) and outdoor raised beds for rent, plus communal planting areas including a soft fruit cage, fruit trees and a herb garden. It is a place for members to grow produce, learn, share and have fun.

Open: Saturday 12 August, noon - 4pm, admission £3.00, children free.

Directions: Take the B9094 from Aboyne or the A96 and B9119 from Aberdeen. Arriving at the village square the gardens will be clearly signposted.

Opening for: Tarland Development Group

Tarland Community Garden

Aberdeenshire

12 TWO GARDENS IN BANCHORY DEVENICK

Banchory Devenick AB12 5XR
Angela and Derek Townsley & Jane and Terry O'Kelly
T: text 07712 528450 E: janeokelly868@gmail.com

Pinetrees Cottage Banchory Devenick AB12 5XR (Angela and Derek Townsley): A mature garden set in three-quarters of an acre, filled with a wide range of hardy plants including rhododendrons, azaleas, acers, topiary and roses, with two ponds. An alpine house is fronted by stone troughs filled with rock plants. Set in a backdrop of mature pine trees to the north and open fields to the south. **Whin Cottage (NEW)** Ardoe, Aberdeen AB12 5XT (Jane and Terry O'Kelly): A cottage garden of just under half an acre surrounded by farmland. It features a border of rhododendrons and azaleas, several mixed borders, two formal rose beds, a wildlife pond and four raised beds growing a variety of vegetables and flowers for the house. The garden reflects a love of colour and structure and an interest in wildlife.

Open: Friday/Saturday/Sunday, 9/10/11 June, 2pm - 5pm. Also open Friday/Saturday/Sunday, 21/22/23 July, 2pm - 5pm. And open by arrangement 1 June - 31 July. Admission £6.00, children free. Plants for sale at Pinetrees Cottage.

Directions: Banchory Devenick is four miles from the Bridge of Dee. **Whin Cottage:** Take the B9077 out of Aberdeen. After approximately three miles turn left immediately after Banchory Devenick Church, signposted *Banchory Devenick*. Turn right after 100 metres and Whin Cottage is on the right immediately after you have turned. **Pinetrees Cottage:** do not turn right to Whin Cottage but continue up the hill to the T-junction and turn right. Next right is Butterywells Steading. Turn into opening and follow track, go around the back of farmhouse (Lochend) and continue on the track to Pinetrees Cottage. Parking: There is limited parking outside Whin Cottage but parking is available on the verge just before the turning to the cottage. More parking is available at Pinetrees Cottage and it would be possible to walk back down to Whin Cottage.

Opening for: Fighting For Sight Aberdeen

13 UPPER THIRD CROFT

Rothienorman, Inverurie AB51 8XY
Lois Thompson and Dr. John W. Graham
T: 01464 871032 or 07765 501775 E: upperthirdgardens@gmail.com

An unusual combination of working croft and plantsman's garden. The garden extends to over half an acre, complementing the croft, home to the prize-winning Shieling flock of Shetland sheep. The L-shaped garden is divided in three, giving a sense of intimacy, each section with its own character. There is an interesting mix of herbaceous plants, shrubs and trees, many grown from seed including *Glaucidium*, *Trillium*, *Paeonia suffruticosa* cultivars, *Prunus serrula*, and *Pterostyrax*. Vintage earthenware troughs contain some unusual and choice alpines. Three small areas of grass with fritillaria, camassia, narcissus and primula are left unmown until late season. The steading, once the local smiddy (the original cartwheel stone may still be seen by the entrance), forms one wall of a drystane 'sitooterie'. A small polytunnel, greenhouses, raised vegetable beds and new kailyard provide food for the house; several hives of bees are kept for interest and pollination.

Open: by arrangement 1 June - 31 August, admission £5.00. Unfortunately the garden is not suitable for dogs, children or wheelchairs. Maximum group size – ten.

Directions: Take the B9001 north through Rothienorman towards Largue. Approximately three miles from Rothienorman turn up left signposted *Logie Newton*, *Fisherford* and *Wells of Ythan*. The croft entrance is the second farm entrance on the left (sign on field gate), half a mile from the junction. Follow the farm track round to park at the garden entrance.

Opening for: Mrs Murray Home For Stray Dogs & Cats

Aberdeenshire

Two Gardens in Banchory Devenick – Whin Cottage

14 **WESTFIELD LODGE**
Contlaw Road, Milltimber, Aberdeen AB13 0EX
Mr and Mrs L. Kinch
E: jamesfraser@kinchmail.com

The gardens at Westfield were first laid out formally in the 1990s and gradually improved and reworked since that date. Since then they have been undergoing some great changes around the garden and estate. We are looking forward to welcoming groups to enjoy a guided walk around the garden, followed by tea/coffee and cake.

Open: by arrangement 26 June - 23 July, admission £5.00, children free. Groups welcome from 10 am to 4pm.

Directions: On North Deeside Road (A93), at Milltimber turn into Contlaw Road. Continue about one mile; turn right into single track road signposted Westfield. From A944 turn off at Mason Lodge on to B979, straight over Carnie Crossroads, turn second left signposted *Contlaw*, take first left and follow road for almost one mile. Westfield turning is on the left.

Opening for: CLAN

15 **WESTHALL CASTLE**
Oyne, Inverurie AB52 6RW
Mr Gavin Farquhar
T: 01224 214301 E: enquiries@ecclesgreig.com

Set in an ancient landscape in the foothills of the impressive and foreboding hill of Bennachie, is a circular walk through glorious daffodils with outstanding views. This interesting garden is in the early stages of restoration, with large groupings of rhododendrons and specimen trees. Westhall Castle is a 16th-century tower house, incorporating a 13th-century building of the bishops of Aberdeen. There were additions in the 17th, 18th and 19th centuries. The castle is semi-derelict, but stabilised from total dereliction. A fascinating house encompassing 600 years of alteration and additions.

Open: Sunday 16 April, 1pm - 4pm, admission £5.00, children free.

Directions: Marked from the A96 at Old Rayne and from Oyne Village.

Opening for: 1st Insch Scout Group

Angus & Dundee

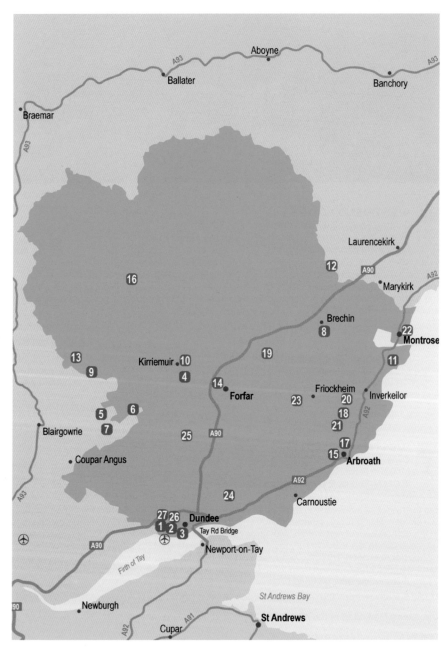

Angus & Dundee

OUR VOLUNTEER ORGANISERS

District Organisers:	Debbie Butler	Top Croft, Arniefoul, Angus DD8 1UD
	Frances Dent	12 Glamis Drive, Dundee DD2 1QL
		E: info@scotlandsgardens.org
Area Organisers:	Pippa Clegg	Easter Derry, Kilry, Blairgowrie PH11 8JA
	Moira Coleman	Templeton House, Arbroath DD11 4QP
	Jan Crow	Lower Duncraig, 2 Castle Street, Brechin DD9 6JN
	Terrill Dobson	Logie House, Kirriemuir DD8 5PN
	Frances Shepherd	Windyridge, 10 Glamis Drive DD2 1QL
	Claire Tinsley	Ethie Mains, Inverkeilor DD11 5SN
Treasurer:	James Welsh	Dalfruin, Kirktonhill Road, Kirriemuir DD8 4HU

GARDENS OPEN ON A SPECIFIC DATE

Kinblethmont House, by Arbroath, Angus	Saturday/Sunday, 25/26 February
Lawton House, Inverkeilor, by Arbroath	Thursday - Saturday 9/10/11/12 March
10 Menzieshill Road, Dundee	Saturday/Sunday, 15/16 April
17a Menzieshill Road, Dundee	Saturday/Sunday, 22/23 April
Forfar Open Garden, 36 Lochside Road, Forfar	Sunday, 23 April
17a Menzieshill Road, Dundee	Saturday/Sunday, 6/7 May
Kirkton Cottage, Aberlemno	Sunday, 7 May
10 Menzieshill Road, Dundee	Saturday/Sunday, 13/14 May
Dalfruin, Kirktonhill Road, Kirriemuir	Sunday, 14 May
Braidestone Farm, Meigle, Blairgowrie	Sunday, 21 May
Westgate and Windyridge, 10 & 12 Glamis Drive, Dundee	Saturday/Sunday, 27/28 May
Forfar Open Garden, 36 Lochside Road, Forfar	Sunday, 28 May
6 Minto Place, Dundee	Saturday/Sunday, 3/4 June
Letham Grange Gardens & Ashbrook Nursery Tours, Letham Grange	Saturday, 10 June
Inverbrothock School Sensory Garden and Forest Garden, Arbroath	Sunday, 11 June
Estir Bogside, Alyth	Saturday, 17 June
St Bride's Cottage, South Kingennie, Broughty Ferry	Saturday/Sunday, 17/18 June
Cotton of Craig, Kilry, Blairgowrie	Saturday, 17 June
Brechin Gardens in Summer, Locations across Brechin	Sunday, 18 June
Kirkton Cottage, Aberlemno	Saturday, 24 June
Braidestone Farm and The Doocot, by Meigle	Sunday, 25 June
Angus Plant Sale, Logie Walled Garden, Kirriemuir	Saturday, 1 July
Hospitalfield Gardens, Hospitalfield House, Westway, Arbroath	Saturday, 8 July
Dunninald Castle, Montrose	Sunday, 9 July
Montrose Gardens, Locations across Montrose	Saturday/Sunday, 15/16 July
Kirkton Cottage, Aberlemno	Saturday, 29 July
Edzell Village Gardens, Edzell	Sunday, 30 July
Torwood, Milton of Ogilvie, Glenogilvy, Glamis by Forfar	Saturday/Sunday, 5/6 August
Westgate, 12 Glamis Drive, Dundee	Saturday/Sunday, 21/22 October

Angus & Dundee

GARDENS OPEN REGULARLY

Inchmill Cottage, Glenprosen, near Kirriemuir — Thursday, 20 April, 18 May, 15 June, 20 July, 17 August and 21 September

Pitmuies Gardens, House of Pitmuies, Guthrie, by Forfar — 1 April - 30 September

Dunninald Castle, Montrose — 1 May - 30 June (Mons, Tues & Suns) 1 July - 31 July (every day) and 1 - 31 August (Mons, Tues & Suns)

Balhary Walled Garden, Balhary, Alyth, Blairgowrie — Saturday, 27 May, 24 June, 29 July, 26 August and 30 September

GARDENS OPEN BY ARRANGEMENT – BOOK A VISIT WITH THE GARDEN OWNER

Inchmill Cottage, Glenprosen, near Kirriemuir — 1 April - 30 September

Braidestone Farm

Angus & Dundee

1 10 MENZIESHILL ROAD
Dundee DD2 1PW
Frances Tait
T: 01382 665719

On a sloping site facing the river, No 10 is home to one of the nine wells in this part of the west end of Dundee. At one time, the well provided drinking water for a nearby farmhouse and two cottages. It was also the first and last water available to carriers' horses on their way to and from Dundee. Now it feeds rhododendrons and camellias, many of which came from the Rothschilds' garden at Exbury, Hampshire. Of particular interest are magnolia 'Manchu Fan' and rhododendrons 'Loderic King George' and 'Lady Chamberlain'. More recently, an area near the well has been given over to bulbs and small herbaceous plants, various irises and primulas.

Open: Saturday/Sunday, 15/16 April & Saturday/Sunday, 13/14 May, 2pm - 5pm, admission £4.00, children free.

Directions: Turn off A85/Riverside Avenue at the roundabout towards the Dundee Botanic Garden. Pass the Botanics and the road bears left and becomes Perth Road. Take a right on to Invergowrie Drive and then first left on Menzieshill Road. Buses 5 and 5A to the foot of Glamis Road and walk west to Invergowrie Drive.

Opening for: Friends Of Dundee University Botanic Garden

10 Menzieshill Road

Angus & Dundee

2 **17A MENZIESHILL ROAD**
Dundee DD2 1PS
Mr and Mrs John Stoa
W: www.johnstoa.com

This Dundee garden is on a fairly steep slope with steps and paths. It features a riot of colour in April/May with thousands of tulip bulbs planted over the years. This display continues with azaleas and rhododendrons. There is a large fig tree and a grapevine 'Brant' growing on south facing walls. In the greenhouse John grows four grapevines, 'Phoenix', 'Seigerrebe', 'Muller Thurgau' and 'Solaris', used for his Muscat flavoured wines, and three varieties of tomato. John is a horticulturist, evidenced by some unusual fruit varieties including Saskatoon, and an artist. His art gallery will be open as well.

Open: Saturday/Sunday, 22/23 April & Saturday/Sunday, 6/7 May, 11am - 4pm, admission £4.00, children free.

Directions: Turn off the A85/Riverside Avenue at the roundabout towards Dundee Botanic Gardens. Pass the Botanics, road bears left and becomes Perth Road. Right onto Invergowrie Drive and first left on Menzieshill Road. Buses 5 and 5A to the foot of Glamis Road and walk west to Invergowrie Drive. In Menzieshill Road look for the garden with the prominent white stemmed birch tree.

Opening for: Cancer Research UK

3 **6 MINTO PLACE**
Dundee DD2 1BR
Heather Berger

Small town garden in the West End of Dundee. Trees, featuring maples, prunus, lilac and laburnum, with palm trees and bamboo adding an unexpectedly exotic note! Shrubs, including several magnolias, cotinus, camellia, paeonia and roses. Bulbs and herbaceous borders. Below the summerhouse is a pond, planted with iris and other aquatic plants.

Open: Saturday/Sunday, 3/4 June, 2pm - 5pm, admission £4.00, children free.

Directions: Take the number 73 or 17 from Dundee city centre or number 16 from Perth City. Get off at Windsor Street and walk down to the bottom. Turn west along Magdalen Yard Road and take the first right onto Minto Place. Number 6 is on your left-hand side.

Opening for: Marie Curie

4 **ANGUS PLANT SALE**
Logie Walled Garden, Kirriemuir DD8 5PN
SGS Angus & Dundee Organisers

Please join us for our annual plant sale. We will offer a good, interesting selection, sourced from private gardens and with some donations from our local nurseries. It's advisable to come promptly and bring boxes and trays. Donations of plants either before or during sales will always be welcome.

Open: Saturday 1 July, 2pm - 5pm, admission £3.00, children free.

Directions: From the A90, take the A926 towards Kirriemuir. Just after Maryton, take a left into

Angus & Dundee

Logie Business Park and then take a second left onto the single track road. Then take the first left onto a beech tree lined drive and follow the signs to *The Walled Garden*.

Opening for: SGS and Beneficiaries

5 BALHARY WALLED GARDEN
Balhary, Alyth, Blairgowrie PH11 8LT
Teri and Paul Hodge-Neale
W: www.facebook.com/balharywalledgarden/

This two-acre organic working walled garden is being lovingly restored back to full production with the development of the 'no dig' method to grow many heritage and new varieties of vegetables with impressive results. The maturing herbaceous borders have the space to encourage drifts of colour and interest throughout the seasons. An opportunity to follow the garden throughout the growing season from late spring to autumn harvest, and to discuss and learn about the benefits of 'no dig'. Paul and Teri will also open their own private Therapy Garden which is a beautiful contemplative space with serene water features, statuary, stonework and unusual plants.

Open: Saturdays 27 May, 24 June, 29 July, 26 August & 30 September, 1pm - 5pm, admission £5.00, children free. Please approach the gardens at low speed due to resident wildlife. Please no dogs.

Directions: Situated between Alyth and Meigle on the B954 opposite the sign to *Jordanstone*.

Opening for: Perennial

6 BRAIDESTONE FARM
Meigle, Blairgowrie PH12 8RE
Leslie and William Robertson

Braidestone is situated in the Valley of Strathmore with views of the Sidlaw Hills, Grampians and surrounding countryside. The garden has year-round interest, although it is particularly colourful in spring, with a selection of shrubs, perennials, bulbs and annuals. There is a walled garden for vegetables, an orchard with a variety of fruit and nut trees and a garden, with several flower borders, surrounding the house. A large Wellingtonia tree stands in the centre of the garden next to a small woodland walk. Seating areas are available to relax and enjoy the views.

Open: Sunday 21 May, 2pm - 5pm, admission £5.00, children free. Parking is available at the Farm Steading.

Directions: From Forfar/A90 take the A94 west to Eassie. Turn right at the crossroads. Turn left at T junction and continue along the road for approximately one-and-a-quarter-miles. From Coupar Angus take the A94 to just before Meigle, follow signs to *Kirriemuir*. The garden is approximately three miles along the road.

Opening for: Scotland's Charity Air Ambulance

Angus & Dundee

7 BRAIDESTONE FARM AND THE DOOCOT
by Meigle PH12 8QX
Leslie & William Robertson and Liz & George McLaren

Braidestone Farm (NEW) Meigle, Blairgowrie PH12 8RE (Leslie and William Robertson): Braidestone is situated in the Valley of Strathmore with views of the Sidlaw Hills, Grampians and surrounding countryside. The garden has year-round interest, although it is particularly colourful in spring, with a selection of shrubs, perennials, bulbs and annuals. There is a walled garden for vegetables, an orchard with a variety of fruit and nut trees and a garden, with several flower borders, surrounding the house. A large Wellingtonia tree stands in the centre of the garden next to a small woodland walk. Seating areas are available to relax and enjoy the views.

The Doocot Kinloch, Meigle, Blairgowrie PH12 8QX (Liz and George McLaren): The house and garden sit in a two-acre site with views to the Sidlaws and Grampians. The house is a converted 18th century steading with a large doo'cot tower, completed in 2009. Garden development began in 2013 with several flowering cherries and two small herbaceous beds, and expanded in 2014 with the creation of a parterre rose garden, and the addition of shrub, herbaceous beds and areas of heather and hard planting including rhododendrons, azaleas and a variety of trees. In 2019 the garden was further developed to create seated areas and themed beds. A wildlife pond was added in 2022 and expansion of the vegetable garden is planned for 2023.

Open: Sunday 25 June, 1pm - 5pm, admission £7.00, children free. Teas will be available at The Doocot.

Directions: The two gardens are four miles apart.
Braidestone Farm: From Forfar/A90 take the A94 west to Eassie. Turn right at the crossroads. Turn left at T junction and continue along the road for approximately one-and-a-quarter-miles. From Coupar Angus take the A94 to just before Meigle, follow signs to *Kirriemuir*. Braidestone Farm is approximately three miles along the road.
The Doocot: Approximately two miles west of Meigle on the A94 (towards Coupar Angus). Just before the hamlet of Longleys there is a turning to the right with a small lodge with red eaves on the roadside. Turn up that tarmac road and The Doocot is 400 metres on the right.

Opening for: The Church of Scotland: Guild & Scotland's Charity Air Ambulance

8 BRECHIN GARDENS IN SUMMER
Locations across Brechin DD9 6AW
The Gardeners of Brechin

9 Pearse Street Brechin DD9 6JR (James Mackie): Opening in memory of its creator Irene Mackie, the well-known plantswoman whose love of plants is reflected in every inch of this beautiful tranquil garden. There's a secluded and rural feel to this town garden. A huge collection of ferns is a unique feature of the garden, unusually planted to mingle with other interestingly planted colourful herbaceous plants.

Bishops Walk 11A Argyll St, Brechin DD9 6JL (Steff and Mike Eyres): A collection of acers grown successfully for years in large pots greets you as you access the unexpected door after viewing several different planting areas. You will find a hidden, walled garden planted with scented climbing and shrub roses, lavenders, perennials and evergreen shrubs and conifers including an established Wollemi, the prehistoric tree recently discovered.

Brechin Cathedral Allotments Chanory Wynd, Brechin DD9 6EU (Brechin Cathedral Allotments Gardeners): Eleven varied plots reflect the interests and personalities of each plot-holder and include fruit, vegetables and herbs. A unique feature is the historical 'College Well' used by medieval monks.

Angus & Dundee

Dalhousie Estate Allotments Brechin Bridge, Arbroath Road, Brechin DD9 6TJ (George Garden): Fourteen varied plots in a beautiful setting making much use of reclaimed materials including a wind powered generator, raised beds and sheds of all shapes and sizes!
Hoodston House Findowrie DD9 6RF (Kat and Aaron Robertson): A work-in-progress family garden and wildlife haven created from scratch, on a tight budget. Currently the garden includes wildlife (and child!) friendly lawns, vegetables and herbs, fruit cage, perennials and shrubs.
Kirkside of Lochty (NEW) Menmuir, by Brechin DD9 6RY (Ed and Fi Troughton): Renovated by a well-known local plantswoman 20 years ago, the current owners are nurturing the existing garden whilst opening up vistas to embrace nearby hills and the Angus Glens. A well-stocked courtyard garden and large island beds extend the garden towards the wildlife meadow.
Kirkton Cottage Aberlemno DD8 3PE (George Henry and Susan Norris): Nestled in a dip beside a stream this country cottage garden is packed with plants. Mown grass paths meander among mature trees, shrubs and perennials in borders, island beds and rockeries. Rustic steps lead to raised vegetable beds, greenhouse and a prolific nursery area.
Latchlea 17A North Latch Road, Brechin DD9 6LE (Pamela Stevens): A new garden begun as a way of coping with bereavement. Inspired by Queen Elizabeth II saying that 'everyone should plant as many trees as possible', 100 trees are newly planted along The Old Lady Walk. Features include some fine stonework, shrubs, herbaceous plants and bulbs and also a courtyard garden.

Open: Sunday 18 June, noon - 5pm, admission £7.00, children free. Teas and tickets will be available at the Gardner Memorial Church Hall, St Ninian Square, Brechin DD9 6AW.

Directions: Gardens are located around the town of Brechin. Look for the *SGS yellow* signs. Map with directions will be provided with tickets.

Opening for: 2nd Brechin Brownie Pack: Guides

---

9 COTTON OF CRAIG
Kilry, Blairgowrie PH11 8HW
Nick Joy

Old walled garden, partially under redesign, with fruit house containing espaliered peach, apricot and cherry trees, herbaceous borders, vegetable garden, greenhouse and specimen trees and shrubs. A robot mower keeps the grass in order. There is also a waterfall walk to explore.

Open: Saturday 17 June, 2pm - 5pm, admission £4.00, children free. Estir Bogside, a mile away on the same road, is also open and serving teas on 17 June from 12 noon – 5pm, so it would be possible to see both gardens on the same day.

Directions: From Perth take the A94 to Coupar Angus and just before Meigle take the B954 and follow signs to *Glen Isla* for approximately four miles until you see the *Garden Open* signs on the right, where there is a left turn signposted *Kilry*. From Dundee take the A923 to Muirhead then the B954 to Meigle, turn right up B954 and follow signs as above. Limited parking on the road and up the drive.

Opening for: RNLI & Scotland's Charity Air Ambulance

Angus & Dundee

10 DALFRUIN
Kirktonhill Road, Kirriemuir DD8 4HU
Mr and Mrs James A Welsh

A well stocked connoisseur's garden of about a third-of-an-acre situated at the end of a short cul-de-sac. There are many less common plants like varieties of trilliums, meconopsis (blue poppies), tree peonies (descendants of ones collected by George Sherriff and grown at Ascreavie), dactylorhiza and codonopsis. There is a scree garden and collection of ferns. The vigorous climbing rose, Paul's Himalayan Musk, grows over a pergola. Interconnected ponds encourage wildlife.

Open: Sunday 14 May, 2pm - 5pm, admission £4.00, children free. Sorry, no dogs.

Directions: From the centre of Kirriemuir turn left up Roods. Kirktonhill Road is on the left near the top of the hill. Park on Roods or at St Mary's Episcopal Church. Disabled parking only in Kirktonhill Road. Bus 20 (from Dundee) getting off at either stop on the Roods.

Opening for: Kirriemuir Day Care Ltd

11 DUNNINALD CASTLE
Montrose DD10 9TD
The Stansfeld family
T: 01674 672031 E: estateoffice@dunninald.com
W: www.dunninald.com

We welcome our visitors to explore our 100 acres of woods, wild garden, policies and a walled garden. From January to May, the main interest is the wild garden and policies where snowdrops in January are followed by daffodils and finally bluebells in May. In June, the emphasis turns to the walled garden, rich in interest and colour throughout the summer. Situated at the bottom of the beech avenue, the walled garden is planted with rose borders, traditional mixed borders, vegetables, herbs, soft fruits and fruit trees and there is a greenhouse.

Open: Sunday 9 July, 2pm - 5pm with homemade teas. Also open 1 May - 30 June (Monday, Tuesday & Sunday), 1 July - 31 July (everyday) and 1 August - 31 August (Monday, Tuesday & Sunday), 1pm - 5pm. Admission £5.00, children free. See website for Castle Tours.

Directions: Three miles south of Montrose, ten miles north of Arbroath, signposted from the A92.

Opening for: Donation to SGS (1 May - 30 June, 1 July - 31 July & 1 August - 31 August) & RNLI: Montrose (Sunday 9 July)

12 EDZELL VILLAGE GARDENS
Edzell DD9 7UA
The Gardeners of Edzell

12 Union Street (NEW) Edzell DD9 7TD (Christy Bing): A walled garden with roses and ancient apple trees.
7 Sladeford Gardens (NEW) Edzell DD9 7SX (Jill & Ali Reid): Hard landscape softened with herbaceous trees and shrubs.
Kinnaber (NEW) Ramsey Street, Edzell DD9 7TT (Anne McIntosh): Medium sized garden with hostas and grasses.
North Lodge 36 Church Street, Edzell DD9 7TQ (Robin and Paul McIntosh): Arts and Crafts style home with large varied garden including woodland, mature trees and shrubs, pond and with Japanese element.

Angus & Dundee

St Andrews Cottage (NEW) Dunlappie Road, Edzell DD9 7UB (Suzie Smith): Small Cottage garden with mixed roses and herbaceous.
Tillytoghills Steading (NEW) Fettercairn AB30 1YJ (Veronica & Steve Engel): Large country garden with herbaceous borders, paddock, pond and vegetable garden.
Westwater (NEW) Dunlappie Road, Edzell DD9 7UB (Judith Gallacher): Large town garden with views of Edzell hill, herbaceous borders and much more.

Open: Sunday 30 July, 2pm - 5pm, admission £7.00, children free. Tickets, teas and maps available at Edzell Cottage Community Centre, Dalhousie Street DD9 7UA.

Directions: Gardens are located around the town of Edzell. Look for the *SGS yellow* signs. Map with directions provided with tickets.

Opening for: Edzell Village Improvement Society: Edzell Garden Club & Edzell Cottage Community Centre

---

 13 ESTIR BOGSIDE
Alyth PH11 8HU
Morag and Andrew Buist

The garden was started in 1995. There are herbaceous borders, a cottage garden created three years ago with traditional plants including lupins, daylilies and foxgloves, a small rose garden and potager. In 2010 the garden was extended to adjacent land to allow planting of native trees, wildflowers, mown paths, two ponds and a glasshouse.

Open: Saturday 17 June, noon - 5pm, admission £4.00, children free. Cotton of Craig, a mile away on the same road, is also open on the 17 June from 2-5pm so it would be possible to see both gardens on the same day.

Directions: From Perth take the A94 to Coupar Angus and just before Meigle take the B954 and follow signs to *Glen Isla* for approximately three miles till you see *Garden Open* signs on the left, by the road. From Dundee take the A923 to Muirhead and then the B954 to Meigle, turn right up B954 towards Glen Isla and follow signs as above.

Opening for: The Haven & Scotland's Charity Air Ambulance

---

 14 FORFAR OPEN GARDEN
36 Lochside Road, Forfar DD8 3JD
Forfar Open Garden Scheme
T: 07796 627023 E: forfaropengardens@gmail.com

Now into its 6th year, this therapeutic and tranquil space consists of a walled garden and woodland. The garden contains a diversity of herbaceous planting, food growing areas, greenhouse, polytunnel and the old well. The woodland is more informal with a cosy bothy room and an abundance of wildlife. As a charity, we support volunteers, and aim to promote the benefits of working alongside others in natural surroundings. We sell plants (mostly perennials) to raise funds. The main garden is fully accessible, with toilet facilities.

Open: Sunday 23 April & Sunday 28 May, 1pm - 4pm, admission £4.00, children free.

Directions: Lochside Road is situated opposite Tesco, with the Factory Shop on the corner. The garden is found towards Forfar Loch on the right, with a large parking bay opposite. The No. 117 bus stops directly opposite.

Opening for: Forfar Open Garden

Angus & Dundee

15 HOSPITALFIELD GARDENS
Hospitalfield House, Westway, Arbroath DD11 2NH
Hospitalfield Trust
E: info@hospitalfield.org.uk
W: www.hospitalfield.org.uk

In 2021 the walled garden at Hospitalfield was comprehensively redeveloped to a design by celebrated garden designer and plantsman, Nigel Dunnett. The new garden tells the 800-year horticultural story of this extraordinary site from its monastic origins in the 13th century through to the Victorian passion for ferns. You will be able to explore the garden in its first few years after planting as it continues to grow into its inspirational design; full of diverse textures and striking colours. The house that overlooks the garden was remodelled in the 19th century by Elizabeth Allan-Fraser and her husband, the artist Patrick Allan-Fraser, who designed their home in the Arts and Crafts style. Their fernery, which sits within the walled garden, has been restored and re-planted with ferns from all over the world and will also be open for visitors. For more information about Hospitalfield and its international cultural programme rooted in contemporary visual arts, please visit the website.

Open: Saturday 8 July, 11am - 4pm, admission £6.00, children free. Admission is for the walled garden and fernery and Angus residents will receive an annual pass with their admission. The new glass house café offers excellent refreshments.

Directions: Comprehensive directions can be found on the website at hospitalfield.org.uk/visit/location/.

Opening for: Donation to SGS

16 INCHMILL COTTAGE
Glenprosen, near Kirriemuir DD8 4SA
Iain Nelson
T: 01575 540452

This is a long, sloping and terraced garden at over 800 feet in the Braes of Angus, developed to be a garden for all seasons. Half is dominated by bulbs, rhododendrons, azaleas, primulas, meconopsis and clematis. The other half is mainly later summer bulbs, herbaceous plants and roses. There is also a rockery/scree.

Open: Thursdays 20 April, 18 May, 15 June, 20 July, 17 August & 21 September, 2pm - 5pm. Also open by arrangement 1 April - 30 September. Admission £4.00, children free.

Directions: Please DO NOT use SatNav. From Kirriemuir take the B955 (signposted *The Glens*) to Dykehead (about five miles). From there follow the *Prosen* sign for about five miles. Inchmill is the white-fronted cottage beside the phone box in the village. There is car parking beside the church (50 yards away) and by the village hall opposite.

Opening for: The Archie Foundation

**17 INVERBROTHOCK SCHOOL SENSORY GARDEN
AND FOREST GARDEN**
East Kirkton Road, Arbroath DD11 4GR
Inverbrothrock Pupils and Staff

These two gardens have been designed and created by the pupils, staff and parents. The Sensory Garden is a great asset to all children and staff, especially children who need additional support. There are areas of raised beds for growing vegetables, a dry river bed

Angus & Dundee

with interesting grasses and plants, large stone features to climb on, and different shelters and corners to play in. A polytunnel is used for outdoor classes and seed sowing. The Forest Garden includes interesting mounds and trees, an area to build dens and play amongst trees. Gardens created by and for young minds.

Open: Sunday 11 June, noon - 4pm, admission by donation.

Directions: Take the A933 towards Arbroath, turn into Kirkton Industrial Estate on Kirkton Road, follow the road to the T junction for East Kirkton Road. Follow the signs to the school which is on the left.

Opening for: Inverbrothock Primary School: Extracurricular Activities

KINBLETHMONT HOUSE
by Arbroath, Angus DD11 4RW
The Ramsay family
E: info@kinblethmont.com
W: www.kinblethmont.com, www.facebook.com/kinblethmont

Kinblethmont is an historic estate which, with its advantageous elevated position, has been settled since Pictish times. In the centre is the Victorian mansion house surrounded by beautiful policy woodlands where specimen trees and snowdrops abound. Paths take you through the woods past the old pet cemetery, the remains of 16th century Kinblethmont and the walled garden with children's play area. A longer walk will take you up around the solar park with spectacular views over to the Angus hills and the North Sea.

Open: Saturday/Sunday, 25/26 February, 10am - 4pm for Snowdrops and Winter Walks, admission £5.00, children free. The estate has some lovely holiday cottages for anyone wanting to make a weekend of it. House tours will also be available, please see website or Facebook for details.

Directions: From Forfar/Brechin, take the A933 towards Arbroath, turn left to Friockheim. Drive through Friockheim and continue along the road, past the crematorium, until you reach a T junction. Turn right and continue along this road, past a crossroads, until you enter Kinblethmont estate on your left.

Opening for: Leysmill (31st Angus) Scout Group

KIRKTON COTTAGE
Aberlemno DD8 3PE
George Henry and Susan Norris

Nestled in a dip beside a stream this country cottage garden is packed with plants. Mown grass paths meander among mature trees, shrubs and perennials in borders, island beds and rockeries. Rustic steps lead to raised vegetable beds, greenhouse and a prolific nursery area.

Open: Sunday 7 May, Saturday 24 June and Saturday 29 July, noon - 5pm. Admission £4.00, children free. Please note that the terrain is uneven in places.

Directions: From the village of Aberlemno, turn off the A9134, cottage is opposite the church.

Opening for: UNICEF UK (Sunday 7 May), The Adam Centre (Saturday 24 June) & The Dalhousie Centre Day Care For The Elderly (Saturday 29 July)

Angus & Dundee

20   LAWTON HOUSE
Inverkeilor, by Arbroath   DD11 4RU
Cate and Simon Dessain

Woodland garden of beech trees, carpeted with snowdrops, aconites and crocuses in spring, set around a 1755 house. There is also a walled garden planted with fruit trees and vegetables. The property was owned for many years by Elizabeth and Patrick Allan-Fraser who remodelled Hospitalfield House in Arbroath.

Open: 9 March - 12 March, 10am - 5pm for Snowdrops and Winter Walks, admission £4.00, children free.

Directions: Take the B965 between Inverkeilor and Friockheim, turn right at the sign for *Angus Chain Saws*. Drive approximately 200 metres, then take the first right.

Opening for: Siobhan's Trust

21   LETHAM GRANGE GARDENS & ASHBROOK NURSERY TOURS
Letham Grange   DD11 4QA
Letham Grange Gardeners & Ashbrook Nursery

Letham Grange Gardens: Come and enjoy a walk from the main house at Letham Grange, through the grounds to visit a selection of gardens. Follow the *yellow* signs. Drive or walk to gardens in Waulkmill, Firhills and Denside areas. Look out for wildlife, birds and insects.
Ashbrook Nursery Tours: Come and see commercial plant production, from seed sowing to the final plant and production of sustainable cut flowers.

Open: Saturday 10 June, 1pm - 5pm, admission £5.00, children free. Ashbrook Nursery will run tours at 2pm, 3pm and 4pm. Cafe available at the nursery.

Directions: To Letham Grange DD11 4QA: On the A933 Arbroath to Brechin Road, turn off at the T-junction at Colliston Church, then continue to the end and turn right. Follow this road to the *Letham Grange* sign and turn into Green Beeches, follow this road to the main house, Letham Grange.
To Ashbrook Nursery and Garden Centre: Forfar Road, Arboath, DD11 3RB: Located on the outskirts of Arbroath, on the west side of the A933 opposite Condor Royal Marine Base.

Opening for: ROFO

22   MONTROSE GARDENS
Locations across Montrose   DD10 8SB
The Montrose Gardeners

36 The Mall Montrose DD10 8SS (Peter Wood): The garden at 36 The Mall has experienced huge changes throughout its lifetime and typically it would have been employed as a kitchen garden providing seasonal fruit and vegetables for the household. Since taking ownership of the property in 2012, we have endeavoured to return the garden to what might be something a little more traditional, albeit with a slightly more modern interpretation. The walled garden, so traditional to the period, now features fruit trees in the form of espaliers on the south facing aspect with additional raised beds comprising both soft fruit and vegetables. Additional borders and pots provide colour in abundance.

Angus & Dundee

Arwin House 17 Renny Crescent, Montrose DD10 9BW (Trish and Andy Winton): Our garden is constantly evolving and has been 10 years in the making. It was designed to bring peace and tranquility and features different themed 'rooms'. In 2015 we created an Asian inspired memorial garden in memory of my late son. Andy and I were fortunate to feature on BBC's *The Beechgrove Garden* in 2019 and we look forward to welcoming you and hope you enjoy your visit.

Dorward House 24 Dorward Road, Montrose DD10 8SB (The Trustees of Dorward House): The original house was built in 1839 and became a care home for the elderly in 1950. There have been many changes over the years including the addition of the garden pavilion. The gardens are tended mainly by volunteers and their hard work and dedication has certainly paid off with stunning herbaceous borders and colourful annuals. There is also a 'sensory garden' to the rear which is dedicated mainly for the vulnerable dementia residents. We hope you enjoy your visit.

Open: Saturday/Sunday, 15/16 July, 1pm - 5pm, admission £5.00, children free. Homemade teas, and tickets on the day, will be available at Dorward House.

Directions: Dorward House is on the corner of Dorward Road and Warrack Terrace, and is adjacent to the Midlinks park and tennis courts. Directions to the other gardens are available with map and tickets from Dorward House.

Opening for: Dorward House, Montrose

 23 PITMUIES GARDENS
House of Pitmuies, Guthrie, by Forfar DD8 2SN
Jeanette and Ruaraidh Ogilvie
T: 01241 828245 E: ogilvie@pitmuies.com
W: www.pitmuies.com

Two renowned semi-formal walled gardens adjoin an 18th-century house and steading, sheltering long borders of herbaceous perennials, superb old-fashioned delphiniums and roses, together with pavings rich with violas and dianthus. An extensive and diverse collection of plants, interesting kitchen garden, spacious lawns, and river, lochside and woodland walks beneath fine trees. A wide variety of shrubs with good autumn colour and a picturesque turreted doocot and a 'Gothick' wash house. Myriad spring bulbs include carpets of crocus following massed snowdrops and daffodils.

Open: 1 April - 30 September, 10am - 5pm, admission £5.00, children free.

Directions: From Forfar take the A932 east for seven miles and gardens are signposted on the right. From Brechin take the A933 south to Friockheim and turn right onto the A932. The gardens are signposted on the left after one-and-a-half miles.

Opening for: Donation to SGS

Angus & Dundee

24 ST BRIDE'S COTTAGE
South Kingennie, Broughty Ferry DD5 3PA
Alison and Donald Gordon

This half-acre garden was started from scratch in 2002 and now provides year-round interest. Planting several trees and making a wildlife pond and stream were the first priorities, as birds were sadly rare visitors to the garden. Parts of the perimeter of the garden are left semi-wild with dense shrubs to provide cover and nesting areas, while the area visible from the house is planted for viewing, with a mixture of shrubs, perennials and bulbs. Some features are inspired by visits to gardens around the world, including a Japanese-themed area with island bed. There is a small bog garden with a lovely early summer display of *Iris sibirica* and many plants justify their existence by attracting a wide variety of bees and butterflies.

Open: Saturday/Sunday, 17/18 June, 1pm - 5pm, admission £4.00, children free. Plants will also be for sale, for the benefit of Dundee Botanic Garden.

Directions: From Kellas take the minor road signed *Murroes Church* for approximately one mile to some steading houses and turn left up the farm track immediately before them. St Bride's is the first house on the left with the conservatory and solar panels.

Opening for: Friends Of Dundee University Botanic Garden

25 TORWOOD
Milton of Ogilvie, Glenogilvy, Glamis by Forfar DD8 1UN
John Gordon
T: 07988 010418 E: j.gordon.82@btinternet.com
W: www.gardendisplays.co.uk

A small, attractively laid-out country garden striving towards year-round interest, enjoyment and relaxation through association and succession planting of trees, shrubs, herbaceous, ornamental grasses, perennials and bulbs. John's aim for his gardening is to focus on ecologically-based, wildlife-friendly planting schemes, guided by natural and semi-natural habitats. This approach is demonstrated beautifully in his garden, separated into rooms focusing on different colour schemes and styles, including a small woodland area, mixed borders and prairie-style planting.

Open: Saturday/Sunday, 5/6 August, 11am - 4pm, admission £5.00, children free. John is an experienced horticulturalist and designer and will provide a half-hour talk on 'Integrating Traditional-style Gardening with Ecological-based Planting' at noon and 2pm on both opening days.

Directions: Take the A928 between Kirriemuir turnoff on the A90 or Glamis turnoff on the A94. Follow the road signposted *Glenogilvy, Handwick, Dryburn*. Torwood is the second house from the end on the left.

Opening for: Alzheimer Scotland

26 WESTGATE
12 Glamis Drive, Dundee DD2 1QL
John and Frances Dent

This established garden, with many mature trees, occupies a south-facing site overlooking the River Tay and Fife hills. The tennis court lawn is surrounded by herbaceous plants and shrubs. A short woodland walk reveals a miniature knot garden, a bower and other surprise features.

Angus & Dundee

There are also two oriental-themed water gardens, rose beds and a newly planted chamomile lawn. As darkness falls, all these scenes will be transformed by floodlighting and other effects.

Open: Saturday/Sunday, 21/22 October, 3pm - 7pm, admission by donation. Children's activities and a variety of floodlighting effects. Torches recommended.

Directions: Buses 5, 22 or 73 from Dundee city centre. Please note there is no roadside parking on Glamis Drive. Limited disabled parking is available at the house.

Opening for: Dr Graham's Homes Kalimpong (UK)

St Bride's Cottage

 27 **WESTGATE AND WINDYRIDGE**
10 & 12 Glamis Drive, Dundee DD2 1QL
Frances & John Dent and Frances Shepherd

These adjacent gardens are each about half-an-acre and sit behind Arts and Crafts era houses. They are south facing with views to the River Tay and Fife hills. Both are well established and have many mature plants and trees.

Westgate 12 Glamis Drive, Dundee DD2 1QL (John and Frances Dent): This garden has a tennis court lawn surrounded by herbaceous plants and shrubs. A short woodland walk reveals a miniature knot garden, a bower and other surprise features. There are also two oriental-themed water gardens, rose beds and a newly planted chamomile lawn.

Windyridge 10 Glamis Drive DD2 1QL (Frances M. Shepherd): The garden, set out in the 1920s, comprises different areas: a terrace at the top looks over a central lawn with a sundial in the middle and wide herbaceous borders on each side. An arbour divides this area from the orchard containing several old and some new fruit trees. Passing under the covered beech hedge at the bottom takes one into the vegetable area.

Open: Saturday/Sunday, 27/28 May, 2pm - 5pm, admission £6.00, children free.

Directions: Buses 5, 22 or 73 from Dundee city centre. Please note there is no roadside parking on Glamis Drive. Limited disabled parking available at Westgate.

Opening for: Maggie Keswick Jencks Cancer Caring Centres Trust (Dundee)

Argyll & Lochaber

Sponsored by

Investec

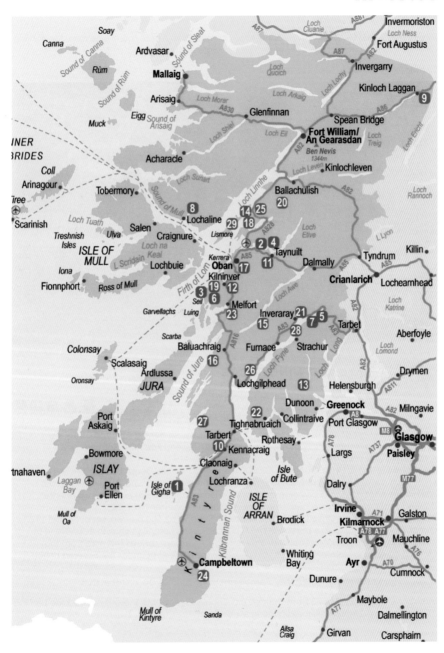

Argyll & Lochaber

OUR VOLUNTEER ORGANISERS

District Organiser:	Minette Struthers	Camasmaddy, Ardmaddy, by Oban PA34 4QY E: info@scotlandsgardens.org
Area Organisers:	Grace Bergius Shian Carlow Mary Lindsay	Craignish House, by Lochgilphead PA31 8QN Balliemore, Loch Striven, Dunoon PA23 8RH Dal an Eas, Kilmore, Oban PA34 4XU
District Photographer:	Maurice Wilkins	Dunrobian, Laurel Road, Oban PA34 5EA
Treasurer:	Shelagh Cannon	Kames Bay, Kilmelford, By Oban PA34 4XA

GARDENS OPEN ON A SPECIFIC DATE

Knock Newhouse, Lochgair	Saturday/Sunday, 6/7 May
Baravalla Garden, by West Loch Tarbert, Argyll	Thursday, 11 May
Achamore Gardens, Isle of Gigha	Saturday, 13 May
Kames Bay, Kilmelford	Saturday/Sunday, 13/14 May
Strachur Flower & Woodland Gardens, Strachur	Sunday, 14 May
Fasnacloich, Appin	Sunday, 21 May
Strachur Flower & Woodland Gardens, Strachur	Sunday, 21 May
Inveryne Woodland Garden, Kilfinan, Tighnabruaich	Saturday/Sunday, 27/28 May
Knock Newhouse, Lochgair	Sunday, 28 May
Ardchattan Priory, North Connel	Sunday, 11 June
Ardverikie with Aberarder, Kinloch Laggan, Newtonmore	Sunday, 11 June
Benmore Botanic Garden, Benmore, Dunoon	Sunday, 1 October

GARDENS OPEN REGULARLY

Ardkinglas Woodland Garden, Cairndow	1 January - 31 December
Ardmaddy Castle, by Oban	1 January - 31 December
Barguillean's 'Angus Garden', Taynuilt	1 January - 31 December
Druimneil House, Port Appin	1 January - 31 December
Ardtornish, by Lochaline, Morvern	1 January - 31 December
Achnacloich, Connel, Oban	1 January - 31 December (Sats only)
Kinlochlaich Walled Garden, Appin	3 March - 31 October
Ardchattan Priory, North Connel	1 April - 31 October (Weds only)
An Cala, Ellenabeich, Isle of Seil	1 April - 31 October
Inveraray Castle Gardens, Inveraray	3 April - 31 October
Crinan Hotel Garden, Crinan	1 May - 31 August

Argyll & Lochaber

GARDENS OPEN BY ARRANGEMENT – BOOK A VISIT WITH THE GARDEN OWNER

Berandhu, Appin, Argyll	1 April - 31 October
Knock Newhouse, Lochgair	1 April - 1 November
Ormsary Gardens, Ormsary, Lochgilphead, Argyll	3 April - 31 October
Ardno, Cairndow	1 May - 30 September
Barochreal, Kilninver, Oban, Argyll	1 May - 30 September
Braevallich Farm, by Dalmally	1 May - 30 September
Dal an Eas, Kilmore, Oban	1 May - 30 September
Eas Mhor, Cnoc-a-Challtuinn, Clachan Seil, Oban	1 May - 31 October
Kildalloig, Campbeltown	1 May - 31 October
The Secret Garden, Isle of Lismore, Oban, Argyll	1 January - 31 December

Barochreal © Maurice Wilkins

Argyll & Lochaber

1 ACHAMORE GARDENS
Isle of Gigha PA41 7AD
The Isle of Gigha Heritage Trust
E: gardens@gigha.org.uk
W: www.gigha.org.uk

Created by Colonel Sir James Horlick with the assistance of Gardener Kitty Lloyd Jones in 1944, Achamore Gardens is the home of Horlick's renowned rhododendron and camellia collection. Flourishing in Gigha's warm microclimate, the 54-acre gardens host many notable and unusual plants and trees from around the world. The woodland walks with rhododendrons, azaleas, camellias, New Zealand tree ferns, hydrangeas and fuchsias complement the walled garden's tender exotics, herbaceous borders and bamboo maze. The garden viewpoint has stunning views over to Islay and Jura while the pond area offers a secluded oasis. After years of decline, The Isle of Gigha Heritage Trust is now actively working to restore and develop Achamore Gardens.

Open: Saturday 13 May, 10am - 4pm, admission £7.00, children free. The garden is also open to visitors through the season.

Directions: Access to Gigha is via CalMac ferry. Gigha can be explored by foot or bicycle so you can choose to leave your vehicle for free at the Tayinloan ferry car park and help to avoid congestion of traffic on Gigha's single track roads. The garden is three-quarters of a mile from the ferry.

Opening for: Gigha Village Hall

2 ACHNACLOICH
Connel, Oban PA37 1PR
Mr T E Nelson
T: 01631 710223 E: charlie_milne@msn.com; cassandhu@gmail.com

The 20-acre woodland garden overlooking Loch Etive has been planted over the last century with a wide range of trees and shrubs from Asia, China, Japan, North America, Chile and New Zealand. Many have grown to considerable size. The light woodland canopy consists of native oaks and a number of magnificent 150-year-old Scots pines and European larch. Amongst these are open glades, carpeted with bluebells and numerous other bulbs. Two ponds and streams are planted with primulas, iris species, lysichitum, and astilbes. The woodland contains innumerable species of rhododendron and azalea, of which the triflorums and yunnanense are outstanding. Amongst these are species of acer, betula, camellia, cercidiphyllum, cornus, crinodendron, drimys, embothrium, enkianthus, eucryphia, hoheria, magnolia, malus, nothofagus, pieris, sorbus, stewartia, telopea and viburnum. Beside the house is a giant Douglas fir from Douglas' original introduction. One of the first Dawyck beeches stands beside the drive. Fine autumn colours.

Open: 1 January - 31 December (Saturdays only), 2pm - 4pm, admission £5.00, children free.

Directions: On the A85 two miles east of Connel. The car park is at the bottom of the drive.

Opening for: Macmillan Cancer Support

Argyll & Lochaber

3 AN CALA

Ellenabeich, Isle of Seil PA34 4RF
Mrs Sheila Downie
W: www.gardens-of-argyll.co.uk/view-details.php?id=447

A wonderful example of a 1930s designed garden, An Cala sits snugly in its horseshoe shelter of surrounding cliffs. A spectacular and very pretty garden with streams, waterfall, ponds, many herbaceous plants as well as azaleas, rhododendrons and cherry trees in spring. Archive material of Thomas Mawson's design was found recently and is available to visitors.

Open: 1 April - 31 October, 10am - 6pm, admission £5.00, children free.

Directions: Proceed south from Oban on Campbeltown Road for eight miles, turn right at the *Easdale* sign, a further eight miles on the B844; the garden is between the school and the village. Bus Oban – Easdale.

Opening for: Cancer Research UK

An Cala © Maurice Wilkins

4 ARDCHATTAN PRIORY

North Connel PA37 1RQ
Mrs Sarah Troughton
T: 01796 481355 E: admin@ardchattan.co.uk
W: www.ardchattan.co.uk

Overlooking Loch Etive, Ardchattan Priory Garden has a mature rockery and extensive herbaceous and rose borders to the front of the house. On either side of the drive, shrub borders, numerous roses and ornamental trees, together with bulbs, give colour throughout the season. The Priory, founded in 1230, is now a private house. The ruins of the chapel and graveyard are in the care of *Historic Environment Scotland* and open with the garden.

Open: 1 April - 31 October (Wednesdays only) 9:30am - 5:30pm. Garden Fete Sunday 11 June, 12noon - 4pm. Admission £5.00, children under 16 free.

Directions: Oban 10 miles. From north, turn left off the A828 at Barcaldine onto the B845 for

Argyll & Lochaber

six miles. From east or from Oban on the A85, cross Connel Bridge and turn first right, proceed east on Bonawe Road.

Opening for: SGS and Beneficiaries

5 ARDKINGLAS WOODLAND GARDEN
Cairndow PA26 8BG
Ardkinglas Estate
T: 01499 600261
W: www.ardkinglas.com

In a peaceful setting overlooking Loch Fyne, the garden contains one of the finest collections of rhododendrons and conifers in Britain. This includes the mightiest conifer in Europe – a silver fir, as well as many other Champion Trees. There is a gazebo with a unique scriptorium based around a collection of literary quotes. For younger visitors, the garden features a Fairy Trail, Gruffalo Trail and Snakey Slide. It is a *VisitScotland* 3-star garden.
Champion Trees: The mightiest conifer in Europe and others..

Open: 1 January - 31 December, dawn – dusk, admission £5.00, children over 3 years £2.50. Tickets available online at www.ardkinglas.com or pay on arrival. All admission fees go to helping maintain and preserve the garden, as well as a donation to SGS charities.

Directions: Entrance through Cairndow village off the A83 Loch Lomond/Inveraray road.

Opening for: Donation to SGS

6 ARDMADDY CASTLE
by Oban PA34 4QY
Mr and Mrs Archie Struthers
T: 01852 300353 E: minette@ardmaddy.com
W: www.ardmaddy.com

The gardens lie in a most spectacular setting in the centre of a horseshoe valley sheltered by mixed mature woodlands and the elevated castle standing on a volcanic mound to seaward. The walled garden is full of magnificent rhododendrons, a collection of rare and unusual shrubs and plants, the clock garden with its cutting flowers, the crevice garden, a NEW border with grasses and coastal theme, fruit and vegetables grown with labour saving formality, all within dwarf box hedging. Beyond, a woodland walk, with its 60-foot *Hydrangea petiolaris*, leads to the water garden which in spring has a mantle of bluebells and daffodils and in early summer a riot of *Primula candelabra*, irises, rodgersias and other damp-loving plants and grasses. Lovely autumn colour. A plantsman's garden for all seasons.

Open: 1 January - 31 December, 9am – dusk, admission £5.00, children free. Holiday cottages available sleeping 4 - 12. Find out more at www.ardmaddy.com

Directions: Take the A816 south of Oban for eight miles. Turn right onto the B844 to Seil Island/Easdale. Four miles on, turn left to Ardmaddy (signposted) and follow for a further two miles.

Opening for: Donation to SGS

Argyll & Lochaber

7 ARDNO
Cairndow PA26 8BE
Kate How
T: Rob Backhouse (Gardener) 01499 302304/Kate How 02072 211996
E: ardnokate@gmail.com

From the rich varied landscape, a romantic garden has been created from scratch over the past 25 years. Visitors can stroll in the walled garden near the house, or explore the old oak wood planted with many interesting shrubs. These are growing up fast, adding shape and colour. Across the burn is the gorge and a wonderful waterfall. The woodland garden ends in the meadow, planted with irises and a collection of unusual trees, which continues down to the beach and a magnificent huge rock. My garden is a place to be peaceful in. Come and enjoy but be prepared as some of the paths are steep with lots of steps and unfortunately not suitable for wheelchairs.

Open: by arrangement 1 May - 30 September, admission £5.00, children free. Small groups of up to six people by application to the Gardener, Robert Backhouse, Ardno Cottage T: 01499 302304 from May – September. The Rediweld Foundation supports Charities in London and the West coast of Scotland that are primarily but not exclusively involved with children's educational activities.

Directions: Situated at the top end of Loch Fyne between Cairndow and St Catherines, off the A815.

Opening for: Rediweld Foundation

8 ARDTORNISH
by Lochaline, Morvern PA80 5UZ
Mrs John Raven
W: www.ardtornish.co.uk

Ardtornish Estate spreads out around Loch Aline, a huge, wooded, U-shaped bay, a natural haven. Wonderful gardens of interesting mature conifers, rhododendrons, deciduous trees, shrubs and herbaceous plantings, set amid magnificent scenery. Much of the garden is covered by native birch, alongside extensive planting of exotic species, under mature groups of larch, firs and pine, whose strong form and colour complement the pink sandstone towers and gables of Ardtornish House.

Open: 1 January - 31 December, 10am - 6pm, admission £5.00, children free. Groups must be pre-booked.

Directions: Three miles from Lochaline along the A884.

Opening for: Donation to SGS

9 ARDVERIKIE WITH ABERARDER
Kinloch Laggan, Newtonmore PH20 1BX
The Feilden family, Mrs P Laing and Mrs E T Smyth-Osbourne
T: 01528 544300 E: amanda@ardverikie.com

Ardverikie Kinloch Laggan, Newtonmore PH20 1BX (Mrs P Laing and Mrs E T Smyth-Osbourne): Lovely setting on Loch Laggan with magnificent trees. Walled garden with large collection of acers, shrubs and herbaceous plants. Architecturally interesting house (not open) featured in *Monarch of the Glen* and *The Crown*.

Argyll & Lochaber

Aberarder Kinloch Laggan, Newtonmore PH20 1BX (The Feilden family): The garden has been laid out over the last 20 years to create a mixture of spring and autumn plants and trees, including rhododendrons, azaleas and acers. The elevated view down Loch Laggan from the garden is exceptional.

Open: Sunday 11 June, 2pm - 5:30pm, admission £5.00, children under 16 free.

Directions: On the A86 between Newtonmore and Spean Bridge.
Ardverikie House entrance is at the east end of Loch Laggan via the bridge by Gatelodge.
Aberarder Lodge entrance is about 200 metres west of the Ardverikie entrance, next to the small cottage.

Opening for: Laggan Parish Church & Highland Hospice

 ## BARAVALLA GARDEN
by West Loch Tarbert, Argyll PA29 6YE
Baravalla Garden Partnership – Matt Heasman – Director
T: 07793 604609 E: mtheasman@outlook.com
W: rscg.org.uk

This wild garden of 26 acres is carved out of typical Argyll woodland, with mature oak, beech, hazel and alder that run down to the shores of the West Loch some seven miles from Tarbert. The 'Two Peters', Sir Peter Hutchison Bt. CBE FRSE and Peter Cox MBE, both botanical travellers, were looking for an area to plant the more tender plants from their colder east coast gardens. They found the site here with the help of the Mackie Campbell Family and some 50 years ago started to create a garden with collections of plants from all over the world, rhododendrons, magnolias, azaleas, camellias, tender shrubs and so much more. The garden now is mature, managed and maintained by the Rhododendron Species Conservation Group. This garden is very rarely open. This is a truly wild garden and stout footwear and clothing for protection against the Argyll weather are recommended.

Open: Thursday 11 May, 10am - 7pm, admission £5.00, children free. Teas on site and picnic tables available if you want to bring a picnic lunch. Groups of 15 or more by arrangement. Plant stall with plants from the garden.

Directions: From Tarbert Village, through the village take the B8024 past the golf course, turn left on the Kilberry road for about seven miles. SGS signs will direct you to a car park just through the gate on the right hand side. Please do not attempt to come down the forest track but follow the signs and walk down the track to the garden. We will provide guided tours at regular intervals.

Opening for: Rhododendron Species Conservation Group

Argyll & Lochaber

11 BARGUILLEAN'S 'ANGUS GARDEN'

Taynuilt PA35 1HY
The Josephine Marshall Trust
T: 01866 822333 E: info@barguillean.co.uk
W: www.barguillean.co.uk

Nine-acre woodland garden around an 11-acre loch set in the Glen Lonan Hills. Spring-flowering shrubs and bulbs, extensive collection of rhododendron hybrids, deciduous azaleas, conifers and unusual trees. The garden contains a large collection of North American rhododendron hybrids from famous contemporary plant breeders. Some paths can be steep. Three marked walks from 30 minutes to one-and-a-half hours.

Open: 1 January - 31 December, 9am - dusk, admission £5.00, children free. Coach tours by appointment.

Directions: Three miles south off the A85 Glasgow/Oban road at Taynuilt, road marked *Glen Lonan*, three miles up a single track road, turn right at the sign.

Opening for: SSAFA Forces Help

12 BAROCHREAL

Kilninver, Oban, Argyll PA34 4UT
Nigel and Antoinette Mitchell
T: 01852 316151 E: antoinettemitchell1946@gmail.com
W: www.barochreal.co.uk

The garden was started in 2006. Fencing and stone walling define it from the rest of Barochreal land. Every year an area has been added, resulting in the gardens you will see today. There are rhododendron banks, a water feature, waterfalls and burns, a pond, a walled rose garden, active beehives (now housed in a purpose-built bee shelter built in 2021), tiered areas, a greenhouse and wild garden across the burn. Maintained walking tracks in the fields lead to viewpoints. Biodiversity studies revealed that rare butterflies inhabit the small glen by the waterfall, there are forty different species of moths including rare micro moths and over seventy species of wildflowers in the fields, including three types of wild orchids. There is an abundance of wildlife including red squirrels, pine martens and a wide range of birds can be seen. This garden is a haven of tranquility, as seen in episode 9 of 2022 *Beechgrove*.

Open: by arrangement 1 May - 30 September, admission £5.00, children free. Visiting by arrangement allows the owners to personally show visitors around if they wish, and explain the history around Barochreal, a village in the 1700s before Oban existed.

Directions: Fifteen minutes south of Oban. On the main A816 Oban to Lochgilphead road just to the south of the village of Kilninver on the left-hand side of the road. Bus Oban – Lochgilpead stops at Kilninver School, short walk after. Please disregard SatNav and use what3words address instead www.w3w.co/albums.forest.tinned

Opening for: Scottish SPCA

Argyll & Lochaber

 13 **BENMORE BOTANIC GARDEN**
Benmore, Dunoon PA23 8QU
A Regional Garden of the Royal Botanic Garden Edinburgh
T: 01369 706261 E: benmore@rbge.org.uk
W: www.rbge.org.uk

Benmore's magnificent mountainside setting is a joy to behold. Its 120 acres boast a world-famous collection of plants from the Himalayas, China and Japan to North and South America, as well as an impressive avenue of giant redwoods, one of the finest entrances to any botanic garden. Established in 1863, these majestic giants stand over 150 feet high. Seven miles of trails throughout lead to a restored Victorian Fernery and a dramatic viewpoint at 420 feet looking out to surrounding mountains and Holy Loch. There are also traditional Bhutanese and Chilean pavilions and the magnificent Golden Gates. Keep an eye out for red squirrels and other wildlife as you explore the garden.
National Plant Collection: Abies, South American Temperate Conifers, Picea.
Champion Trees: Many rare trees and giant conifers.

Open: Sunday 1 October, 10am - 5pm, admission details can be found on the garden's website. Also see website for details of regular opening times – www.rbge.org.uk

Directions: Seven miles north of Dunoon or 22 miles south from Glen Kinglass below Rest and Be Thankful pass. On the A815. Bus service is limited.

Opening for: Donation to SGS

 14 **BERANDHU**
Appin, Argyll PA38 4DD
John and Fiona Landale
T: 01631 730585 mobile 07900 377414 E: johnllandale@gmail.com

A sheltered one-and-a-half acre coastal garden in a scenic setting offering fabulous views over Loch Laich to Loch Linnhe, Castle Stalker and the Morvern hills beyond. Craggy limestone abounds on the undulating site, some of which forms natural rockeries. Native trees mix with introduced firs and conifers. A variety of rhododendrons and azaleas provide spring and early summer colour. A mix of limestone overlaid with peat gives an unusual mix of wild flowers. This well-tended garden also has lovely wild areas of bog garden and woodland.

Open: by arrangement 1 April - 31 October, admission £5.00, children free.

Directions: In Appin turn off the A828 Connel to Ballachulish road at Gunn's Garage signposted for *Port Appin*. After one mile when the road turns uphill, first entrance on the right, half way up the hill.

Opening for: The Appin Village Hall & Alzheimer Scotland

Argyll & Lochaber

15 BRAEVALLICH FARM

by Dalmally PA33 1BU
Mr Philip Bowden-Smith
T: 01866 844246 E: philip@brae.co.uk

Discover two gardens, one at the farm and an upper garden further up the hill. The former is approximately one and a half acres and developed over the last 40 years. Its principal features include dwarf rhododendron, azaleas (evergreen and deciduous), large drifts of various primula and meconopsis and bluebells, and mixed herbaceous perennials/shrubs; there is also quite a serious kitchen garden. The second garden has been developed over the last 30 years out of a birch and sessile oak wood and is a traditional West Coast glen garden intersected by two pretty burns with waterfalls. The garden has been extended over the last few years and now covers nearly ten acres with extensive new paths, and a suspension bridge over the ravine. Whilst the plants are important, many say that it is the topography with its differing vistas which make this garden such a peaceful and special place.

Open: by arrangement 1 May - 30 Sept, admission £5.00, children free. Dogs must be on leads.

Directions: South-east of Loch Awe on the B840, 15 miles from Cladich, seven miles from Ford.

Opening for: Mary's Meals

16 CRINAN HOTEL GARDEN

Crinan PA31 8SR
Mrs N Ryan
T: 01546 830261 E: nryan@crinanhotel.com
W: www.crinanhotel.com

Small rock garden, now open for 25 years, with azaleas and rhododendrons created in a steep hillside over a century ago; with steps leading to a sheltered, secluded garden with sloping lawns, herbaceous beds and spectacular views of the canal and Crinan Loch.

Open: 1 May - 31 August, dawn – dusk, admission by donation. Raffle of signed, limited edition fine art print by Frances Macdonald. Tickets available at the coffee shop, art gallery and hotel.

Directions: Take the A83 to Lochgilphead, then the A816 to Oban, then the A841 Cairnbaan to Crinan. Daily bus.

Opening for: Feedback Madagascar

17 DAL AN EAS

Kilmore, Oban PA34 4XU
Mary Lindsay
T: 01631 770246 E: dalaneas@live.com

An informal country garden with the aim of increasing the biodiversity of native plants and insects while adding interest and colour with introduced trees, shrubs and naturalised perennials. There is a structured garden round the house and beyond there are extensive flower-filled 'meadows' with five different species of native orchid. Grass paths lead to waterfalls, vegetable plot, woodland garden, views and ancient archaeological sites.

Open: by arrangement 1 May - 30 September, admission £5.00, children free. Teas on request.

Directions: From Oban take the A816 to Kilmore three-and-a-half miles south of Oban. Turn left on road to Barran and Musdale. Keep left at junction for Connel. Dal an Eas is approximately one mile on the left before the big hedges.

Opening for: SGS and Beneficiaries

Argyll & Lochaber

18   **DRUIMNEIL HOUSE**
Port Appin PA38 4DQ
Mrs J Glaisher (Gardener: Mr Andrew Ritchie 07484 165749)
T: 01631 730228 E: druimneilhouse@btinternet.com

Large garden overlooking Loch Linnhe with many fine varieties of mature trees and rhododendrons and other woodland shrubs. Nearer the house, an impressive bank of deciduous azaleas is underplanted with a block of camassia and a range of other bulbs. A small Victorian walled garden is currently being restored. Owner, Janet Glaisher, is the winner of the Diana Macnab Award 2020. She has opened Druimneil House for Scotland's Garden Scheme for a remarkable 40 years.

Open: 1 January - 31 December, dawn – dusk, admission by donation. Teas normally available.

Directions: Turn in for Appin off the A828 (Connel/Fort William Road). After two miles take a sharp left at Airds Hotel and it's the second house on the right.

Opening for: The Queen's Nursing Institute Scotland & The Appin Village Hall

19   **EAS MHOR**
Cnoc-a-Challtuinn, Clachan Seil, Oban PA34 4TR
Mrs Kimbra Lesley Barrett
T: 01852 300469 E: kimbra1745@gmail.com

All the usual joys of a west coast garden plus some delightful surprises! A small contemporary garden on a sloping site – the emphasis being on scent and exotic plant material. Unusual and rare blue Borinda bamboos (only recently discovered in China) and bananas. The garden is at its best in mid to late summer when shrub roses and sweet peas fill the air with scent. The delightful, sunny deck overlooks stylish white-walled ponds with cascading water blades. Recent additions include a 20-foot citrus house, Chinese pergola walk and peony border.

Open: by arrangement 1 May - 31 October, admission £5.00, children free.

Directions: After arranging a visit and agreeing a time, you will be met at the Tigh An Truish Car Park by the Atlantic Bridge, Isle of Seil. Or if travelling by bus, you will be met off the bus and taken to Eas Mhor. Please inform Mrs Barrett the time of your arrival. The bus stops at the bottom of Cnoc-a-Challtuinn Road.

Opening for: ABWA: Argyll & Bute Woman's Aid-support for domestic abuse – Oban Branch

Eas Mhor © Maurice Wilkins

Argyll & Lochaber

20 FASNACLOICH
Appin PA38 4BJ
Mr and Mrs David Stewart

South-facing 15-acre woodland garden sloping down to Loch Baile Mhic Cailein in Glen Creran. Partly laid out in the mid-19th century with extensive structural water features added in the early 20th century. The garden mainly consists of hybrid and species rhododendrons, azaleas and magnolias with, over the last 25 years, a more recent addition of trees from Eastern Europe, Central Asia and the Northern United States (including a small pinetum).

Open: Sunday 21 May, noon - 5pm, admission £5.00, children free.

Directions: On the A828 at the roundabout on the north side of Creagan Bridge take the road for Invercreran. At the head of the loch go straight ahead for about one-and-a-half miles. The house is on the right hand side.

Opening for: Mary's Meals

21 INVERARAY CASTLE GARDENS
Inveraray PA32 8XF
The Duke and Duchess of Argyll
T: 01499 302203 E: manager@inveraray-castle.com
W: www.inveraray-castle.com

The castle gardens are a blaze of yellows with varieties of narcissus in the spring, followed by bluebells in May. Rhododendrons and azaleas abound and flower from April to June and the newly restored rose garden is a mass of pinks in late June and July. Very fine specimens of *Cedrus deodara*, *Sequoiadendron giganteum* (Wellingtonia), *Cryptomeria japonica*, *Taxus baccata* and others thrive in the damp climate. The Flag-Borders on each side of the main drive with paths in the shape of Scotland's national flag, the St Andrew's Cross, are outstanding in spring with *Prunus* 'Ukon' and *P. subhirtella* and are underplanted with rhododendrons, eucryphias, shrubs and herbaceous plants giving interest all year.

Open: 3 April - 31 October, 10am - 5pm, admission £8.50 (Garden only) children under 5 free. Tearoom and shop on site. Free parking with castle and garden entrance. Pre-booking via website recommended. Tours with the Head Gardener can be arranged in advance. Only assistance dogs within the castle and garden. Please check the website for opening days (currently shut Tuesdays and Wednesdays) and times, further information and accessibility. www.inveraray-castle.com

Directions: Inveraray is 60 miles north of Glasgow and 45 miles from Oban. Regular bus services from Glasgow, Oban and Campbeltown. SatNav PA32 8XF.

Opening for: Donation to SGS

22 INVERYNE WOODLAND GARDEN
Kilfinan, Tighnabruaich PA21 2ER
Mrs Jane Ferguson

In ten acres of a 100-year-old amenity wood at Inveryne Farm, on a sloping site, somewhat sheltered from Loch Fyne, the garden was begun in 1994. Scrub birches were gradually cleared, bridges installed and amongst rocky outcrops were planted rhododendrons, azaleas, dogwoods, Japanese maples, sorbuses, eucryphias, hydrangeas and more. Gunnera, primulas and rodgersias cling to the banks of the burn and ferns provide the backdrop for our growing shrubs.

Argyll & Lochaber

Storms have varied its character and created features, and it is still a work in progress. Spring and autumn colour and an interest in varied vistas and textures of bark and leaf inspire us.

Open: Saturday/Sunday, 27/28 May, 1pm - 5pm, admission £5.00, children free. Please park at the red-roofed barn.

Directions: Approximately six miles north of Tighnabruaich towards Kilfinan on the B8000. After turning right at the crossroads at Millhouse, follow the road past the turning to Ardmarnock, over the little bridge at the bottom of the hill. The next track on the left is unpaved and leads to Inveryne.

Opening for: Cowal Elderly Befrienders SCIO

---

 23 KAMES BAY
Kilmelford PA34 4XA
Stuart Cannon
T: 01852 200205 E: stuartcannon@kames.co.uk

Kames Bay garden has evolved from two acres of scrub and bracken on an exposed lochside hill into a natural, almost wild garden spread over 13 acres, which blends into the contours of the coastal landscape. A garden where visitors can wander at peace on the woodland walk, or the hillside walk edged with wild primroses and violets, or around the pond edged with hydrangeas. Relax on hidden benches to enjoy the magnificent views over Loch Melfort and the islands to the west. An enchanting garden full of vibrant colours, especially in the spring, with more than 100 varieties of azaleas and rhododendrons.

Open: Saturday/Sunday, 13/14 May, 2pm - 6pm, admission £5.00, children free.

Directions: On the A816 Oban to Lochgilphead road. Opposite Kames Bay and the fish farm. Two-and-a-half miles south of Kilmelford and two-and-a-half miles north of Arduaine.

Opening for: St Columba's – Poltalloch

---

 24 KILDALLOIG
Campbeltown PA28 6RE
Mr and Mrs Joe Turner
T: 07979 855930 E: kildalloig@gmail.com

Coastal garden with some interesting and unusual shrubs including Australasian shrubs and trees, climbing roses, and herbaceous perennials. There is a woodland walk and a pond garden with aquatic and bog plants.

Open: by arrangement 1 May - 31 October, admission £5.00, children free. Group visits must be pre-booked.

Directions: Take the A83 to Campbeltown, then three miles south-east of the town past Davaar Island.

Opening for: Marie Curie & Macmillan Cancer Support

Argyll & Lochaber

25 | **KINLOCHLAICH WALLED GARDEN**
Appin PA38 4BD
Miss F M M Hutchison
T: 07881 525754 E: fionakinlochlaich@gmail.com
W: www.kinlochlaichgardencentre.co.uk

Octagonal walled garden incorporating a large Nursery Garden Centre with a huge variety of plants growing and for sale. Bluebell woodland walk and spring garden. Many rhododendrons, azaleas, trees, shrubs and herbaceous plants, including many unusual ones such as embothrium, davidia, stewartia, magnolia, eucryphia and tropaeolum. A quarter of the interior of the walled garden is borders packed with many unusual and interesting plants, espaliered fruit trees, and with an ancient yew in the centre, and another quarter is vegetable growing.

Open: 3 March - 31 October, 10am - 4pm, admission by donation. Winter by appointment – we are generally about. Accommodation available, see www.kinlochlaichgardenselfcatering.co.uk/

Directions: On the A828 in Appin between Oban, 18 miles to the south, and Fort William, 27 miles to the north. The entrance is next to the police station. Infrequent bus Oban to Fort William – request stop.

Opening for: The Appin Village Hall & Down's Syndrome Scotland: West of Scotland Branch

26 | **KNOCK NEWHOUSE**
Lochgair PA31 8RZ
Mrs Hew Service
T: 01546 886628 E: corranmorhouse@aol.com

Like all good gardens, it has evolved over time. It is centred on a 250 foot lochan, a small waterfall and lily pond. The first trees and rhododendrons were planted in the 60s, with major additions in the 90s. A variety of cut leaf and flowering trees were added after the storms of 2011/12. As a result the garden now has a wide range of specimen trees, camellias, hoheria, eucryphia, stewartia to name a few in addition to the azaleas and rhododendrons. January flowering is followed with spring flowers and bluebells and then into the autumn with spectacular colours. I am delighted to welcome visitors at any time so please let me know when you would like to visit.

Open: Saturday/Sunday, 6/7 May & Sunday 28 May, 1pm - 5pm. Also open by arrangement 1 April - 1 November. Admission £5.00, children free. Plants for sale.
Tours and groups must be pre-booked.

Directions: On the A83. The house is not visible from the road. From Lochgilphead, half-a-mile south of Lochgair Hotel and on the left-hand side of the road, and from Inveraray on the right-hand side of the road half-a-mile after the Lochgair Hotel; the drive opening is marked and enters the woods. Bus Route – Inveraray to Lochgilphead

Opening for: Cancer Research UK & The Lochgair Association (SCIO): Village Hall Fund

27 | **ORMSARY GARDENS**
Ormsary, Lochgilphead, Argyll PA31 8PE
Lady Lithgow
T: 01880 770738 E: mclithgow@ormsary.co.uk

Ormsary is on the shore of Loch Caolisport looking across to Islay and Jura. The house policies are resplendent in spring with bluebells and daffodils under fine oak trees. There are woodland gardens with azaleas, rhododendrons and a collection of trees and shrubs. The walled garden, which has evolved over a couple of centuries, is on two levels. The top half is a kitchen garden producing plants, fruit and vegetables for the house; a winter garden and 'Muscat of Alexandria'

Argyll & Lochaber

vinery have been heated by hydroelectric power for 100 years. A magnificent *Polylepis australis* beckons to the lower Secret Garden with its lawn, roses, magnolias and long mixed border. It opens onto the banks of Ormsary Water. There are also woodland walks accessed via the upper woodland garden with specimens of Wollemi Pine, Gingko and Turkish Oak.

Open: by arrangement 3 April - 31 October, admission £5.00, children free.

Directions: Take the A83 road from Lochgilphead towards Campbeltown for four miles, then take the B8024 signposted to *Kilberry*, travel ten miles and follow signs to the *Estate office* for directions to the garden.

Opening for: Mary's Meals

---

  28   ## STRACHUR FLOWER & WOODLAND GARDENS
Strachur PA27 8BX
Sir Charles and Lady Maclean

The flower garden is sheltered by magnificent beeches, limes, ancient yews and Japanese maples. There are herbaceous borders, a burnside rhododendron and azalea walk, rockery, tulips and spring bulbs. Enjoy the old woodland of Strachur Park, laid out in 1782, and the wildlife rich lochan.

Open: Sunday 14 May & Sunday 21 May, 1pm - 5pm, admission £5.00, children free.

Directions: Turn off the A815 at Strachur House Farm entrance. Park in farm square. Bus Dunoon – Inveraray. From Edinburgh/Glasgow take the ferry from Gourock to Dunoon.

Opening for: British Red Cross

---

  29   ## THE SECRET GARDEN
Isle of Lismore, Oban, Argyll PA34 5UL
Eva Tombs
T: 01631 760128 E: eva.tombs@gmail.com

A unique garden at the centre of a biodynamic farm on the Island of Lismore in the Inner Hebrides. The garden created from a field has a strong geometric layout that reflects the ecclesiastical history of the island. It has a vegetable garden, a tree nursery, a physic garden, an orchard and a polytunnel. The garden is a haven for wildflowers, birds, bees and butterflies. Standing stones, meadows, mountains and the sea encompass the whole. There is also a herd of rare breed Shetland cattle, chickens, ducks and friendly cats.

Open: by arrangement 1 January - 1 December, admission £5.00, children free. Plants, seeds, fruit and vegetables, flowers, meat and eggs for sale. No dogs please, there are lots of animals around. Refreshments by arrangement.

Directions: Please telephone for directions. Approximately two miles from Port Appin ferry.

Opening for: SGS and Beneficiaries

Ayrshire & Arran

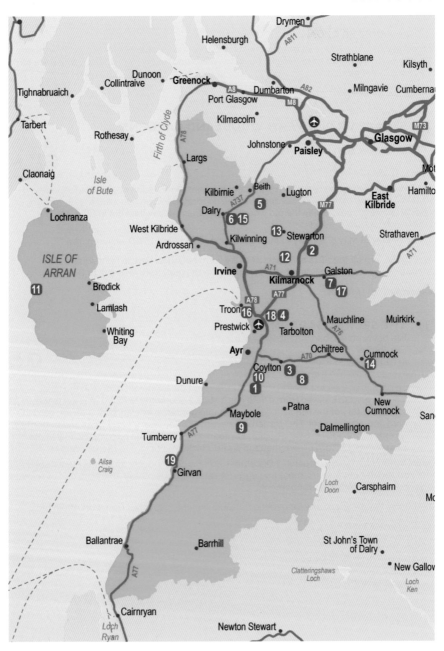

Ayrshire & Arran

OUR VOLUNTEER ORGANISERS

District Organisers:	Rose-Ann Cuninghame	45 Towerhill Avenue, Kilmaurs KA3 2TS
		E: racuninghame@gmail.com T: 07748 280036
	Lavinia Gibbs	Dougarie, Isle of Arran KA27 8EB
		E: info@scotlandsgardens.org
Area Organisers:	Kim Donald MBE	
	Sarah Hay	
	Pattie Kewney	
	Fiona McLean	
	Wendy Sandiford	
	Jane Tait	
	Sue Veitch	
District Photographers:	David Blatchford	
	Rob Davis	
Treasurers:	Lizzie Adam	Bayview, Pirnmill, Isle of Arran KA27 8HP
	Carol Freireich	18 Netherblane, Blanefield, Stirling G63 9JW
		E: carol.freireich@btinternet.com T: 07980 164404

GARDENS OPEN ON A SPECIFIC DATE

Blair Castle & Estate, Dalry, Ayrshire	Sunday, 30 April
Kirkfauld, 5 Kirkton Road, Kilmarnock	Saturday/Sunday, 13/14 May
Burnhouse, Cemetery Road, Galston	Saturday/Sunday, 20/21 May
The Wildings, Bankwood, Galston	Saturday, 27 May
Kirkmuir Cottage, Stewarton	Saturday/Sunday, 3/4 June
Barrmill Community Garden, Barrmill Park and Gardens	Sunday, 18 June
Underwood Lodge, Craigie, Kilmarnock, South Ayrshire	Saturday, 1 July
Barnweil Garden, Craigie, near Kilmarnock	Sunday, 2 July
Dougarie, Isle of Arran	Tuesday, 4 July
The Wildings, Bankwood, Galston	Saturday, 8 July
The Pines, Southwood Road, Troon	Saturday/Sunday, 15/16 July
Dalhowan Farm, Dalhowan Farm, Crosshill, Maybole	Saturday, 29 July
Netherthird Community Garden, Craigens Road, Cumnock	Saturday, 12 August

GARDENS OPEN REGULARLY

Dalrymple Community Garden, Barbieston Road, Dalrymple	1 January - 31 December
Whitewin House, Golf Course Road, Girvan	Saturday/Sunday, 15 July - 20 August

Ayrshire & Arran

GARDENS OPEN BY ARRANGEMENT – BOOK A VISIT WITH THE GARDEN OWNER

Burnside, Littlemill Road, Drongan	1 April - 30 September
The Carriage House, Blair Estate, Dalry	1 April - 30 November
Auldbyres Farm Garden, Coylton	9 April - 30 September
19 Waterslap, Fenwick	15 April - 17 September
The Wildings, Bankwood, Galston	1 May - 30 September
Barnweil Garden, Craigie, near Kilmarnock	14 May - 20 July
Dougarie, Isle of Arran	22 May - 30 August
1 Burnton Road, Dalrymple	1 June - 31 August
Whitewin House, Golf Course Road, Girvan	1 July - 31 August
Barnweil Garden, Craigie, near Kilmarnock	9 October - 19 October

19 Waterslap © David Blatchford

Ayrshire & Arran

1 BURNTON ROAD
Dalrymple KA6 6DY
David and Margaret Blatchford
T: 01292 561988 E: d.blatchford273@btinternet.com

A tiny slice of jungle nestled within a small triangular plot. To the front of the house are two beds planted with nectar-secreting plants. In a larger bed, a sea of *Stipa tenuissima* is studded with perennials. To the rear,a small patio is home to some bonsai, a collection of potted terrestrial ferns and stone troughs hold tender and hardy succulents. A serpentine path meanders through dense planting of palms, bamboos, bananas and tree ferns. Of particular note, is the use of hardy and tender bromeliads and a collection of aroids such as *Arisaemia, Alocasia* and *Colocasia*. Flower highlights are provided by lilies (species and cultivars) and later in the season, cannas and hardy gingers such as *Hedychium* and *Roscoea*. A large specimen of *Schefflera taiwaniana* cloaks the side of a summer house and rare *Cordyline indivisa* is staging a modest resurgence after the winter of 2021.

Open: by arrangement 1 June - 31 August, admission £5.00, children free.

Directions: From the north take the A77 Ayr to Stranraer. At the roundabout, turn left onto the A713 and follow the road past the hospital to the junction with B742, turn right into the village and park in the White Horse car park at the T junction. The garden is on the corner of Burnton and Barbieston Roads. From the south take the A77 towards Ayr, turn right onto the B7034. Follow into the village, at Kirkton Inn junction turn left onto Barbieston Road. Bus 52 from Ayr.

Opening for: Dalrymple, Skeldon and Hollybush Project

2 19 WATERSLAP
Fenwick KA3 6AJ
Mrs Kim Donald
T: 07836 583546 E: kd581@aol.com

This south facing garden began life in 2015 with only four mature chestnut, lime and willow trees. A challenging site, the owner has designed it to give year-round colour. Traditional hedging provides shelter for this contemporary cottage garden, planted with a wide variety of now well established trees, shrubs, perennials, roses and many clematis. Snowdrops, daffodils and hellebores are planted in abundance for spring interest. For summer, herbaceous borders and shrubberies frame a lawn. Paths link raised vegetable beds, greenhouse, cold frames, fruit trees, beds and a small woodland area with many hydrangeas, ferns and a composting area. The burn on the south side inspired the flow of the garden, the banks of which are planted with water loving trees, shrubs and gunnera, giving shelter from frosts and winds. The garden remains a work in progress.

Open: by arrangement 15 April - 17 September, admission £6.00, children free. Coffees or teas can be ordered when booking. Email or phone Kim to book. Individuals and small groups welcome. Sorry no dogs.

Directions: M77 from the south take J8 signed *Fenwick*. Into the village, past the coffee shop and turn right into Waterslap. From the north take J7 signed *Fenwick*, down Main Road, at the bottom turn left into Waterslap.

Opening for: SGS and Beneficiaries

Ayrshire & Arran

3 AULDBYRES FARM GARDEN
Coylton KA6 6HG
Marshall and Sue Veitch
E: su.pavet@btinternet.com

Surrounded by a working farm, this compact, established garden has mature shrubs, wildlife pond, bog garden and stream, borrowing stunning countryside views towards Ayr and Arran. Well behaved spring borders give way to a riot of summer perennial favourites. Many 'found objects' of agricultural interest. Extensive containers brighten the farmyard with seasonal displays.

Open: by arrangement 9 April - 30 September, admission £7.50, children free. Personal tour and tea/coffee on request. Ideal for couples and small groups. Extend your visit by walking the adjacent community nature trail.

Directions: In Coylton take the road signposted *B742*, past Coylton Arms Pub in Low Coylton, *Auldbyres* is signposted on the left after half-a-mile.

Opening for: Beatson West of Scotland Cancer Centre

4 BARNWEIL GARDEN
Craigie, near Kilmarnock KA1 5NE
Mr and Mrs Ronald W Alexander
E: ronaldwalexander@btinternet.com

Developed over the past 50 years by the current owners, the garden surrounds an 18th century house. On the south lies a lawn flanked by herbaceous borders, the east one in soft colours, the other stronger. Surrounded by woodland, bordered by azaleas, rhododendrons and other woodlanders. Oscar's ditch – planted with primulas, meconopsis, ferns, woodland geraniums, smilacina, rodgersias and gunnera. The walk passes through the Golden Glade with golden leaved acers, philadelphus, rhododendron and hostas. On the north side are herbaceous borders flanking the view to Ben Lomond, sixty miles away. Long shrub rose borders are backed by beech hedges. The autumn is mostly about leaf colour – parrotia, acers, American oaks and liquidambar with underplanting of sedums, anemones, asters and dahlia.

Open: Sunday 2 July, 2pm - 5pm. Also open by arrangement 14 May – 20 July and 9 October – 19 October. Admission £6.00, children free.

Directions: From the south take the A719 off the A77 at Sandyford roundabout continue on the A719 for two-and-a-half miles before turning left onto the B730. Take the first left signposted *Barnweil Monument*, and the garden is on the right. From the north on the A77 take the left at the B730 Tarbolton (past Hayes). Go two miles on the right, signposted *Barnweil Monument* and the garden is on the right.

Opening for: Tarbolton Parish Church of Scotland & The Ridley Foundation

Ayrshire & Arran

5 BARRMILL COMMUNITY GARDEN

Barrmill Park and Gardens KA15 1HW
The Barrmill Conservation Group
T: 07920 098171 E: fionafisher.bcg@yahoo.com

This large woodland garden is carved from a 19th-century whinstone quarry and situated within an 1890's parkland, once known for the quoiting green provided for the village thread mill and ironstone pit workers of that time. Enhancement of the gardens began in 2010 by volunteers, with assistance from *Beechgrove*. Features include: enchanted woodland walks, a fairy trail, a nature trail, the Vale Burn, views of the Dusk Water, a restored 19th-century cholera pit aka 'The Deid Man's Plantin', guided walks and traditional Ayrshire quoits game. The woodland backdrop is complemented by an understorey of natural planting throughout.

Open: Sunday 18 June, 2pm - 5pm, admission £4.00, children free.

Directions: From Stewarton take the A735 to Dunlop, go left down Main Street B706 to Burnhouse, over at crossroads to Barrmill B706. From Lugton south on the A736, take the right at Burnhouse, B706 to Barrmill. From Glasgow on the M8 take J28a signposted *Irvine*, on Beith bypass take the left at B706 to Barrmill.

Opening for: Barrmill and District Community Association

6 BLAIR CASTLE & ESTATE

Dalry, Ayrshire KA24 4ER
Siobhan Nanson, Head of Business Development and Events
T: 01294 833100 E: Siobhan@blairestate.co.uk

Blair has beautiful landscaped gardens, with a collection of trees dating back to the 18th century. The gardens have undergone a major restoration project, with new beds created including a collection of rhododendrons, magnolias and azaleas. Walks around the estate will include the stunning private gardens. Sorry dogs are not allowed.

Open: Sunday 30 April, noon - 4pm, admission £6.00, children free.

Directions: Exit the A737 at the Highfield roundabout. Take the first exit towards Stewarton on the B707. Follow this road for 0.8 mile and then turn right onto Blair Road. Turn left to enter the estate at the north gates. We will be operating a one-way system on the day for visitors.

Opening for: Dalry Community Development Hub

Ayrshire & Arran

7 BURNHOUSE
Cemetery Road, Galston KA4 8LL
Kevin and Marjorie Quinn
T: 07927 907853 E: mbquinn2018@gmail.com

The garden surrounds the house which dates from the 17th century. Mature beech and lime trees shelter an abundance of rhododendrons and azaleas. Newer plantings of trees and shrubs add year-round colour and interest with underplantings of perennials and bulbs. Perfumed roses are along the entrance to the house and cottage. Raised beds have recently been added for vegetables, fruit trees and herbs. A colourful maple grove, a den for the youngsters and a rockery with alpines and small rhododendrons beside the burn all add interest. Cross the bridge to the main lawn which is framed with trees and shrubs chosen for different seasons. There are various seats in sheltered spots to enjoy, wildflowers and fruit trees.

Open: Saturday/Sunday, 20/21 May, 11am - 5pm, admission £6.00. Sorry no dogs.

Directions: At the roundabout near Tesco take the B7037 into Galston. Go over the bridge and straight ahead at the traffic lights. After 100 metres turn left following the sign to *Sorn* (B7037). At the outskirts of the village turn sharp right into Cemetery Road and Burnhouse is immediately on the left.

Opening for: *Ayrshire Cancer Support & Refuweegee*

8 BURNSIDE
Littlemill Road, Drongan KA6 7EN
Sue Simpson and George Watt
T: 01292 592445 E: suesimpson33@btinternet.com

This maturing and constantly changing six-and-a-half acre garden began in 2006. There is a wide range of plants from trees to alpines, giving colour and variability all year. Next to the road flows the Drumbowie Burn, parallel to which is a woodland border with snowdrops, erythroniums, hellebores, trilliums, rhododendrons and acers. Near the house are a raised bed and large collection of troughs, with an interesting range of alpines. The garden boasts herbaceous beds, ericaceous garden, screes, three alpine glasshouses with award-winning plants, an extensive Streptocarpus collection, polytunnel, pond and arboretum – underplanted with daffodils, camassia, fritillaries and crocus. With a view towards matrimonial harmony, there are two sheds which may be of interest. The garden is only 15 minutes from Dumfries House.

Open: by arrangement 1 April - 30 September, admission £6.00, children free. Sue and George are happy to receive any size of group, large or small, even individuals. If we don't answer, simply send an email – we check regularly. Hot drinks and baking available on request from £2.50. Visit the Scotland's Gardens Scheme website for additional openings.

Directions: From A77 Ayr bypass take A70 Cumnock for five-and-a-quarter miles, at Coalhall, turn onto B730 Drongan (south) for two-and-a-half miles. Burnside entrance is immediately adjacent to a black/white parapeted bridge. Ordnance survey grid ref: NS455162.

Opening for: *IFDAS*

Ayrshire & Arran

 9 DALHOWAN FARM
Dalhowan Farm, Crosshill, Maybole KA19 7RN
Fiona and Robbie Baird
T: 07850 282130 E: crosshill.fionabaird@tiscali.co.uk

Dalhowan is on the edge of the village, the garden of this working dairy farm has clear views towards the Heads of Ayr. Central to the garden is the lawn, around which are a wide range of mixed perennial borders providing colour into the autumn. In spring these are highly colourful with a variety of daffodils. A raised pond complements some of the external walls and border edges, constructed from recycled sandstone. A long hosta border stretches the length of the farmhouse, where it benefits from shade. Mature trees and shrubs help to protect the garden from the prevailing winds. Two greenhouses protect tender plants over winter, from which a large number of cuttings are taken to fill numerous containers around the farmyard.

Open: Saturday 29 July, 2pm - 5pm, admission £5.00, children free. Sorry no dogs. Plants for sale.

Directions: Follow the A77 south from Ayr to Maybole, take the B7023 towards the village of Crosshill, continue to the end of the village. Parking is available in the field at the end of the village, with a short walk along the road to enter the garden.

Opening for: Ayrshire Hospice

 10 DALRYMPLE COMMUNITY GARDEN
Barbieston Road, Dalrymple KA6 6DY
Dalrymple Community Landscape Project

Opened in September 2019, the garden, situated opposite the shops in Barbieston Road, is run by a dedicated team of volunteers; part of the Dalrymple, Skeldon and Hollybush Project. A large central lawn is surrounded by extensive areas of original meadow turf and already we have seen the appearance of wildflowers, with a concomitant increase in insect diversity, and the appearance of butterflies associated with wild grasses. Damselflies and amphibians have begun to visit the two ponds. We have planted several thousand spring bulbs including snake's head fritillaries and camassias as well as willows and other native shrubs to provide a richer habitat.

Open: 1 January - 31 December, dawn - dusk.

Directions: From the north take the A77 Ayr to Stranraer. At the A713 junction take the left turn and follow the road past the hospital to the B742 junction, turn right into the village and park behind the shops in the centre of the village. From south of the A77, take the B7034 and turn right. Bus 52 from Ayr.

Opening for: Dalrymple, Skeldon and Hollybush Project

Ayrshire & Arran

 11 DOUGARIE
Isle of Arran KA27 8EB
Mrs S C Gibbs
E: laviniagibbs@btopenworld.com

Most interesting terraced garden in a castellated folly built in 1905 to celebrate the marriage of the 12th Duke of Hamilton's only child to the Duke of Montrose. Good selection of tender and rare shrubs and herbaceous border. Small woodland area with trees including azara, abutilon, eucryphia, hoheria and nothofagus.

Open: Tuesday 4 July, 2pm - 5pm. Admission £4.00, children free. Also open by arrangement 22 May - 30 August. Admission £5.00, children free. Cash payments only. There is free parking.

Directions: Five miles from Blackwaterfoot. Regular ferry sailing from Ardrossan and Claonaig (Argyll). Information from Caledonian MacBrayne, Gourock, T: 01475 650100. Parking is free.

Opening for: Pirnmill Village Association

 12 KIRKFAULD
5 Kirkton Road, Kilmarnock KA3 2NW
Mr and Mrs Frank Murray
T: 07449 775333 / 01563 538350 E: frankmm@btinternet.com

A one acre garden on an historic site. Two significant buildings are in the grounds: a crow-stepped dovecot dated 1636, with many of the original stone nestboxes in good condition. It probably served as a larder for the adjacent ruins of Tour. Timothy Pont, visiting Tour in 1604 reported that it had many rooms and was probably the vicarage of the collegiate priory once standing near the site. Only nobles and clerics were allowed to keep pigeons. A burn runs through the garden, the south side being maintained as a woodland walk. The north side lawns are divided by dry stone dykes and feature a mature Alaskan cedar *(nootkatensis)* and large horse chestnuts. They are surrounded by shrubberies. At the rear of the house are two polytunnels and a greenhouse, growing chrysanthemums, dahlias, roses and vegetables.

Open: Saturday/Sunday, 13/14 May, 1pm - 5pm, admission £5.00, children free. Dogs are allowed but must be on a lead.

Directions: Kirkton Road lies off the A735 . It is a narrow lane down past the Kirk and Kilmaurs Cemetery. Park outside Kilmaurs Glencairn Kirk (limited parking at the house for disabled access).

Opening for: Ayrshire Hospice

 13 KIRKMUIR COTTAGE
Stewarton KA3 3DZ
Mr and Mrs Brian Macpherson
T: 01560 483816 E: dhmmacp@gmail.com

A one-and-a-half-acre mature garden with paths weaving through many different areas including woodland, formal borders, laburnum arch, herbaceous borders, rhododendrons and azaleas. Large lawn area and wildlife pond. The garden also features many interesting and unusual artefacts and sculptures.

Open: Saturday/Sunday, 3/4 June, 10am - 4pm, admission £6.00, children free.

Ayrshire & Arran

Directions: From the M77 take the B778 to Stewarton. At the traffic lights turn left, and continue to the mini-roundabout. Turn right at the mini-roundabout signposted *B778 Kilwinning*. Continue for 100 yards under the railway bridge, take an immediate left at the war memorial. Parking for Kirkmuir Cottage will be well signposted.

Opening for: Capability Scotland

14 NETHERTHIRD COMMUNITY GARDEN

Craigens Road, Netherthird, Cumnock KA18 3AR
Netherthird Community Development Group
E: jamielor@aol.com
W: www.facebook.com/Netherthird-Community-Development-Group-174476469271910

Netherthird Community Garden will be opening with a 'wildlife for families theme' to suit all ages. See our long cottage garden border bursting with shrubs, perennials and annuals, vegetable beds and polytunnels where we grow tomatoes and plants. The striking wooden gazebos were funded by the Prince's Trust for outdoor lessons. Visit the vast sandpit and take part in a treasure hunt and fancy dress class for young dog owners. All run by, and for, volunteers and the local community.

Open: Saturday 12 August, 2pm - 5pm, admission £4.00, children free.

Directions: Driving south on the A76 Cumnock Bypass, look for the roundabout signposted *B7083*. Take this exit which heads to Cumnock and after a few hundred yards take a right turn into Craigens Road. Netherthird Primary School is on the right and parking is available there. The Community Garden is nearby. There is disabled parking at the garden.

Opening for: Netherthird Community Development Group

15 THE CARRIAGE HOUSE

Blair Estate, Dalry KA24 4ER
Mr and Mrs Luke Borwick
T: 01294 832816 E: lina@blairtrust.co.uk

Built on a rocky outcrop with little soil depth (c1800), the garden has evolved over the past 22 years and has been designed by the owners to provide colour and interest all year round. Divided into a variety of different 'rooms', some contain sculptures by artists including Lucy Poett, Lucy Fisher and Mary Stormonth Darling and the Ironwork by Kev Paxton. Look out for the Victorian Zodiac table, the prehistoric fossilised fern 'seed' (approximately 358.9 million years old), the mermaids rescuing a girl carved from the severed trunk of a Portuguese Laurel and the wellingtonia grown from seed. In the last three years an arboretum of over 170 rare trees has been planted in the adjoining field offering a beautiful tranquil space of interest and colour. We are proud that the collection has been recognised with the *Platinum Jubilee Green Canopy Award*. The trees have been selected from Northern Hemisphere environments and include an avenue of eight varieties of limes.

Open: by arrangement 1 April - 30 November, admission £6.00, children free. A minimum of four people, email us or text 07831 301294 using 'Garden Visit' as the subject. SatNav takes you to right spot.

Directions: A737 from Beith. At the roundabout before Dalry take the first left signposted *Stewarton*. Then go straight on, signposted *Bike Route Irvine*. Keep going for approximately two miles and keep the estate wall on the right until you come to South Lodge (white building). Turn right down the drive for Blair Estate – The Carriage House is on the right. Public transport to Dalry.

Opening for: The National Trust for Scotland & Friends of Hilary Storm School Uganda

Ayrshire & Arran

16   THE PINES

Southwood Road, Troon KA10 7EL
Cheryll & Alasdair Cameron
T: 01292 314316 or 07702 807561 E: cheryllcameron2@gmail.com

In eight years our one acre plot has been transformed from a barren children's playground, with mature pine trees and rhododendrons only, to a colourful seaside garden. Our exposed coastal situation causes windburn in many supposedly hardy plants, so we have formed a windbreak for the borders with mixed shrubs including griselinia, hawthorn, and photinia. Billowing grasses sit alongside perennials including helenium, euphorbia and agapanthus, all interspersed with tulips, lilies and alliums. The coastal theme is accentuated by cordyline, phormium, *Fatsia japonica* and eucalyptus. We have barked woodland paths, and our garden is a haven for birds, bees and butterflies.

Open: Saturday/Sunday, 15/16 July, 2pm - 5pm, admission £5.00, children free.

Directions: From the A77 at Dutch House Roundabout, follow the A78 and then the A79, then immediately right to Troon on the B749. Southwood Road is first left and The Pines is the last property. Stagecoach X14 passes the property.

Opening for: Cancer Research UK

17   THE WILDINGS
Bankwood, Galston KA4 8LH
Mr and Mrs Jim Tait
T: 07854 474028 E: jane.d.tait@gmail.com

The garden was created from part woodland and a field in 1999. It nestles in a beautiful setting overlooking low lying hills to the east and a bluebell wood to the south planted with mature rhododendrons. There is a cottage garden to the front with a more formal area to the south side which includes a large pond and lawned areas surrounded by mature shrubs, trees and herbaceous plants. There are various paths that wind through the garden with seating hideaways to view different aspects of the garden. The garden is a wildlife haven and there are numerous nest boxes for a wide variety of woodland birds. The garden has been designed to provide interest through all seasons.

Open: Saturday 27 May and Saturday 8 July, 12 noon- 5pm. Also open by arrangement 1 May - 30 September, email Jane to book. Teas can be ordered when booking. Admission £6.00, children free. Sorry no dogs.

Directions: From Galston take the Sorn Road B7037 and follow for approx one and a half miles. Just before reaching Sorn Hill turn left where signposted *Gibbs Animal Feeds*. Turn left again immediately and follow the lane for half a mile and The Wildings is the first house on the left. Please note parking is limited.

Opening for: The Purim Trust

Ayrshire & Arran

18 UNDERWOOD LODGE

Craigie, Kilmarnock, South Ayrshire KA1 5NG
Marilyn Badman
T: 01563 830439 E: mbadman1@sky.com

Underwood Lodge has a secluded garden surrounded by farmland and woodland which give some protection and adds to the ambience. The main structure of the garden has been in place for about 20 years, however, significant remodelling has taken place in the last few years. The one-acre garden comprises a variety of mature trees, shrubs, herbaceous and wallgrown plants. A woodland garden is at an embryonic stage with the construction of a woodland path, the planting of some semi-mature rhododendrons and some underplanting of woodland plants. The planting within all areas of the garden demonstrates an understanding of form and texture of plants, which adds to its enjoyment.

Open: Saturday 1 July, 11am - 5pm, admission £5.00, children free. Visitors should make contact in advance and will be given a timed slot during the open days.

Directions: Southbound on the A77, pass Hansel Village and take the next left signposted *Underwood/Ladykirk*. Northbound on the A77 take the exit to Symington, then first right, to join the Southbound Carriageway. Take the Underwood/Ladykirk turning. At the stone bridge, turn left and Underwood Lodge is the first house on the left. Please note daytime contraflow on the A77.

Opening for: Annbank Parish Church Of Scotland

19 WHITEWIN HOUSE

Golf Course Road, Girvan KA26 9HW
Linda Finnie and Graeme Finnie
T: 01465 712358 M: 07855 269247 E: lafinnie@hotmail.com

Historic Whitewin House was built for Baronet Henry Tate of Tate and Lyle. The house stands in one acre of formal Victorian Garden, redesigned over a five year period in the form of an English Manor House Garden, which of course, comes with its challenges, because of its coastal location. The rockeries, beautiful scalloped lawns and the plethora of statuary all complement the use of authentic Victorian bedding plants, trees and shrubs, ideally mirroring the ambience and grandeur of the house interior. In 2022, two water features were added to the garden. Whitewin House is fortunate in having prime position in Golf Course Road, having been the first house built there, standing majestically overlooking the Firth of Clyde, Ailsa Craig, Arran and the Kintyre Peninsula.

Open: Saturdays/Sundays, 15/16 July, 22/23 July, 29/30 July, 5/6 August, 12/13 August and 19/20 August, 2pm - 5pm. Also open by arrangement 1 July - 31 August. Admission £6.00, children free. Teas and coffees will be served in the conservatories and the garden.

Directions: Approaching Girvan from the north on the A77 the turning to Golf Course Road is on the right-hand-side of the road before the town centre follow signs for the *Golf Course*. From the south on the A77 come through Girvan, turn left at the lights, then first left and follow signs for the *Golf Course*. Entrance to the property will be signposted.

Opening for: SGS and Beneficiaries

Berwickshire

Map of Berwickshire showing locations:
St Abb's Head, Eyemouth (6), Berwick-upon-Tweed, Norham, Etal, Chirnside, Granthouses, Coldstream (4), Preston, 2 5 7, Duns (3), 8, Eccles, Greenlaw (1), Kelso, Gordon, Gifford, Lauder, Melrose

Berwickshire

OUR VOLUNTEER ORGANISERS

District Organiser:	Christine McLennan	Marlfield, Coldstream TD12 4JT E: info@scotlandsgardens.org
Area Organisers:	Candy Philip Susan Vassallo	34 Trinity Park, Duns TD11 3HN 4 Lambton Green, Coldstream TD12 4EN
Cartographer:	Christine Johnston	
District Photographer:	Malcolm Ross	2 Dall Hollow, North Berwick EH39 5FN
Treasurer:	Forbes McLennan	Marlfield, Coldstream TD12 4JT

GARDENS OPEN ON A SPECIFIC DATE

Broomhill Villa, 4 Edinburgh Road, Greenlaw	Sunday, 14 May
Duns Open Gardens , Volunteer Hall, Langtongate, Duns	Sunday, 18 June
Ruthven House, Coldstream	Sunday, 25 June
The Moorhouse, Duns	Sunday, 16 July
Marlfield, Coldstream	Sunday, 23 July

GARDENS OPEN REGULARLY

Bughtrig, near Leitholm, Coldstream	1 June - 1 September

GARDENS OPEN BY ARRANGEMENT – BOOK A VISIT WITH THE GARDEN OWNER

Ruthven House, Coldstream	1 January - 30 September
Netherbyres, Eyemouth	1 May - 31 August
Lennel Bank, Coldstream	1 May - 31 October
Broomhill Villa, 4 Edinburgh Road, Greenlaw	1 June - 31 July
Marlfield, Coldstream	1 June - 31 October

Berwickshire

1 **BROOMHILL VILLA**
4 Edinburgh Road, Greenlaw TD10 6XF
Tatyana Aplin
T: 07957 288557 E: aplin848@btinternet.com

Broomhill garden is on the northern side of Greenlaw comprising half-an-acre of spring colour nestled between village and farmland. The garden is maintained by a passionate plant collector featuring narcissuses, tulips, meconopses, and hundreds of other flowers. The collection has been developed along informal lines with treats at every turn. A radiant display of blooms that changes through the year is intended not only for the visual pleasure of the garden but also for the house with cut flower arrangements as well as produce for the table and larder.

Open: Sunday 14 May, 1pm - 5pm. Also open by arrangement 1 June - 31 July. Admission £5.00, children free.

Directions: On the A697 at the northern end of Greenlaw Village

Opening for: Cancer Research UK

Broomhill Villa

2 **BUGHTRIG**
near Leitholm, Coldstream TD12 4JP
Mr and Mrs William Ramsay
E: ramsay@bughtrig.co.uk

A traditional hedged Scottish family garden with an interesting combination of sculpture, herbaceous plants, shrubs, annuals and fruit. It is surrounded by fine specimen trees, which provide remarkable shelter.

Open: 1 June - 1 September, 11am - 5pm, admission £5.00, children free.

Directions: Quarter-of-a-mile east of Leitholm on the B6461.

Opening for: Donation to SGS

Berwickshire

 3

DUNS OPEN GARDENS
Volunteer Hall, Langtongate, Duns TD11 3AF
The Gardeners of Duns

Duns, formally the county town of Berwickshire, lies approximately 12 miles north of the border between Scotland and England and still retains a thriving market square reminiscent of an ancient Scottish burgh. It is home to an award-winning motor sport museum depicting the life and career of Formula 1 Champion, Jim Clark OBE. There are extensive green areas in and around the town offering delightful walks all year round. After two hugely successful years of opening our gardens in August 2021 and again in August 2022 we decided to show our visitors how varied our gardens are in Duns and have chosen a different season for 2023. Our gardens are lovingly tended by enthusiastic gardeners, happy to share them with like-minded people. They offer a wonderful variety of size, layout and planting, ensuring that there is something for everyone. We are sure you will enjoy your time in Duns, meeting and chatting with other garden lovers and sharing ideas and plans for future garden projects.

Open: Sunday 18 June, 12 noon - 5pm, admission £5.00, children free. Teas/coffees available to purchase at the Volunteer Hall where you can also purchase tickets and route maps. For our visitors wishing a more substantial lunch or treat, our Market Square cafes offer a variety of hot and cold food with seating both inside and out.

Directions: Duns is situated on the crossroads of the A6112 and A6105, approximately 14 miles west of Berwick upon Tweed and is easily accessible from the A1 onto the A6112 and from the A68/697 onto the A6105.

Opening for: A Heart for Duns

Lennel Bank © Kenneth Patterson

Berwickshire

4 | LENNEL BANK
Coldstream TD12 4EX
Mrs Honor Brown
T: 01890 882297 E: honor.b.brown@gmail.com

Lennel Bank is a terraced garden overlooking the River Tweed, consisting of wide borders packed with shrubs and perennial planting, some unusual. The water garden, built in 2008, is surrounded by a rockery and utilises the slope, ending in a pond. There is a small kitchen garden with raised beds in unusual shapes. Different growing conditions throughout the garden from dry, wet, shady and sunny, lend themselves to a variety of plants and enhance interest in the garden.

Open: by arrangement 1 May - 31 October, admission £5.00, children free.

Directions: On the A6112 Coldstream to Duns road, one mile from Coldstream.

Opening for: SGS and Beneficiaries

5 | MARLFIELD
Coldstream TD12 4JT
Christine and Forbes McLennan
T: 01890 840700 M: 07717 237357 E: forbes.mclennan@gmail.com

Marlfield, previously a traditional 80 acre farm, now a quiet hamlet with three lovely gardens:
Marlfield Farmhouse (Christine and Forbes McLennan) – this two acre garden has been open for the past six years with extensive lawns, specimen trees, herbaceous borders and a large raised bed allotment style vegetable garden.
West Cottage (Max and Kate Lowe) – a beautiful cottage garden, intensively planted with herbaceous borders, mixed shrubberies, vegetable and fruit plot.
The Lodge (Ron Whittaker 07766 296453) – newly re-designed, this half-acre garden, with fine views of the surrounding countryside, is a lovely mix of lawns, herbaceous borders, wild flower meadow, vegetables and fruit. A chance to observe a lovely garden in development.

Open: Sunday 23 July, 1pm - 5pm. Also open by arrangement 1 June - 31 October. Admission £5.00, children free.

Directions: Four miles north of Coldstream on the old Duns road. Half-a-mile off the main road.

Opening for: Charity to be confirmed

6 | NETHERBYRES
Eyemouth TD14 5SE
Col S J Furness
T: 01890 750337

An unusual elliptical walled garden, dating from 1740, with a mixture of flowers, fruit and vegetables. A very old pear tree, possibly dating from the 18th century, and the largest rose in Berwickshire, *Rosa filipes* 'Kiftsgate'. A wide variety of roses and herbaceous borders.

Open: by arrangement 1 May - 31 August, admission £5.00, children free. Only open for parties of four or more.

Directions: Half-a-mile south of Eyemouth on the A1107 to Berwick.

Opening for: SGS and Beneficiaries

Berwickshire

7 RUTHVEN HOUSE

Coldstream TD12 4JU
Keith and Karen Fountain
T: 01890 840680 E: ruthvenhouse@btconnect.com

The three acres of Ruthven's garden have lovely views towards the Cheviots. The garden's central feature is two ponds joined by a winding stream. The garden is composed of various differing areas – herbaceous borders, woodland areas, a gravel garden, a knot garden, rockeries, an orchard laid to meadow, a kitchen garden, a nuttery, a small lavender field and, adjacent to the house, a formal rose garden. Much of the work to create the garden from the original few small beds around the house has only been undertaken in the last few years, so the garden has not yet reached complete maturity. New for this year is a shade bed under the plum trees. The small fold of Highland cattle in the adjacent field complete the scene.

Open: Sunday 25 June, 1pm - 5pm. Also open by arrangement 1 January - 30 September. Admission £5.00, children free. Groups and individuals are welcome.

Directions: Four miles north of Coldstream on the old Duns road.

Opening for: Macmillan Cancer Support (Sunday 25 June) & Scottish Association For Mental Health (1 January - 30 September)

8 THE MOORHOUSE

Duns TD11 3RY
Mike and Bridget Bevan
T: 07848 803776 E: bordersecoflowers@gmail.com

The Borders Eco Flowers garden at The Moorhouse is designed to produce organic cut flowers and foliage throughout the year. Whilst most cut flowers sold in Scotland are imported, our flowers are grown here, not flown here! All are grown in an environmentally friendly manner without the use of chemical fertilisers and pesticides. Not only are we eco-friendly gardeners, we are eco-friendly florists too! We harvest the flowers at their peak and create posies, bouquets and all kinds of unique floral creations.

Open: Sunday 16 July, 1pm - 5pm, admission £5.00, children free. Dogs must remain on leads, as we have free range hens and ducks.

Directions: Ignore the SatNav, once you have left the A6112. From Duns, take the A6112 towards Grantshouse. Ignore the left-hand turn (B6355) signposted *Abbey St Bathans*. Proceed through the village of Preston and three miles further on, turn left signposted *Edin's Hall Brock*. Continue up the hill for a mile-and-a-half and you will see *The Moorhouse* (painted yellow) on the right. From the A1, turn off at Grantshouse onto the A6112, signposted Dun. After three-and-a-half-miles, turn right signposted *Edin's Hall Brock*. Continue up the hill for a mile-and-a-half and you will see *The Moorhouse* (painted yellow) on the right.

Opening for: Borders Pet Rescue

Caithness & Sutherland

Sponsored by
Investec

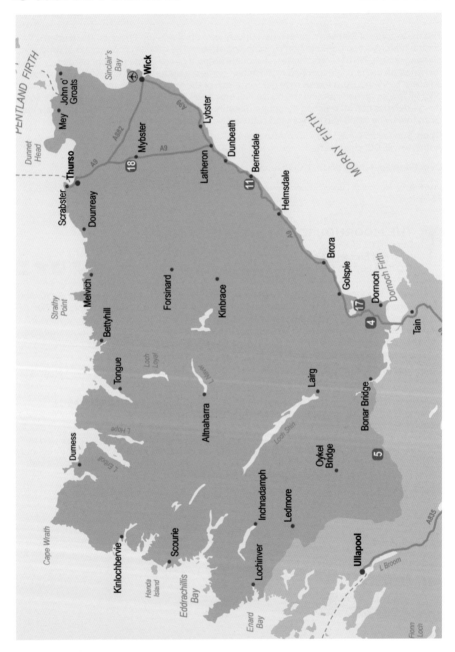

Caithness, Sutherland, Orkney & Shetland

Orkney

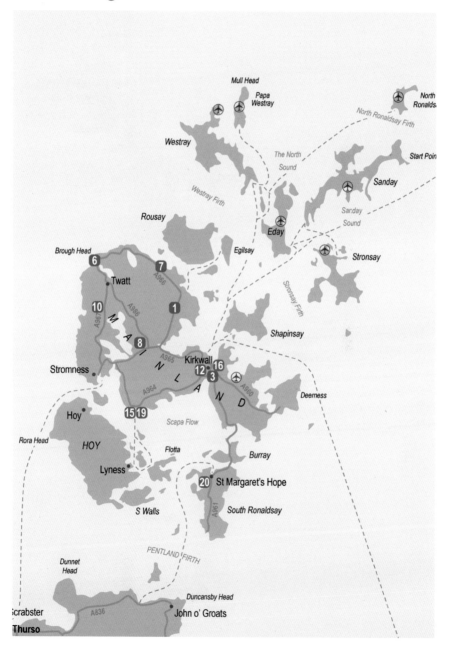

Shetland

Sponsored by
⊕ Investec

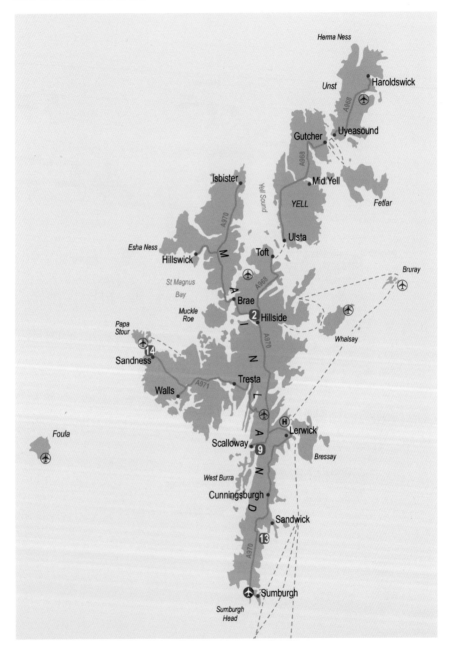

Caithness, Sutherland, Orkney & Shetland

OUR VOLUNTEER ORGANISERS

District Organiser:	Sara Shaw	Amat, Ardgay, Sutherland IV24 3BS E: info@scotlandsgardens.org
Area Organisers:	Caroline Critchlow Miranda Jones Mary Leask Steve Mathieson	Old Granary Quoy, Orphir, Orkney KW17 2RD Rowanlea, Main Street, Sutherland IV27 4DD VisitScotland, Market Cross, Shetland ZE1 0LU VisitScotland, Market Cross, Shetland ZE1 0LU
District Photographer:	Colin Gregory	Iona, Reay, Caithness, KW14 7RG
Treasurer:	Nicola Vestey	

GARDENS OPEN ON A SPECIFIC DATE

16 Mulla, Voe, Shetland	Saturday/Sunday, 15/16 April
Old Granary Quoy, The Quoy of Houton, Orphir, Orkney	Sunday, 14 May
The Quoy of Houton, Orphir, Orkney	Sunday, 14 May
Linfirlea, Pipersquoy Road, Kirkwall	Sunday, 21 May
19 Burnside, Kirkwall, Orkney	Sunday, 18 June
Finya, Grimeston Road, Harray, Orkney	Sunday 25 June
Westlea, Cromarty Square, St Margaret's Hope, Orkney	Sunday, 25 June
16 Mulla, Voe, Shetland	Saturday/Sunday, 1/2 July
Westlea, Cromarty Square, St Margaret's Hope, Orkney	Sunday, 2 July
Old Granary Quoy, The Quoy of Houton, Orphir, Orkney	Sunday, 9 July
The Quoy of Houton, Orphir, Orkney	Sunday, 9 July
Kierfiold House, Kierfiold House, Sandwick, Orkney	Sunday, 9 July
Amat, Amat Lodge, Ardgay	Saturday/Sunday, 15/16 July
Linfirlea, Pipersquoy Road, Kirkwall	Sunday, 16 July
Annie's Place, Old Manse, Palace Village, Birsay, Orkney	Sunday, 16 July
Finya, Grimeston Road, Harray, Orkney	Sunday 16 July
Kierfiold House, Kierfiold House, Sandwick, Orkney	Sunday, 16 July
Round House, Berstane Road, Kirkwall, Orkney	Sunday, 16 July
19 Burnside, Kirkwall, Orkney	Sunday, 16 July
Skelbo House, Skelbo, Dornoch	Saturday/Sunday, 22/23 July
42 Astle, Dornoch	Saturday/Sunday, 22/23 July
11 Lyron, Rendall, Orkney	Saturday, 29 July
Annie's Place, Old Manse, Palace Village, Birsay, Orkney	Sunday, 30 July
Castlehill B&B, Evie, Orkney	Sunday, 30 July
Langwell, Berriedale	Sunday, 30 July
11 Lyron, Rendall, Orkney	Saturday, 5 August
Linfirlea, Pipersquoy Road, Kirkwall, Orkney	Sunday, 13 August
Annie's Place, Old Manse, Palace Village, Birsay, Orkney	Sunday, 20 August
The Garden at the Auld Post Office B&B, Spittal-by-Mybster	Sunday, 20 August

Caithness, Sutherland, Orkney & Shetland

GARDENS OPEN REGULARLY

Norby, Burnside, Sandness, Shetland	1 April - 31 December

GARDENS OPEN BY ARRANGEMENT

16 Mulla, Voe, Shetland	1 April - 30 September
Highlands Garden, East Voe, Scalloway, Shetland	1 May - 31 October
Nonavaar, Levenwick, Shetland	1 May - 30 September

Orkney Summer Festival

Eleven Orkney gardens are opening as part of the Orkney Summer Festival this year. You can visit the gardens from 14 May to 20 August and will have the chance to speak to Garden Owners who are gardening under Orkney's challenging conditions. The gardens are all of very different sizes and styles but will certainly offer interest to visitors, so be sure to include some in your plans for the summer. To help you plan your visits, the gardens are listed by date order below. Details of each garden are shown in the following pages. Look for the ORKNEY SUMMER FESTIVAL sign to find out information on all participating gardens.

Old Granary Quoy, The Quoy of Houton, Orphir	Sunday, 14 May
The Quoy of Houton, Orphir	Sunday, 14 May
Linfirlea, Pipersquoy Road	Sunday, 21 May
19 Burnside, Kirkwall	Sunday, 18 June
Finya, Grimeston Road, Harray	Sunday 25 June
Westlea, Cromarty Square, St Margaret's Hope	Sunday, 25 June
Westlea, Cromarty Square, St Margaret's Hope	Sunday, 2 July
Old Granary Quoy, The Quoy of Houton, Orphir	Sunday, 9 July
The Quoy of Houton, Orphir	Sunday, 9 July
Kierfiold House, Kierfiold House, Sandwick	Sunday, 9 July
Linfirlea, Pipersquoy Road, Kirkwall	Sunday, 16 July
Annie's Place, Old Manse, Palace Village, Birsay	Sunday, 16 July
Finya, Gremestone Road, Harray	Sunday, 16 July
Kierfiold House, Kierfiold House, Sandwick	Sunday, 16 July
Round House, Berstane Road, Kirkwall	Sunday, 16 July
19 Burnside, Kirkwall,	Sunday, 16 July
11 Lyron, Rendall, Orkney	Saturday, 29 July
Annie's Place, Old Manse, Palace Village, Birsay	Sunday, 30 July
Castlehill B&B, Evie, Orkney	Sunday, 30 July
11 Lyron, Rendall, Orkney	Saturday, 5 August
Linfirlea, Pipersquoy Road, Kirkwall, Orkney	Sunday, 13 August
Annie's Place, Old Manse, Palace Village, Birsay, Orkney	Sunday, 20 August

Caithness, Sutherland, Orkney & Shetland

 11 LYRON
Rendall, Orkney KW17 2NZ
Ursula Porterfield

ORKNEY SUMMER FESTIVAL

Small south facing garden that is open to salt sea breezes and is inclined to poor drainage problems. I garden organically and have areas devoted to insect/bee/wildlife, raised veg/fruit beds and a small polytunnel, as well as perennial borders with a variety of plants that I am experimenting with to find ones suitable for our Orkney climate short growing season! I have a special interest in making as much of my own compost as possible, which is badly needed to improve the soil in my gardening area!

Open: Saturday 29 July and Saturday 5 August, 10am - 5pm. Admission by donation. There may be some plants for sale.

Directions: If travelling from Kirkwall/Finstown, take the Tingwall road through Norseman village and Lyron is the first road on the right as you go past Rendall Community Hall. Our house if the last one at the end of the road.

Opening for: CLAN

 16 MULLA
Voe, Shetland ZE2 9XQ
Linda Richardson
T: 07765 037516 E: linda@lindarichardson.co.uk

A garden on the Clubb of Mulla, a hillside overlooking Olnafirth with views of the sea and Lower Voe. Started in October 2016, the steep overgrown plot looked like a continuation of the moor at the back of the house. This garden shows what can be achieved in a very windy and exposed situation, battling against the extremes of the Shetland weather. Gardening with wildlife in mind, trees were planted in the spring of 2017, now providing shelter for birds. Six years on, there are herbaceous borders, rockery, a vegetable bed, 3.6 x 2.4 metre greenhouse, mini wildflower meadow strips and a natural water feature which is a long drainage ditch planted up with willows and water-loving plants. Always a work in progress, more trees will be added this year. The owner is an artist-printmaker with an open studio that folk are welcome to look round too.

Open: Two plant sale weekends – Saturday/Sunday 15/16 April and Saturday/Sunday, 1/2 July, 10am - 5pm. Tea and cake will be available on these dates. Also open by arrangement 1 April - 30 September. Look for the open sign for 16 Mulla on the main road. If the sign is out the garden and studio are open or telephone us to arrange a visit. Admission by donation.

Directions: Eighteen miles north of Lerwick on the A970 is Voe. Pass the North Isles junction and Tagon Stores on your right. Turn right into Mulla and number 16 is up the hill on your left. Bus no. 21 (Hillswick) and 23 (Toft) stop on the main road at the bottom of Mulla.

Opening for: Shetland UHI: Shetland Community Wildlife Group

Caithness, Sutherland, Orkney & Shetland

 3 **19 BURNSIDE**
Kirkwall, Orkney KW15 1TF
Jenny Marriott

ORKNEY SUMMER FESTIVAL

This small sloping town garden makes the most of the thin topsoil and steep slopes. The winding grass pathway edged with meadow planting and punctuated by perennials brings a breath of countryside into the town. Difficult areas have been left to naturalise and this work in progress gives everyday gardeners some great, budget saving ideas.

Open: Sunday 18 June and Sunday 16 July, 2pm - 5pm. Admission by donation.

Directions: Burnside is near the Highland Park Distillery, on the south side of Kirkwall. Access from Holm Road, A961, near the junction with Holm Branch Road. Bringsvard, number 19 is near the top of Burnside, corner plot on right side of road. Bus number 4 (the Airport bus) goes past the bottom of Burnside. The X1 bus (from Stromness to St Margaret's Hope) goes up Holm Branch Road. Alight at the top of the hill, turn left onto Holm Road and Burnside is immediately first right.

Opening for: LHDR

 4 **42 ASTLE**
Dornoch IV25 3NH
Fay Wilkinson

Organic wildlife garden at the edge of boggy moorland. Mature trees and shrubs are mixed with herbaceous perennials, vegetables and flowers for cutting. Changes are continually being made to focus on providing food and homes for pollinating insects.

Open: Saturday/Sunday, 22/23 July, 11am - 4pm, admission £4.00, children free.

Directions: A9 from the south: pass the turn off to Dornoch, take the first left after the Tall Pines Restaurant, signposted *Astle*. After one and a half miles take the left fork, cross the river and no. 42 is the second house on the left. A9 from the north: turn right 100 yards before the Tall Pines Restaurant. As above.

Opening for: Bumblebee Conservation Trust

 5 **AMAT**
Amat Lodge, Ardgay IV24 3BS
Jonny and Sara Shaw
T: 07712 266500 E: sara.amat@aol.co.uk

Over the last two years there have been big changes in the garden and there is now much more interest during the summer months. There is a new mini stumpery and many changes to original borders . The river Carron flows around the edge of the garden and the old Amat Caledonian Forest is close by. Large specimen trees surround the house, plus many new ones planted in the policies in the last few years. There are several herbaceous borders, rhododendrons, trees and shrubs, all set in a large lawn. It is possible to go on a short woodland and river walk and you may see red squirrels which were reintroduced some years ago and are often in and around the garden.
Champion Trees: Abies Procera, Noble Fir.

Open: Saturday/Sunday, 15/16 July, 2pm - 5pm, admission £5.00, children free.

Caithness, Sutherland, Orkney & Shetland

Directions: Take the road from Ardgay to Croick, nine miles. Turn left at the red phone box and the garden is 500 yards on the left.

Opening for: Marie Curie

 6   ### ANNIE'S PLACE
Old Manse, Palace Village, Birsay, Orkney KW17 2LX
Anne and Robin Barr

ORKNEY SUMMER FESTIVAL   NEW

Annie's Place is in the historic village of Palace on the extreme north-west coastline of Mainland Orkney. This small, floral garden is a stone's throw from the Atlantic beach and demonstrates gardening on the edge. It features hardy herbaceous plants as well as annuals which have proved they can withstand the extremes of weather in these northern parts. The garden was featured in the 2021 Orkney International Science Festival due to its links with the 18th century botanist, George Low. Visitors can enjoy live fiddle music during their visit.

Open: Sunday 16 July, Sunday 30 July and Sunday 20 August, 10am - 4pm. Admission by donation. Hot and cold drinks and home baking are available for purchase in the adjacent village shop.

Directions: The garden is on the northwest tip of Mainland Orkney. Follow the A967 on Google maps, turning down into Palace Village, Birsay. The garden is in the centre of the village adjacent to Palace Stores. It is at the terminus of Stagecoach bus service number 7 from Kirkwall Town Centre.

Opening for: Music in Hospitals and Care

Amat

Caithness, Sutherland, Orkney & Shetland

7 CASTLEHILL B&B
Evie, Orkney KW17 2PJ
Denise Campbell

ORKNEY SUMMER FESTIVAL

The garden has evolved from turning a corner of a field, at 300 feet above sea level, battling the elements, and letting nature lead with quirky upcycling, it is a work in progress.

Open: Sunday 30 July, 11am - 3pm, admission by donation.

Directions: From Finstown 10 miles through Evie Village to the *RSPB Birsay Moor* sign. Turn left and follow the road up and round to the right. Stay on the tarmac road until the T junction with a track. Engage 1st gear as track has drainage humps and subject to rain erosion. *Castlehill* is signposted on the left and is the first house on the left.

Opening for: FOTNW

8 FINYA
Grimeston Road, Harray, Orkney KW17 2JT
Ann Marwick

ORKNEY SUMMER FESTIVAL

The garden was created in an overgrown field when new house was built. A summer house and polycrub can be toured. There is a pond, four large flower beds and six raised beds for vegetables and cut flowers.

Open: Sunday 25 June and Sunday 16 July, 12pm - 4:30pm. Admission £4.00, children free.

Directions: Finya is situated on Grimeston Road which can be reached via The Stone Hill Road or signposted *Grimeston Road* from the A986.

Opening for: FOTNW

9 HIGHLANDS GARDEN
East Voe, Scalloway, Shetland ZE1 0UR
Sarah Kay
T: 01595 880526/ 07818 845385 E: info@easterhoull.co.uk
W: www.selfcatering-shetland.co.uk/the-garden/ and www.sarahkayarts.com

The garden is in two parts. The upper garden is mostly a rockery, with a large selection of plants, shallow pond, seating area, polycrub and greenhouse with fruit and vegetables. The lower garden is on a steep slope with a spectacular sea view over the village of Scalloway. There is a path to lead visitors around and the garden features a large collection of plants, vegetable patch, deep pond and pergola. It was awarded a *Shetland Environmental Award* in 2014 for its strong theme of recycling. The owner also has an art studio which you are most welcome to visit when you view the garden.

Open: by arrangement 1 May - 31 October, admission £3.50, children free. Dogs are not allowed.

Directions: Follow the A970 main road towards the village of Scalloway. Near the top of the hill heading towards Scalloway take a sharp turn to the left, signposted *Easterhoull Chalets*. Follow the road to chalets (painted blue with red roofs) and you will see the yellow *SGS* sign for the garden. Bus 4 from Lerwick/Scalloway.

Opening for: Macmillan Cancer Support

Caithness, Sutherland, Orkney & Shetland

 10 **KIERFIOLD HOUSE**
Kierfiold House, Sandwick, Orkney KW16 3JE
Fiona and Euan Smith

ORKNEY SUMMER FESTIVAL

A 150 year old walled garden in Orkney's West Mainland, which provides a unique micro climate against the windy, coastal conditions. The 'gardens within gardens' layout provides sheltered growing for hostas, irises, grasses and a collection of more than 120 species and hybrids of perennial geraniums. Organically gardened, the space is alive with birds, bees and butterflies. The garden has featured in the *Scottish Field, Scotland on Sunday* and *BBC's The Beechgrove Garden*. It is included in the books *Island Gardens* by Jackie Bennet, and *Scotland for Gardeners* by Ken Cox.

Open: Sunday 9 July and Sunday 16 July, 11am - 4:30pm. Admission £5.00, children free.

Directions: Located on the B9057, a quarter of a mile north of Skaill Loch.

Opening for: Orkney Foodbank

Kierfiold House

 11 **LANGWELL**
Berriedale KW7 6HD
Welbeck Estates
T: 01593 751278 / 751237 E: caithness@welbeck.co.uk

A beautiful and spectacular old walled garden with outstanding borders situated in the secluded Langwell Strath. Charming wooded access drive with a chance to see deer.

Open: Sunday 30 July, noon - 4pm, admission £5.00, children free.

Directions: Turn off the A9 at Berriedale Braes, up the private (tarred) drive signposted *Private – Langwell House*. It is about one-and-a-quarter miles from the A9.

Opening for: RNLI

Caithness, Sutherland, Orkney & Shetland

12 **LINFIRLEA**
Pipersquoy Road, Kirkwall, Orkney KW15 1BW
Susan Byers

ORKNEY SUMMER FESTIVAL

Informal town garden with a wildlife pond, trees and vegetable patch with raised beds and a greenhouse.

Open: Sunday 21 May, Sunday 16 July and Sunday 13 August, 10am - 5pm. Admission £4.00, children free. There may be plants for sale.

Directions: The garden is located on Pipersquoy Road in Kirkwall, a very short distance from the old Balfour Hospital.

Opening for: Macmillan Cancer Support

13 **NONAVAAR**
Levenwick, Shetland ZE2 9HX
James B Thomason
T: 01950 422447

This is a delightful country garden, sloping within drystone walls and overlooking magnificent coastal views. It contains ponds, terraces, trees, bushes, varied perennials, annuals, vegetable garden and greenhouse.

Open: by arrangement 1 May - 30 September, admission £5.00, children free.

Directions: Head south from Lerwick. Turn left at the *Levenwick* sign soon after Bigton turnoff. Follow the road to the third house on the left after the Midway stores. Park where there is a *Garden Open* sign. Bus 6 from Lerwick – Sumburgh.

Opening for: Cancer Research UK

14 **NORBY**
Burnside, Sandness, Shetland ZE2 9PL
Mrs Gundel Grolimund
T: 01595 870246 E: gundel.g5@btinternet.com

A small but perfectly formed garden and a prime example of what can be achieved in a very exposed situation. Blue painted wooden pallets provide internal wind breaks and form a background for shrubs, climbers and herbaceous plants, while willows provide a perfect wildlife habitat. There are treasured plants such as *Chionochloa rubra*, pieris, Chinese tree peonies, a selection of old-fashioned shrub roses, lilies, hellebores and grasses from New Zealand. There is also a lovely selection of interesting art and textiles in the house.

Open: 1 April - 31 December, dawn – dusk, admission £3.00, children free.

Directions: Head north on the A970 from Lerwick then west on the A971 at Tingwall. At Sandness, follow the road to Norby, turn right at the Methodist Church, Burnside is at the end of the road. Bus 10 Sandness – Walls.

Opening for: Survival International

Caithness, Sutherland, Orkney & Shetland

15 **OLD GRANARY QUOY**
The Quoy of Houton, Orphir, Orkney KW17 2RD
Caroline Critchlow

ORKNEY SUMMER FESTIVAL

A newly planted and designed garden, adjacent to The Quoy of Houton. Fabulous views over Scapa Flow, ponds and a water garden. The home of Orkney perennial geraniums and an extensive range of plants suitable for this exposed coastal location. The lantern greenhouse is a new acquisition featuring an indoor fig tree. Caroline Critchlow has designed award winning gardens and is the resident gardening guru on *BBC Radio Orkney*.

Open: Sunday 14 May and Sunday 9 July, 10am - 4pm. Admission £4.00, children free. Plant sale and refreshments at the Quoy.

Directions: From Orphir take the turning to Houton Ferry at the first junction signed *Quoy of Houton*, turn right by the car park. Park here and walk 10 minutes along coastal road around bay to the gardens. Disabled access please ring to arrange as parking is very limited. The gardens are a 10 minute walk from the bus stop.

Opening for: FOTNW

Old Granary Quoy

Caithness, Sutherland, Orkney & Shetland

16 ROUND HOUSE
Berstane Road, Kirkwall, Orkney KW15 1SZ
David and Gill Newstead

ORKNEY SUMMER FESTIVAL

Half-an-acre site (including the house) with a view towards North Isles. Established windbreak surround of mixed shrubs and trees, seven raised beds for vegetables and flowers, bog garden with huge gunnera and water-loving plants. A very large rockery, non alpine, with a path over the top. There are two small wooded areas, one with bluebells and areas of grass made over to a wildflower meadow.

Open: Sunday 16 July, 1pm - 4pm, admission by donation.

Directions: There is no parking up our lane. Vehicles can be left on the verge at the top of Berstane Road and it's a 100 meter walk from there. The town bus no 9 stops at Berstane Loan at the top of our lane.

Opening for: Orkney Seal Rescue

17 SKELBO HOUSE
Skelbo, Dornoch IV25 3QG
Alison Bartlett
E: SkelboHouseGarden@gmail.com

Extensive woodland garden with spectacular views over Loch Fleet. Mixed herbaceous borders, rose garden and shrubberies surround the house. Lawns slope down to a small lochan and river walkway. Mature trees throughout. Large kitchen garden.

Open: Saturday/Sunday, 22/23 July, 11am - 4pm, admission £5.00, children free.

Directions: from the south: On the A9 take the small turning opposite the Trentham Hotel (just past the Dornoch turn offs). At the side of Loch Fleet turn left, at the ruined castle take the second farm road which is fairly rough, and follow round to your right. If coming from the north take the Loch Fleet road signposted to *Embo* from the A9.

Opening for: Mary's Meals

18 THE GARDEN AT THE AULD POST OFFICE B&B
Spittal-by-Mybster, Caithness KW1 5XR
Lynne and Weyland Read
T: 01847 841391 E: auldpostoffice@btinternet.com
W: www.auldpostoffice.com

Surrounded by eight acres of Alaskan Lodgepole pine trees, this secluded garden has a variety of beds and borders containing evergreen plants, shrubs, grasses and perennials. The one-third acre garden provides a meandering walk under the pergola to beds set in the lawn. The fish share their pond with grasses and lilies, and the garden walk continues beneath 20-year-old pine trees, under-planted with shade-loving perennials. Heather, junipers and conifers provide an all-year-round centrepiece. There are many seating areas to rest awhile and, for the hardy, a stout footwear walk can be taken through the surrounding woodland. Planting has been chosen to encourage bees, birds and butterflies.

Open: Sunday 20 August, 2pm - 4pm, admission £4.50, children free.

Directions: On the A9 at Spittal.

Opening for: Spittal Village Hall

Caithness, Sutherland, Orkney & Shetland

19   **THE QUOY OF HOUTON**
Orphir, Orkney KW17 2RD
Dr Colleen Batey

ORKNEY SUMMER FESTIVAL

An unusual historic walled panoramic garden with 60-foot rill which leads the eye to the spectacular coastal views of Scapa Flow. Carefully planted to withstand winds in excess of 60 mph, with floral interest from March to September. Winner of *Gardeners' World* Britain's best challenging garden 2017 and listed in the top ten *UK coastal gardens*. Featured on *Beechgrove* and in the book *Island Gardens.*

Open: Sunday 14 May and Sunday 9 July, 10am - 4pm. Admission £4.00, children free. Plant sale and refreshments at the Quoy.

Directions: From Orphir take the turning to Houton Ferry at the first junction signed Quoy of Houton, turn right by the car park. Park here and walk 10 minutes along coastal road around bay to the gardens. Disabled access please ring to arrange as parking is very limited. The gardens are a 10 minute walk from the bus stop.

Opening for: FOTNW

20   **WESTLEA**
Cromarty Square, St Margaret's Hope, Orkney KW17 2SN
Shaun Hourston-Wells

ORKNEY SUMMER FESTIVAL

This relatively sheltered garden (by Orkney standards!), centrally placed within the village of St Margaret's Hope, has a wonderful, established tree backdrop. The garden demonstrates that a relatively small space can be transformed into a plant packed paradise! Plants that are usually difficult to grow in Orkney thrive here and the lush green paths give wonderful access to a rich range of plants.

Open: Sunday 25 June and Sunday 2 July, 11am - 4pm. Admission by donation. There may be plants for sale.

Directions: Westlea is at the top of Cromarty Square, furthest from the sea, and sits adjacent to the Cromarty Hall, in St Margaret's Hope (known locally as "The Hup"). Parking is available in Cromarty Square. The X1 bus (Stromness and Kirkwall, to St Margaret's Hope) stops right outside Westlea.

Opening for: FOTNW

Dumfriesshire

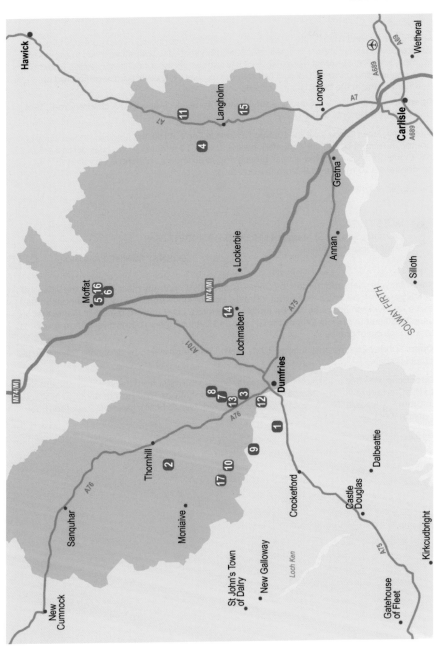

Dumfriesshire

OUR VOLUNTEER ORGANISERS

District Organiser:	Sarah Landale	Dalswinton House, Dalswinton, Auldgirth DG2 0XZ E: info@scotlandsgardens.org
Area Organisers:	Fiona Bell-Irving	Bankside, Kettleholm, Lockerbie DG11 1BY
	Liz Mitchell	Drumpark, Irongray DG2 9TX
District Photographer:	Stuart Littlewood	E: stu@f8.eclipse.co.uk
Treasurer:	Leslie Jack	Gledenholm House, Ae, Dumfries DG1 1RF

GARDENS OPEN ON A SPECIFIC DATE

Craig, Langholm	Sunday, 19 February
Tinnisburn Plants, Upper Millsteads, Canonbie	Saturday/Sunday, 18/19 March
Dalswinton House with Gardens Cottage, Dalswinton	Sunday, 7 May
Portrack, The Garden of Cosmic Speculation, Holywood	To be confirmed
Craigieburn House, by Moffat	Sunday, 28 May
Langholm Gardens Day Trail, Langholm	Sunday, 4 June
Capenoch, Penpont, Thornhill	Sunday, 4 June
Leap Cottage, West Cluden, Dumfries	Sunday, 11 June
Bonerick House, Irongray , Dumfries	Sunday, 11 June
Dunesslin, Dunscore	Sunday, 18 June
Cowhill Tower, Holywood	Sunday, 25 June
Whiteside, Dunscore	Sunday, 9 July
Craigieburn House with Waterside Garden, By Moffat	Sunday, 30 July
Dalswinton Mill, Dalswinton	Sunday, 6 August
Shawhead, 7 Vendace Drive, Lochmaben	Sunday, 13 August

GARDENS OPEN REGULARLY

Tinnisburn Plants, Upper Millsteads, Canonbie	1 April - 30 July (Saturday & Sunday)

GARDENS OPEN BY ARRANGEMENT – BOOK A VISIT WITH THE GARDEN OWNER

Drumpark, Irongray	1 May - 30 September
Waterside Garden, Moffat	1 May - 30 September

Dumfriesshire

1   BONERICK HOUSE

Irongray , Dumfries DG2 9SE
Isobel Strathmore
T: 01387 730415 E: isostrathmore@hotmail.com

Stunning views of gorse covered White Hill, with ruins of a Roman fort at the top. The garden is one acre with a wooded stepped climb to a 'Hobbit House'. Close to the road is a border of peonies and fleur-de-lys, with plenty of thistles and roses. Alastair Clark, the retired gardener from Portrack, has been working on developing the garden over the last year.

Open: Sunday 11 June, 2pm - 5pm, admission £5.00, children free. An ice-cream van will be at the garden. Leap Cottage is also open the same day and it is easily possible to visit both gardens as they are very close to one another.

Directions: Take the Terregles Road from Dumfries for approximately 4 miles, past Terregles and on towards Shawhead. The house is on the right opposite a white farm steading. Bus route 373 (Dumfries-Shawhead) passes directly by the house. Timetables available online.

Opening for: Maggie's

2   CAPENOCH

Penpont, Thornhill DG3 4LZ
Mr and Mrs John Gladstone
E: jbgladstone@gmail.com

There are rare trees throughout the grounds and the main garden is the remnant of that laid out in Victorian times. There is a pretty little raised knot garden called the Italian Garden and a lovely old Victorian conservatory. Parking is available in a field half way up the drive, but you may prefer to park in Penpont Village and walk the whole way to Capenoch. There are lovely wildflowers in the oak woods on either side of the drive.

Open: Sunday 4 June, 2pm - 5pm, admission £5.00, children free. Please note there is disabled parking at the House and picnics are allowed, as there will be no teas available.

Directions: Take the A702 west from Thornhill, drive through Penpont and the entrance to the house is at the lodge on the left-hand side, just at the speed restriction sign.

Opening for: The Jo Walters Trust

3   COWHILL TOWER

Holywood DG2 0RL
Mr and Mrs P Weatherall
T: 01387 720304 E: clara@cowhill.co.uk

This is an interesting walled garden. There are topiary animals, birds and figures and beautiful woodland and river walks. Splendid views can be seen from the lawn right down the Nith Valley. There is also a variety of statues, including several from the Far East.

Open: Sunday 25 June, 2pm - 5pm, admission by donation.

Directions: Holywood is one-and-a-half miles off the A76, five miles north of Dumfries.

Opening for: Maggie's

Dumfriesshire

4 CRAIG
Langholm DG13 0NZ
Mr and Mrs Neil Ewart
T: 013873 70230 E: nmlewart@googlemail.com

Craig snowdrops have evolved over the last 40 or so years. Round the house and policies, a large variety has been planted with a varied flowering season stretching from the start of January until April and peaking mid-February. Large drifts of *Leucojum vernum* (winter snowflake) have started to naturalise here, and along the riverbank a variety of snowdrops swept down by the river have naturalised in the adjacent woodland, known as the Snowdrop Walk.

Open: Sunday 19 February, noon - 4pm for Snowdrops and Winter Walks, admission £5.00, children free. Teas will be available at Bentpath Village Hall. Bentpath is one mile further on towards Eskdalemuir. Snowdrops for sale.

Directions: Craig is three miles from Langholm on the B709 towards Eskdalemuir.

Opening for: Kirkandrews Kirk Trust: The Friends of Kirkandrews Church

5 CRAIGIEBURN HOUSE
by Moffat DG10 9LF
Janet and Peter McGowan
T: 07557 928648 E: bideshi@aol.com

A beautiful and varied five-acre, plant-lovers' garden in a natural location in scenic Moffatdale. Meconopsis, trilliums, rhododendrons, magnolias, arisaemas, bamboos, hoherias and many more types of plants flourish in the shelter of mature woodland. Garden Manager, Datenji Sherpa has recreated a Himalayan gorge with native plants where the Craigie Burn tumbles down through a series of waterfalls. Candelabra primulas, rodgersias, cardiocrinum, ferns and other rare plants thrive in the bog garden and woodland glades. Double herbaceous borders come into their own later in the summer and keep the display going throughout the season. Other garden areas include a rose garden, formal pond and autumn garden. A nursery sells hardy plants propagated on site, many of them rare or unusual. The garden has been created over the past 25 to 30 years, building on its old setting. Its links to Robert Burns – including his song 'Craigieburn Wood' – provide another layer of history.

Open: Sunday 28 May, 2pm - 5pm, admission £5.00, children free. Please note that parking is very limited. Look out for signs prior to Craigieburn (from Moffat direction). There is a short walk in through the woods and some transport to and from the car park. Please check on the website for updated details before visiting.
Also open on 30 July with Waterside Garden which is further along the A708, travelling towards St Mary's Loch.

Directions: Three miles from the motorway (junction 15), two miles east of Moffat on the A708 Selkirk Road. Coming from Moffat, there are traffic lights straight ahead at the end of the bend. You can't miss the lodge and prayer flags.

Opening for: MOOL

Dumfriesshire

6 CRAIGIEBURN HOUSE WITH WATERSIDE GARDEN
by Moffat DG10 9LF
Jane and Peter McGowan & Ronnie Cann

A lovely opportunity to visit these two beautiful Moffat Dale gardens on the same day. Please check both Gardens' other listings in this section for full garden details. Teas will be served in Moffat Village Hall.

Craigieburn House by Moffat DG10 9LF (Janet and Peter McGowan): A beautiful and varied five-acre, plant lovers' garden in a natural location in scenic Moffat Dale.
Waterside Garden Waterside, Moffat, Dumfriesshire DG10 9LF (Ronnie Cann): Set in beautiful Moffat Dale and bounded on one side by the Moffat Water, Waterside Garden is a plantsman's delight and home to woods, riverside walks and three acres of cultivated garden.

Open: Sunday 30 July, 1pm - 5pm, admission, one garden £5.00 or two gardens £8.00, children free. Please note that parking is very limited at both gardens. You will need to use each car park for the relevant garden. **Craigieburn House:** Look out for signs prior to Craigieburn (driving from Moffat direction). There is a short walk in through the woods and some transport to and from the car park. **Parking for Waterside Garden:** There is a small area opposite the Garden and ample parking at The Moffat Water Village Hall, where teas are available throughout the afternoon. The Hall is located beyond the Garden driving towards St Mary's Loch. There will be transport to and from the Garden. Please note that it is not possible to walk along the road between the two gardens as this stretch of road is particularly dangerous. Please check on the website for updated details before visiting.

Directions: Craigieburn: Three miles from the motorway (Junction 15), two miles east of Moffat on the A708 Selkirk Road. Coming from Moffat, there are traffic lights straight ahead at the end of the bend. You can't miss the lodge and prayer flags.
Waterside: Three miles north of Moffat on the A708 opposite Craigieburn Forest Car Park. There is some limited parking here. The garden is half a mile beyond Craigieburn. From Selkirk, the garden is about 14.5 miles south of St Mary's Loch.
See notes on Parking

Opening for: Moffat Water Hall

7 DALSWINTON HOUSE WITH GARDENS COTTAGE
Dalswinton DG2 0XZ
Mr and Mrs Peter Landale
T: 01387 740220 E: sarahlandale@gmail.com

Dalswinton House Dalswinton DG2 0XZ (Mr and Mrs Peter Landale): Late 18th-century house sits on top of a hill surrounded by herbaceous beds and well-established shrubs, including rhododendrons and azaleas, overlooking the loch. Attractive walks through woods and around the loch. It was here that the first steamboat in Britain made its maiden voyage in 1788 and there is a life-sized model beside the water to commemorate this. Over the past years, there has been much clearing and development work around the loch, which has opened up the views considerably.

This year we also have **Gardens Cottage (NEW)** opening in its own right. This is the Head Gardener, Sandy Hutchison's Cottage. It is a wonderful little gem and lies beside the Walled Garden, where he lives with his wife Netty. It serves as a wonderful contrast with the large gardens of Dalswinton House and is a testament to Sandy's comprehensive horticultural skills.

Open: Sunday 7 May, 2pm - 5pm, admission £5.00, children free.

Dumfriesshire

Directions: Take the A76 north from Dumfries to Thornhill. After seven miles, turn right to Dalswinton. Drive through Dalswinton village, past the orange church on the right and follow estate wall on the right. Entrance is by either the single lodge or double lodge entrance set in the wall.

Opening for: Kirkmahoe Parish Church of Scotland

---

8 ### DALSWINTON MILL
Dalswinton DG2 0XY
Colin and Pamela Crosbie
T: 01387 740070 E: colincrosbiehort@btinternet.com

A newly-created, plantsman's garden set around an 18th-century watermill with the Pennyland Burn running through it. The garden contains a wide range of perennials, trees and shrubs that favour the local climate and have been planted during the last few years. A variety of statuary can be found throughout the garden which sits in a hollow and can be only accessed by steps and there are slopes throughout the garden. Unfortunately, this makes the garden unsuitable for anyone with mobility requirements.

Open: Sunday 6 August, 2pm - 6pm, admission £5.00, children free.

Directions: Garden lies in Dalswinton, halfway between the A76 and the A701 on the Auldgirth to Kirkton Road. From Auldgirth take the first left after the Dalswinton Village Hall. The Mill is on the corner before the bridge. We are unable to offer disabled parking.

Opening for: IFDAS : River Garden Auchincruive

---

9 ### DRUMPARK
Irongray DG2 9TX
Mr and Mrs Iain Mitchell
T: 01387 820323 or 07743 895351 E: iain.liz.mitchell@gmail.com

Well-contoured woodland garden and extensive policies nurture mature azaleas, rhododendrons and rare shrubs among impressive specimen trees. Water garden with primulas and meconopsis. Victorian walled garden with fruit trees and garden produce. There is also a beautiful herbaceous border. All planting is set in a natural bowl providing attractive vistas.
Champion Trees: *Abies cephalonica, Abies procera, Chamaecyparis lawsoniana, Cryptomeria japonica.*

Open: by arrangement 1 May - 30 September, admission by donation.

Directions: Dumfries bypass, head north on the A76 for a half mile, turn left at the signpost to *Lochside Industrial Estates* and immediately right onto Irongray Road; continue for five miles; gates in sandstone wall on left (half-mile after Routin' Brig).

Opening for: Loch Arthur

Dumfriesshire

10 DUNESSLIN
Dunscore DG2 0UR
Iain and Zara Milligan
E: zaramilligan@gmail.com

Set in the hills with wonderful views and borrowed landscapes, the principal garden consists of a series of connecting rooms filled with a great and interesting variety of herbaceous plants, beautifully designed and maintained. There is a substantial rock garden with alpines and unusual plants and a very pretty pond. There is a short walk to three cairns by Andy Goldsworthy, through an evolving woodland garden.

Open: Sunday 18 June, 2pm - 5pm, admission £5.00, children free.

Directions: From Dunscore, follow the road to Corsock. About one-and-a-half miles further on, turn right at the post box, still on the road to Corsock and at small crossroads half-a-mile on, turn left.

Opening for: Alzheimer Scotland

11 LANGHOLM GARDENS DAY TRAIL
Langholm DG13 0HL
Kate Knott, Helen Knowles, Mary Buckley

A selection of three lovely and quite different gardens around Langholm, forming a day's trail for the garden aficionado.

The Walled Garden at Arkleton (NEW) Arkleton, Ewes, Langholm DG13 0HL (Kate Knott): The restoration of the Walled Garden at Arkleton has been a labour of love and is an on-going project. Kate and her family flung open the gates to the public at the very beginning of the journey so that people could share in the progress. Highlights include the recently restored Mackenzie and Moncur Glasshouse, the rose garden and the peace and quiet one can find within the garden walls with glimpses of the rolling Ewes Valley hills in the distance.
Tinnisburn Plants (NEW) Tinnisburn Plants, Upper Millsteads, Canonbie, Dumfriesshire DG14 0RY (Helen Knowles): Developed over the last 36 years, this one acre plantsman's garden is home to an eclectic mix of truly hardy perennials, trees and shrubs. Planted for year-round colour and interest and to provide habitats for wildlife, there is something new to see each month. There is a woodland garden, rockery, bog garden, herbaceous borders and much more. Meconopsis grow well here and more are being planted out every year. In addition to the garden, there is a small orchard, wildlife ponds and mown paths through the wildflower meadows and, if you're lucky, you may spot red squirrels.
Westerhall Bentpath, Langholm DG13 0NQ (Mary Buckley): An extensive collection of azaleas, rhododendrons, rare shrubs and mature trees set in a landscape of follies, sculpture and stunning vistas. The Walled Garden has been redesigned and contains a glasshouse with some exotic plants collected from around the world.

Open: Sunday 4 June, 11am - 6pm, admission £12.00, children free. Entrance may be paid at any of the three gardens or £5.00 per individual garden. Refreshments are available at both Arkleton and Tinnisburn Plants

Directions: The Walled Garden at Arkleton: is five miles North of Langholm just off the A7. Opposite the Ewes Community Hall follow the track over the bridge and along to the Walled Garden where there is parking available behind the cottage. The X95 bus stops at the Ewes Hall.
Tinnisburn Plants: take the B6357 north from Canonbie. At Harelaw turn left onto the B6318 and after one mile turn right onto our track. It is 1.5 miles long and is untarmacked but suitable for all vehicles. Just drive slowly and carefully.

Dumfriesshire

Westerhall: from Langholm take the B709 towards Eskdalemuir. After approximately five miles, in the village of Bentpath, turn right by white house. Go down through the village, over a bridge and turn right by the church. Continue on this road for approximately one mile. Parking at farm which will be signed.

Opening for: SGS and Beneficiaries

Langholm Trail, Arkleton Walled Garden © Polly Armstrong-Wilson

 12 **LEAP COTTAGE**
West Cluden, Dumfries DG2 9UW
Mr Raymond Nelson
T: 07906 022 632 E: nelson_nomad@yahoo.com.au

Leap Cottage sits on the site of a former mill dating back to the 1600s. It is situated in the most amazing setting, right down on the banks of the Cluden Water, a tributary of the River Nith with wonderful views of the river's twists and turns. The tiny and enchanting garden is filled to the brim with a variety of plants and colour. There is a lovely walk through the trees right down to the river's edge, just beside the cottage.

Open: Sunday 11 June, 2pm - 5pm, admission £5.00, children free. Bonerick House is also open the same day and it is easily possible to visit both gardens as they are very close to one another.

Directions: Take the A76 Dumfries/Thornhill Road. Turn left to Irongray Industrial Estate/Park on the outskirts of Dumfries. Follow Irongray Road, past all the houses until barn on the right. Turn in here and park – access and parking to the cottage is difficult and limited so parking is at the farm. From there, following the yellow signs, walk to the T-junction, turn right and keep going to the end of the road. About 150 yards walk.

Opening for: The Linda Norgrove Foundation

Dumfriesshire

13 PORTRACK, THE GARDEN OF COSMIC SPECULATION

Holywood DG2 0RW
John Jencks
W: www.gardenofcosmicspeculation.com

Forty major areas, gardens, bridges, landforms, sculpture, terraces, fences and architectural works. Covering 30 acres, The Garden of Cosmic Speculation, designed by the late Charles Jencks, uses nature to celebrate nature, both intellectually and through the senses, including the sense of humour.

Open: Date to be confirmed. Please see Scotland's Gardens Scheme website for details.

Directions: Portrack is one-and-a-half miles off the A76, five miles north of Dumfries.

Opening for: Maggie's

14 SHAWHEAD

7 Vendace Drive, Lochmaben DG11 1QN
Mr and Mrs Ian Rankine
T: 01387 811273 E: srankine298@btinternet.com

A relatively young garden situated on the edge of Lochmaben with delightful views overlooking Mill Loch. It has immaculately maintained lawns and well-furnished borders bursting with colour and a great collection of hardy perennials and grasses with conifers, shrubs and trees providing all year round interest.

Open: Sunday 13 August, 1pm - 4pm, admission £5.00, children free. The walk around Mill Loch takes about 30-40 minutes from the House. Wear suitable walking shoes. For keen walkers, the nearby Castle Loch also has a lovely walk of three miles.

Directions: From Dumfries, turn left opposite The Crown Hotel, turn left at the *give way* sign and then sharp left. From Lockerbie, take the right fork beside the Town Hall and after half a mile, take left turn.

Opening for: Castle Loch Lochmaben Community Trust

15 TINNISBURN PLANTS
Upper Millsteads, Canonbie DG14 0RY
Helen Knowles
T: 07544 373815 E: helen@tinnisburnplants.co.uk
W: tinnisburn.co.uk

Developed over the last 36 years, this one acre plantsman's garden is home to an eclectic mix of truly hardy perennials, trees and shrubs. Planted for year-round colour and interest and to provide habitats for wildlife, there is something new to see each month. There is a woodland garden, rockery, bog garden, herbaceous borders and much more. Meconopsis grow well here and more are being planted out every year. In addition to the garden, there is a small orchard, wildlife ponds and mown paths through the wildflower meadows and, if you're lucky, you may spot red squirrels.
National Plant Collection: *Scilla (Chionodoxa).*

Open: Saturday/Sunday, 18/19 March, 10am - 4pm. Scilla open weekend. Also open 1 April - 30 July (Saturday & Sunday), 10am - 4pm. Admission £5.00, children free. The Old Byre Tearoom is open 10.30am-3.30pm for tea, coffee and cold drinks and homemade cakes, scones and savoury snacks.

Dumfriesshire

Also Open: on Sunday 4 June, 11am - 6pm as part of the Langholm Gardens Day Trail, admission £12.00, children free. Entrance may be paid at any of the three gardens or £5.00 per individual garden. Refreshments are available at both Arkleton and Tinnisburn Plants.

Directions: Take the B6357 north from Canonbie. At Harelaw turn left onto the B6318 and after 1 mile turn right onto our track. It is 1.5 miles long and is untarmacked but suitable for all vehicles. Just drive slowly and carefully.

Opening for: Macmillan Cancer Support

 16 ## WATERSIDE GARDEN
Moffat DG10 9LF
Ronnie Cann
T: 01683 221583 E: waterside-garden@holestone.net
W: holestone.net

Set in beautiful Moffatdale and bounded on one side by the Moffat Water, Waterside Garden is a plantsman's delight, home to woods, riverside walks and three acres of cultivated garden. There are many mature trees including oak, birch, beech and much more. Collections of species and hybrid rhododendrons and azaleas, bamboos, and other flowering shrubs give year-round interest. There are herbaceous beds, giving colour in spring and summer, alpines, mixed plantings, spring bulbs, especially daffodils, and wildflower meadows.

Open: by arrangement 1 May - 30 September, admission £5.00, children free. There is also a joint opening on Sunday 30th July with Craigieburn House. See joint entry details.

Directions: Three miles north of Moffat on the A708 opposite Craigieburn Forest Car Park. From Selkirk the garden is about 14.5 miles south of St Mary's Loch.

Opening for: Moffat Water Hall

 17 ## WHITESIDE
Dunscore DG2 0UU
John and Hilary Craig
T: 01387 820501 and 07972 503895 E: hjcraig19@gmail.com

The garden, which extends to several acres, is 600 feet above sea level on a north-facing slope with views across to Queensberry and the Lowther Hills. There are some mature trees around the house but the rest of the garden is relatively new, having been created from a bare hillside over the last 20 years. There are shrubs, young trees, a rowan avenue, a walled vegetable garden, orchard and courtyard garden. Several burns run through the property and there is a pond and an enclosure for runner ducks.

Open: Sunday 9 July, 1pm - 5pm, admission £5.00, children free. Also open by arrangement with the owners from April 1st to September 30th.

Directions: From Dunscore, take the Corsock road. Continue two miles on, turn right opposite the post box. Continue for one and three quarters miles, over the humpback bridge and past the white farmhouse on the left. *Whiteside* is signed on the left.

Opening for: Music in Dumfries

Dunbartonshire

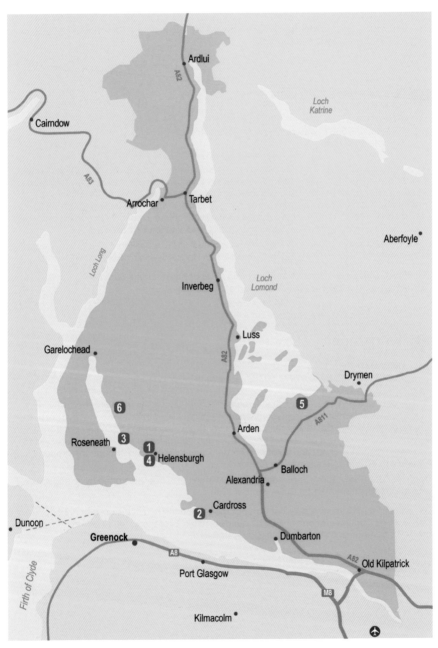

Dunbartonshire

OUR VOLUNTEER ORGANISERS

District Organiser:	Tricia Stewart	High Glenan, 24a Queen Street, Helensburgh G84 9LG E: info@scotlandsgardens.org
Area Organisers:	Adrienne Kerr	Stonecroft, Ardenconnel Way, Rhu, G84 8RZ
	Kathleen Murray	4 Cairndhu Gardens, Helensburgh G84 8PG
	Lesley and Norman Quirk	Glenard, Upper Torwoodhill Road, Rhu, G84 8LE
Treasurer:	Claire Travis	54 Union Street, Alexandria G83 9AH

GARDENS OPEN ON A SPECIFIC DATE

Stuckenduff, Shore Road, Shandon	Sunday, 19 February
18 Duchess Park with Westburn, Helensburgh	Sunday, 14 May
Ross Priory, Gartocharn	Sunday, 21 May
Geilston Garden, Main Road, Cardross	Sunday, 4 June
James Street Community Garden Plant Sale, Helensburgh	Saturday, 2 September

GARDENS OPEN REGULARLY

Glenarn, Glenarn Road, Rhu, Helensburgh	21 March - 21 September

Dunbartonshire

1 **18 DUCHESS PARK WITH WESTBURN**
Helensburgh G84 9PY
Stewart & Sue Campbell and Mrs Baker

18 Duchess Park G84 9PY (Stewart and Sue Campbell): The garden is small, about 40 years old, and is still being developed. The site was originally a paddock on the edge of Duchess Wood, which backs on to the garden, and is our local nature reserve. The rear garden is sloping with steps on one side and a gravel path on the other to get to the upper garden. It is a woodland garden with two large oak trees, many species and hybrid rhododendrons and other interesting plants. More rhododendrons, acers and other woodland shrubs and plants have been planted over the last two years. Mid-May should be a good time to enjoy many of the rhododendrons in full bloom. Almost all the plants are clearly named!
Westburn 50 Campbell Street G84 9NH (Mrs Baker): A woodland garden of just over two acres. The Glenan Burn runs through a woodland of oak and beech trees with bluebells in the springtime. Some of the paths are steep, but there are bridges over the burn and handrails in places. There is also an air raid shelter and the remains of a kiln where James Ballantyne Hannay manufactured artificial diamonds in the 1800s. A lawn is surrounded by rhododendrons and azaleas, and there is a vegetable garden. Over the years, the garden has been enjoyed by children, with lots of room to play and fish in the burn.

Open: Sunday 14 May, 2pm - 5pm, admission £5.00, children free. Short guided wild flower walks in Duchess Wood will be offered during the afternoon by the Friends of Duchess Wood. The bluebells should be in bloom. If the weather is poor, 'stout' shoes are recommended. Homemade teas will be served at 18 Duchess Park and there will be a plant stall at Westburn.

Directions: Duchess Park: From Sinclair Street, travel west along Queen Street until it becomes Duchess Park, a cul de sac. Number 18 is at the far end on the right. **Westburn**: Proceed along West Montrose Street from Sinclair Street and take the fourth turn on the right. The entrance of Westburn is 100 yards up Campbell Street on the right-hand side.

Opening for: Friends of Duchess Wood & St Michael & All Angels Church

2 **GEILSTON GARDEN**
Main Road, Cardross G82 5HD
The National Trust for Scotland
T: 01389 849187 E: geilstongarden@nts.org.uk
W: www.nts.org.uk/visit/places/Geilston-Garden/

Geilston Garden has many attractive features including the walled garden with herbaceous border providing summer colour, tranquil woodland walks and a large working kitchen garden. This is the ideal season for viewing the Siberian iris in flower along the Geilston Burn and the Japanese azaleas.

Open: Sunday 4 June, 1pm - 5pm, admission details can be found on the garden's website. Plant Sale and Homemade Teas will be served.

Directions: On the A814, one mile from Cardross towards Helensburgh.

Opening for: Donation to SGS

Dunbartonshire

3 ### GLENARN
Glenarn Road, Rhu, Helensburgh G84 8LL
Michael and Sue Thornley
T: 01436 820493 E: masthome@btinternet.com
W: www.glenarn.com

Glenarn survives as a complete example of a ten-acre garden which spans from 1850 to the present day. There are winding paths through miniature glens under a canopy of oaks and limes, sunlit open spaces, a vegetable garden with beehives, and a rock garden full of surprise and season-long colour. The famous collections of rare and tender rhododendrons and magnolias give way in midsummer to roses rambling through the trees and climbing hydrangeas, followed by the starry white flowers of hoherias and eucryphias to the end of the season. There is a Silent Space at the top of the garden with views over the Gareloch. Champion Trees: Notably *Magnolia rostrata.*

Open: 21 March - 21 September, dawn – dusk, admission £5.00, children free. There may be local plants for sale.

Directions: On the A814, two miles north of Helensburgh, up Pier Road. Cars to be left at the gate unless passengers have limited mobility.

Opening for: *Rhu & Shandon Community Centre*

Glenarn

Dunbartonshire

4　JAMES STREET COMMUNITY GARDEN PLANT SALE
James Street, Helensburgh G84 8EY
The Gardeners of James Street

Developed from a children's derelict playground, the Community Garden is a relaxed area for contemplation with mixed herbaceous beds, a maze and young trees. The plant sale will include a wide selection of nursery-grown perennials and locally grown trees, shrubs, herbaceous, alpine and house plants.

Open: Saturday 2 September, noon - 3pm, admission by donation.

Directions: Travel west along Princes Street from Sinclair Street through Colquhoun Square, turn right up James Street and the Community Garden is on the left. Park on the street.

Opening for: James Street Community Garden

James Street Community Garden Plant Sale © Stephen Skivington

5　ROSS PRIORY
Gartocharn G83 8NL
University of Strathclyde

Mansion house with glorious views over Loch Lomond with adjoining garden. Wonderful rhododendrons and azaleas are the principal plants in the garden, with a varied selection of trees and shrubs throughout. Spectacular spring bulbs, border plantings of herbaceous perennials, shrubs and trees. Extensive walled garden with glasshouses, pergola and ornamental plantings. Children's play area and putting green beside the house.

Open: Sunday 21 May, 2pm - 5pm, admission £5.00, children free.

Directions: Ross Priory is one and a half miles off the A811 at Gartocharn. Bus from Balloch to Gartocharn.

Opening for: Friends Of Loch Lomond & The Trossachs & Loch Lomond Rescue Boat

Dunbartonshire

6 STUCKENDUFF

Shore Road, Shandon G84 8NW
Colin & Louise Burnet

Stuckenduff is a three-and-a-half acre garden overlooking the Gareloch with mature trees, rhododendrons, azaleas, mixed borders and a magical carpet of bluebells in May. The garden was partially re-landscaped in 2001 when a tennis court was laid alongside the original old walls. The annual snowdrop display spreads from January to March and is a treat to behold for any galanthophile.

Open: Sunday 19 February, 1pm - 4pm for Snowdrops and Winter Walks, admission £5.00, children free. Live music will be performed during the afternoon.

Directions: Stuckenduff is on Shore Road, off the A814, take the Kings Point/Queens Point exit then turn sharply left onto the slip road. Entrance is opposite the post box.

Opening for: Muscular Dystrophy UK: Georgie's Genes & Ellen MacArthur Cancer Trust

Geilston Garden © NTS

East Lothian

Sponsored by

⊕ Investec

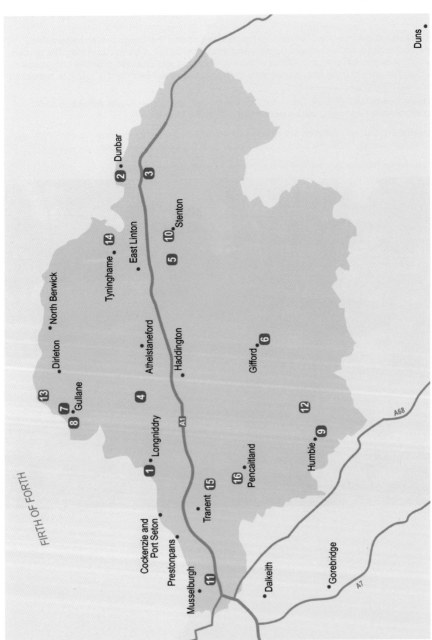

Duns

Dunbar
2
3

Stenton
East Linton
10

Tyninghame
14

5

North Berwick

Dirleton
Athelstaneford
Haddington

13
Gullane
7
8

4

Gifford
6

Longniddry
1

A1

12

Humbie
9

FIRTH OF FORTH

Cockenzie and
Port Seton

Prestonpans

Musselburgh
11

Tranent
15

16
Pencaitland

Dalkeith

Gorebridge

A68

A7

East Lothian

OUR VOLUNTEER ORGANISERS

District Organiser:	Joan Johnson	The Round House, Woodbush, Dunbar EH42 1HB E: info@scotlandsgardens.org
Area Organisers:	Jane Craiglee Frank Kirwan Judy Riley Claire Turnbull	
District Photographers:	Delia Ridley-Thomas Malcolm Ross	
Treasurer:	Colin Wilson	

GARDENS OPEN ON A SPECIFIC DATE

Winton Castle, Pencaitland	Sunday, 26 March
Tyninghame House and The Walled Garden, Dunbar	Sunday, 7 May
Stobshiel House, Humbie	Sunday, 4 June
Bowerhouse, Dunbar	Friday/Saturday, 16/17 June
Camptoun House, Camptoun, East Lothian	Saturday/Sunday, 17/18 June
Belhaven House, Edinburgh Road, Belhaven, Dunbar	Saturday, 24 June
The Gardens at Archerfield Walled Garden, Dirleton	Sunday, 25 June
Tyninghame House and The Walled Garden, Dunbar	Sunday, 25 June
Gullane House, Sandy Loan, Gullane	Friday/Saturday, 30 June/1 July
Papple Steading, Papple, Haddington	Saturday/Sunday, 1/2 July
Gifford Village and Broadwoodside, Gifford	Sunday, 9 July
West Bank, West Bank House, Macmerry, Tranent	Sunday, 30 July
Greywalls, Gullane	Saturday, 5 August

GARDENS OPEN REGULARLY

Stobshiel House, Humbie	11 January - 14 December (Wednesdays only)
Shepherd House, Inveresk, Musselburgh	Tues & Thurs, 7 February - 2 March Sat/Sun, 18/19 February Tues & Thurs, 18 April - 27 July Sat/Sun 13/14 May
Humbie Dean, Humbie	Wednesday, 29 March, 12 & 26 April, 17 May, 7 & 21 June, 19 July & 16 August
A Blackbird Sings, 20 Kings Park, Longniddry	Saturday, 29 April, 27 May, 24 June, 29 July and 26 August

East Lothian

Camptoun House

Gullane House

Shepherd House

East Lothian

 A BLACKBIRD SINGS
20 Kings Park, Longniddry EH32 0QL
Graham and Maxine Pettigrew
T: 01875 853003

A long garden (35m) in a corner site of Glassel Park Estate. Planting is mostly by plant type – heathers, hosta, grasses, ferns, paeony, iris, alpine, rose – in 'gardens within the garden'. Water features abound and an unheated conservatory contains cacti and insectivorous plants. Liquidambar, 'kousa' cornuses, contorted robinia, cherries, magnolia and rowan hupehensis provide vertical structure within the limited space. A flowering presence throughout the year complements our interest in bees and butterflies.

Open: Saturday 29 April, Saturday 27 May, Saturday 24 June, Saturday 29 July & Saturday 26 August, 10am - 5pm, admission by donation. Please telephone us on 01875 853003 if you intend to come so that we can manage numbers. Groups by arrangement.

Directions: By car: Enter Dean Road from A198, right at Kings Avenue, right at Kings Park. By bus (124): Old Dean Road stop, down Old Dean Road, right at Kings Avenue, right at Kings Park.

Opening for: Scottish Wildlife Trust Ltd & Leuchie

 BELHAVEN HOUSE
Edinburgh Road, Belhaven, Dunbar EH42 1NS
Mr and Mrs Bruneau

Belhaven House has four acres of formal Georgian gardens. It comprises raised herbaceous borders with topiary features for structure, beautiful abundant rose archways and a walled vegetable and fruit garden with box-edged borders. There is also a woodland area with specimen trees dating from the early 20th century and in springtime this area is carpeted with daffodils and bluebells. The garden has been associated with a succession of people interested in plants since the 19th century, most notably Sir George Taylor, a former director of Kew gardens.

Open: Saturday 24 June, 2pm - 5pm, admission £6.00, children free.

Directions: By car – approaching Dunbar from the A1 at Thistly Cross roundabout, take the A199 then the A1087. After one-and-a-half miles, Belhaven House is opposite Brewery Lane on the junction with Duke Street. Parking is on the street. Public transport – bus X7 to Dunbar from Edinburgh.

Opening for: Can-Do

East Lothian

3 BOWERHOUSE
Dunbar EH42 1RE
Mr and Mrs Mark Tyndall

The 1835 David Bryce mansion is set in gardens, parkland, orchard and woodland covering some 17 acres. The formal gardens nearest the house are made up of herbaceous borders and lawns, a fountain courtyard garden and a walled greenhouse garden with box edged parterres. Rising behind the house, walking through the thorn garden, is the first of a planned series of glade gardens in the woodland. Further out from the house, the newest garden is a formal pond garden. Enclosed by double yew hedges with a secret path between them, this part of the garden contains lawns, shrub beds, a sorbus avenue, rose and clematis arches and paved pathways.

Open: Friday/Saturday, 16/17 June, 2pm - 6pm, admission £7.00, children free.

Directions: One mile south of Dunbar off the westbound carriageway of the A1.

Opening for: Leuchie

4 CAMPTOUN HOUSE
Camptoun, East Lothian EH39 5BA
Shane Corstorphine

Built in the early 1800s, Camptoun House is a Georgian family house surrounded by eight acres of private garden and paddocks. The gardens comprise a walled garden with herbaceous borders and rose beds, an orchard, a kitchen garden, a kids play area and a small 'fairy wood'. Close to the house is a more formal style. The family keeps bees and favours bee and wildlife friendly planting wherever possible.

Open: Saturday/Sunday, 17/18 June, noon - 4:30pm, admission £7.00, children free.

Directions: Camptoun House is situated on the C106 road between Haddington and Drem. Coming from Haddington, after 1.6 miles you will cross the B1343 by East Garleton, heading north staying on the C106. The house is a further 0.6 miles on the left hand side. Please park in the field beside the house which will be clearly signed. The house is 1.6 miles from Drem station and 0.6 miles from East Garleton bus stop (Athelstaneford route).

Opening for: Our Community Kitchen

5 EASTFIELD AND REDCLIFF GARDENS
Whittingehame EH41 4QA
Mr & Mrs J Harper and Mr & Mrs D Shaw-Stewart

These complementary gardens, very different in style and planting, are set against the backdrop of Deuchrie Dod and Pressmennan Wood.

Redcliff (Joe and Jenny Harper): Redcliff was built as the factor's house to Whittingehame Estate, home of Prime Minister A J Balfour. The established garden is terraced and runs down to the Whittingehame water. The garden has many different rooms, formal terraces, woodland, herbaceous borders and lawns, vegetable garden and steep steps running down to a bridge over the river. The setting and views to rolling hills are lovely and the garden has a country, informal ambience. Redcliff provides the visitor with a tempting stroll through a garden on different levels. It is therefore not suitable for very young children or disabled visitors.

East Lothian

Eastfield (Mr & Mrs D Shaw-Stewart): Eastfield is a 20-year-old house and garden created from a field and a disused farm steading. There is a meadow and woodland walk, a wildlife pond, a courtyard garden and flower/herb garden.

Redcliff and Eastfield gardens together make for a lovely walk in a lovely setting. Visitors are welcome to bring a picnic with them to the gardens.

Open: Late cancellation

Directions: A199 to East Linton bypass and turn right, follow road to Whittinghame for 2.4 miles. Redcliff is the red sandstone house at the top of the hill at Whittinghame.

Opening for: Leuchie

 ### GIFFORD VILLAGE AND BROADWOODSIDE
Gifford EH41 4QU
The Gardeners of Gifford Village & Mr and Mrs Dalrymple

Gifford Village Gifford EH41 4QY (The Gardeners of Gifford): The gardens vary in size and type, from the compact and informal to the large and formal, with a wide range of plants, shrubs and trees. Gifford was laid out in the early 18th century and has retained much of its original charm. The village includes a beautiful church built in 1708, the Lime Avenue of Yester House, a community woodland and a wide range of gardens – all within walking distance of each other.

Broadwoodside Gifford EH41 4JQ (Anna and Robert Dalrymple): "Tucked into a fold in the landscape near Gifford in East Lothian sits a collection of traditional farm buildings that were imaginatively restored to form an elegant family home. Broadwoodside steading is an exercise in polished vernacular, from the yellow limewash of its low, ogee-roofed tower to the oxblood paintwork around its many windows. This is a house that seems to grow out of its environment, the hue of its stone walls and pantiled roof echoed in the colours of the fertile soil of the surrounding farmland, and around the steading has grown up. It has been described as one of the finest contemporary gardens in Scotland, a garden that employs all the classical devices of symmetry, perspective and precise alignment but does so in such a witty fashion that here, in this agricultural setting, the familiar becomes fresh and exciting." *Garden Design Journal.*

Open: Sunday 9 July, noon - 5pm, admission £7.00, children free. Tickets and maps can be purchased either outside the Village Hall or at Broadwoodside.

Directions: Gifford sits between the A1 and the A68 roads about five miles south of Haddington. The village is well signposted from Haddington, Pencaitland and Duns. On the Gifford Circle 123 Bus Route from Haddington. Broadwoodside is just off the B6355 going out of Gifford towards Pencaitland, at the Golf Course junction.

Opening for: Gifford Horticultural Society

East Lothian

 7 **GREYWALLS**
Gullane EH31 2EG
Dr and Mrs Dominic Hoar
W: greywalls.co.uk

Six-acre formal garden attributed to Gertrude Jekyll, surrounding Greywalls Hotel with stunning views over East Lothian and the Forth. The garden was featured in *The Beechgrove Garden* in September 2015, *The English Garden* in July 2019 and *Scottish Field* in September 2019. Highlights of the garden are straight and curved walls which create rooms and vistas, with radiating paths that link entrances and exits. Everywhere there are places to sit, in the sun and in the shade.

Open: Saturday 5 August, 2pm - 5pm, admission £5.00, children free.

Directions: Signposted on the A198 south east of Gullane. From Edinburgh take the A1 south, then the A198 to Gullane, then last turning on the left side. From the south take the A1 north to Haddington, *Gullane* is signposted. Further information is on our website.

Opening for: Leuchie

 8 **GULLANE HOUSE**
Sandy Loan, Gullane EH31 2BH
William and Judy Thomson

A traditional walled garden of three acres. The front of the house looks onto rose-hedged twin herbaceous borders with successional planting, the south border having been refreshed for 2023. A small lily pond leads through to the rose and lavender garden planted in 2018. The next 'room' is reached through a beech hedge and houses soft fruits and vegetables and an informal barbecue area. The orchard boasts a selection of fruit trees and there are magnificent mature trees throughout the garden.
Champion Trees: Elm, Oak.

Open: Friday 30 June & Saturday 1 July, 2pm - 5pm, admission £5.00, children free.

Directions: Gullane House is situated on Sandy Loan about 30 yards from the main street in Gullane. Public transport: regular buses from Edinburgh stop in Gullane.

Opening for: The Ridge SCIO

 9 **HUMBIE DEAN**
Humbie EH36 5PW
Frank Kirwan
E: frank.kirwan@gmail.com

A two-acre ornamental and wooded garden on a variety of levels, sandwiched between two burns at 600 feet, planted for interest throughout the season. A limited palette of plants with hosta, hellebores, perennial geraniums, primula, meconopsis, martagon lilies, clematis, spring bulbs, ground cover, herbaceous and shrub planting, bluebell meadow, mature and recent azalea and rhododendron planting. The lower sections of the garden are only accessible by a series of steps.

Open: Wednesday 29 March, Wednesday 12 April, Wednesday 26 April, Wednesday 17 May, Wednesday 7 June, Wednesday 21 June, Wednesday 19 July & Wednesday 16 August, 10:30am - 4pm, admission £6.00, children free.

East Lothian

Directions: Enter Humbie from the A68, pass the school and the village hall on the left then immediately turn right just before the Humbie Hub. Take the second left and Humbie Dean is on the left between two small bridges. Limited parking.

Opening for: Mamie Martin Fund

---

 10 PAPPLE STEADING
Papple, Haddington EH42 1TE
George and Eri Mackintosh
T: 07941 157785. E: verity.sinclair@papple.com
W: www.papple.com

Papple Steading is a collection of rural farm buildings built in 1860 by AJ Balfour. The gardens (maintained using natural and environmentally friendly methods) have a wonderful herbaceous collection, lawns, a very productive fruit patch, large informal beds and a small herb area. The paddock is largely unmown with a meandering path cut through tall grasses and wildflowers. The adjoining Papple Wood is an ancient, largely deciduous woodland where a trail takes you past follies and sculptures set amongst native trees. A short walk from the Steading is Papana Wood and Wildflower Meadow. The Papana Water flows alongside the meadow which was planted two years ago with native wildflowers. In Autumn 2022 we are planting a forest garden in the grounds and within Papple Wood; in the next few years this will become a wild foraging paradise!

Open: Saturday/Sunday, 1/2 July, 11am - 4pm, admission £6.00, children free.

Directions: From the A199 at East Linton, follow signs to Traprain and Whittingehame, signposted to Papple, 1.5 miles. What3words: formation.painted.honest

Opening for: Leuchie

---

 11 SHEPHERD HOUSE
Inveresk, Musselburgh EH21 7TH
Sir Charles and Lady Fraser
T: 0131 665 2570 E: ann.shepherdhouse@gmail.com
W: www.shepherdhousegarden.co.uk

A constantly evolving artist's garden that never stands still, with lots of surprises including a shell house built in 2014, lavender parterres, a rill and fountains. At its heart are the plants filling every border, spilling over arches and lining paths, which are the inspiration for Ann's paintings. The season starts with the snowdrop collection of over 70 cultivars, moves on through hellebores, tulips, irises and roses. One of the garden's features is a mirror steel diamond sculpture to commemorate the Frasers' diamond wedding anniversary and 60 years in this garden.

Open: Tuesdays and Thursdays from 7 February to 2 March, 2 - 4pm and Saturday/Sunday 18/19 February, 11am - 4pm for Snowdrops. Then open on Tuesday and Thursdays, from 18 April to 27 July, 2 - 4pm. Also open on Saturday/Sunday 13/14 May, 11am - 4pm. Admission £5.00, children free.

Directions: The garden is near Musselburgh. From the A1 take the A6094 exit signposted Wallyford and Dalkeith and follow signs to Inveresk.

Opening for: Trees For Life

East Lothian

12 STOBSHIEL HOUSE
Humbie EH36 5PD
Mr Maxwell and Lady Sarah Ward
T: 01875 833646 E: stobshiel@gmail.com

The garden at Stobshiel House is effectively split into four main parts viz., the walled garden, the shrubbery, the pond and lawns and the woodland areas. Each area is laid out and planted to provide the visitor with all year round interest from swathes of aconites, snowdrops, narcissi in spring to a vast array of perennials, roses, clematis and annuals throughout summer and autumn. The extensive collection of shrubs and mature trees offer a fantastic backdrop during all seasons.

Open: Sunday 4 June, 10am - 4pm. Also open 11 January - 14 December (Wednesdays only), 10am - 3pm. Admission £6.00, children free.

Directions: On the B6368 Haddington/Humbie road; sign to *Stobshiel* one mile.

Opening for: Fostering Compassion, SCIO (11 January - 14 December) & British Red Cross (Sunday 4 June)

13 THE GARDENS AT ARCHERFIELD WALLED GARDEN
Archerfield Walled Garden Archerfield Estate, Dirleton, North Berwick, East Lothian EH39 5HQ
Kerry Lyall, Head Gardener
W: www.archerfieldwalledgarden.com

The Gardens are a series of themed garden rooms divided by broad paths, framed by clipped yew hedging. Explore our perennial meadow and orchard, rose garden, wildlife area, cut and dried flower beds, light and dark borders, potager, productive polytunnel and perennial veg beds. Benches are sited to take advantage of the best views. We are located on a one-acre plot next to Archerfield Walled Garden Café and Shop, entrance beside the well. Enjoy a wander on the wider estate featuring a willow walk, pond, labyrinth and fairy wood.

Open: Sunday 25 June, 10am - 5pm, admission £5.00, children free. Garden tours with Head Gardener at 11am, 1.30pm and 3pm.

Directions: By bus East Coast Buses no 124 from Edinburgh. Bus stops (2nd stop) after Gullane, at entrance to Archerfield Estate then a 10 min walk to Archerfield Walled Garden. By car via the A198 East Lothian coast road, turn in to Archerfield Estate, one minute drive to car park at Archerfield Walled Garden. Or refer to our website.

Opening for: Stepping Out Project

14 TYNINGHAME HOUSE AND THE WALLED GARDEN
Tyninghame House, Dunbar EH42 1XW
Mrs C Gwyn, Tyninghame Gardens Ltd

The formal walled garden combines the lawn, sculpture and yew hedges, an Apple Walk and extensive herbaceous planting, including roses and peonies with an informal arboretum. Splendid 17th century sandstone Scottish baronial house, remodelled in 1829 by William Burn. The gardens include herbaceous border, formal rose garden, Lady Haddington's Secret Garden with old fashioned roses and an extensive wilderness spring garden with rhododendrons, azalea, flowering trees and bulbs. Grounds include a one-mile beech avenue to the sea. The Romanesque ruin of St Baldred's Church commands views across the Tyne Estuary and Lammermuir Hills. Tyninghame has been awarded 'Outstanding' for every category in the Inventory of Gardens and Designed Landscapes of Scotland.

East Lothian

Champion Trees: Two British and seven Scottish.

Open: Sunday 7 May, 1pm - 5pm. Also open Sunday 25 June, 1pm - 5pm. Admission £6.00, children free.

Directions: Gates on the A198 at Tyninghame Village. Bus 120.

Opening for: Lynton Day Centre (Sunday 7 May) & Tyninghame Village Hall (Sunday 25 June)

---

15 WEST BANK
West Bank House, Macmerry, Trenent EH33 2AH
Katherine and Mike Lodge

Situated on the edge of a 'bank' at 120m above sea level, the garden has amazing views but is correspondingly exposed. It occupies about 3 acres and was designed from scratch 10 years ago. The only original features remaining are the big old sycamores, limes, two apple trees and a stunning espaliered pear. There is a formal ornamental garden with herbaceous beds, an orchard and wildflower meadow, a vegetable garden, a shady walk and the paddock with a mix of trees

Open: Sunday 30 July, 11am - 5pm, admission £6.00, children free.

Directions: From the village of Macmerry take West Bank Road by the Miners Welfare Club. Continue up the hill on the private road up to West Bank House.

Opening for: Walk With Scott Foundation

---

16 WINTON CASTLE
Pencaitland EH34 5AT
Sir Francis Ogilvy, Winton Trust
T: 01875 340222
W: www.wintoncastle.co.uk

An historic Renaissance Castle estate in East Lothian, just 30 minutes from Edinburgh. Set in mature and colourful grounds. A glorious spring display of daffodils and cherry blossom surrounds the castle, whilst extensive mixed borders and wisteria walkway provide interest in the Walled Garden. Take a walk around Sir David's Loch, the natural woodland area at The Dell and enjoy the beautiful borders of the castle terraces, accessed by gravelled sloping pathways and stone steps. Home baking and lunch offerings will be provided along with informative garden tours. A visit to Winton Castle is a wonderful family day out.

Open: Sunday 26 March, noon - 4:30pm, admission £6.00, children free. Guided Castle and Garden Tours, family activities with teas, home baking and light lunches available at Cafe Winton. Dogs are welcome.

Directions: Entrance off the B6355 Trenent/Pencaitland Road.

Opening for: East Lothian Foodbank

Edinburgh, Midlothian & West Lothian

Sponsored by

⊕ Investec

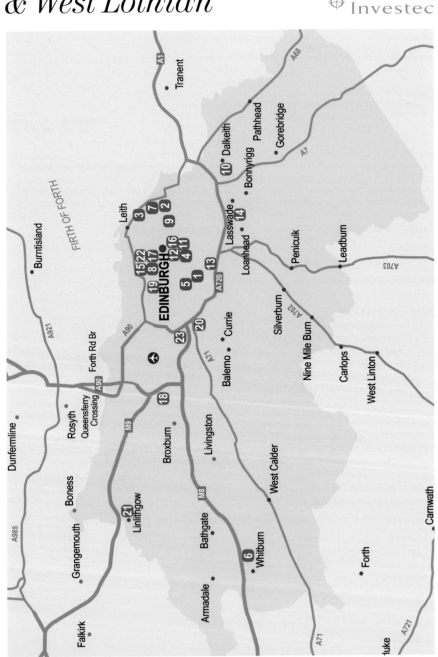

Edinburgh, Midlothian & West Lothian

OUR VOLUNTEER ORGANISERS

District Organiser:	Victoria Reid Thomas	Riccarton Mains Farmhouse, Currie EH14 4AR
		E: info@scotlandsgardens.org
Area Organisers:	Kate Fearnley	23 Lasswade Road, Eskbank EH22 3EE
	Jerry & Christine Gregson	101 Greenbank Crescent, Edinburgh EH10 5TA
	Caroline Pearson	42 Pentland Avenue, Edinburgh EH13 0HY
	Gillian Polley	3 Swanston Road, Edinburgh EH10 7BB
Treasurer:	Michael Pearson	42 Pentland Avenue, Edinburgh EH13 0HY

GARDENS OPEN ON A SPECIFIC DATE

41 Hermitage Gardens, Edinburgh	Saturday, 29 April
Dr Neil's Garden, Duddingston Village	Saturday/Sunday, 6/7 May
Greentree, 18 Green Hill Park, Edinburgh	Sunday, 7 May
Redcroft, 23 Murrayfield Road, Edinburgh	Saturday/Sunday, 13/14 May
14 East Brighton Crescent, Portobello, Edinburgh	Sunday, 14 May
5 Greenbank Crescent, Edinburgh	Sunday, 14 May
Moray Place and Bank Gardens, Edinburgh	Sunday, 21 May
Hunter's Tryst, 95 Oxgangs Road, Edinburgh	Sunday, 4 June
Dean Gardens, Edinburgh	Sunday, 4 June
Eskbank Village Gardens, 23 Lasswade Road, Eskbank	Saturday, 17 June
Claremont, Redmill	Sunday, 18 June
Meadow Place, 19 Meadow Place	Sunday, 18 June
Rivaldsgreen House, 48 Friars Brae, Linlithgow	Sunday, 18 June
Stockbridge Gardens, Edinburgh	Sunday, 25 June
Riccarton Mains House, Currie	Sunday, 2 July
Suntrap Garden, 43 Gogarbank Edinburgh	Saturday/Sunday, 8/9 July
Falcon Bowling & Tennis Club, 84 Newbattle Terrace, Edinburgh	Sunday, 9 July
Maggie's Edinburgh, Western General Hospital, Crewe Road, Edinburgh	Sunday, 16 July
Claremont, Redmill	Sunday, 16 July
14 East Brighton Crescent, Portobello, Edinburgh	Sunday, 23 July
Craigentinny Telferton Allotments, Telferton Road, Edinburgh	Sunday, 23 July
39 Nantwich Drive, Edinburgh	Saturday/Sunday, 5/6 August
Claremont, Redmill	Sunday, 6 August

GARDENS OPEN REGULARLY

Newliston, Kirkliston	Wednesday - Sunday, 3 May - 4 June

Edinburgh, Midlothian & West Lothian

GARDENS OPEN BY ARRANGEMENT – BOOK A VISIT WITH THE GARDEN OWNER

Kevock Garden, 16 Kevock Road, Lasswade	1 January - 31 December
Hunter's Tryst, 95 Oxgangs Road, Edinburgh	1 April - 30 September
101 Greenbank Crescent, Edinburgh	15 April - 30 September

Riccarton Mains House

Edinburgh, Midlothian & West Lothian

 1 ## 101 GREENBANK CRESCENT
Edinburgh EH10 5TA
Jerry and Christine Gregson
T: 0131 447 6492 E: jerry_gregson@yahoo.co.uk

After 12 years of holding open days, we are showing our garden 'by arrangement' this year. We welcome individuals and groups of any size, for guided tours or simple walkabouts. The house is on a busy bus route but hides a fascinating garden on a steeply sloped site. There are views over Braidburn Valley Park to the Pentland Hills. Paths wind down from the oval lawn, past a handsome magnolia tree, to a terrace which overlooks a water feature and established flowering shrubs. Less common species include *Neillia thibetica* and dierama. Further steps lead past a scree bed of azalea and rhododendron to a productive area of vegetable beds and fruit trees and a neatly concealed composting area. We aim to have colour, contrast and interest all year round.

Open: by arrangement 15 April - 30 September, admission £5.00, children free. Refreshments by arrangement. Unfortunately, the layout still makes the garden unsuitable for those of limited mobility.

Directions: From the city centre take the A702 through Morningside. Continue uphill and turn right at Greenbank Church on to Greenbank Crescent. Buses 5 and 16; the stop is for Greenbank Row.

Opening for: Shelter Scotland

2 ## 14 EAST BRIGHTON CRESCENT
Portobello, Edinburgh EH15 1LR
Jim and Sue Hurford
E: sue.hurford@gmail.com

Roughly two thirds of an acre suburban garden, developed over 40 years. People have said the following about it: 'A little bit of countryside in the town', 'Booming with green', 'A bosky bower' and 'There is such a wide range of plant material and every little corner holds a new gem'.

Open: Sunday 14 May and Sunday 23 July, 2pm - 5pm. Admission £5.00, children free.

Directions: Buses 21, 12 and 49 to Brighton Place, and 15, 26, 40 and 45 to Portobello High Street. Brighton Place intersects Portobello High Street just east of the bus stops.

Opening for: The Trussell Trust

 3 ## 39 NANTWICH DRIVE
Edinburgh EH7 6RA
Michael and Susan Burns

Large wildlife friendly garden run on organic principles. Includes mini orchard, pond, mixed borders, greenhouse and a secret garden. There are mini woodland walks and an allotment for vegetables, plus a compost area, worm bin and rotary bin.

Open: Saturday/Sunday, 5/6 August, 2pm - 5pm, admission £5.00, children free.

Directions: Bus 19 to Craigentinny Road or bus 26 to Kekewich Drive.

Opening for: The Henry Doubleday Research Association : Garden Organic

Edinburgh, Midlothian & West Lothian

4 41 HERMITAGE GARDENS

Edinburgh EH10 6AZ
Dr and Mrs Tony Toft
E: toft41@hotmail.com

This relatively large city garden on the corner of Hermitage Gardens and Hermitage Drive is at its best in spring with its rock garden, rhododendrons, camellias, acers, tulips and mature trees.

Open: Saturday 29 April, 2pm - 5pm, admission £6.00, children free.

Directions: Buses 5, 11, 15, 16, 23.

Opening for: The Edinburgh Clothing Store

5 5 GREENBANK CRESCENT

Edinburgh EH10 5TE
Sandy Corlett
T: 0131 447 1119 E: sandycorlett@hotmail.co.uk

South-facing, newly designed, sloping terraced garden with views over Braidburn Valley Park to the Pentlands. Colourful chaos of herbaceous plants, shrubs, roses and small trees. Hard features include a gazebo, pergola, greenhouse and water feature.

Open: Sunday 14 May, 2pm - 5pm, admission £5.00, children free.

Directions: From the city centre take the A702 through Morningside, continue uphill on Comiston Road, turn right at Greenbank Church on to Greenbank Crescent. Buses 5, 16, 11.

Opening for: Parkinsons UK

6 CLAREMONT

Redmill EH47 0JY
Trevor and Faye Yerbury
E: info@yerburystudio.com

Claremont is situated only two minutes from the Junction 4 off the M8 and is yet an idyllic oasis. It is an eclectic garden created over 19 years; before we moved in it was just grass with a few rhododendrons. The garden has three areas: to the front we have various herbaceous borders, to the side we have some of our hosta collections containing over 150 hostas, to the rear there are herbaceous borders, plus a stumpery/fernery created in 2022. There are three ponds, a rockery, a dovecot, a newly created rose garden and interesting trees including a grand monkey puzzle.

Open: Sunday 18 June, Sunday 16 July, and Sunday 6 August, 2pm - 5pm. Admission £5.00, children free.

Directions: Take the M8 and leave at Junction 4 heading for Whitburn. At the first set of traffic lights turn right for Whitburn. After only 100 metres turn first right at a slightly hidden turning with bollards, come straight down, without turning, to the bottom of the hill to Claremont. The house name is on the small pillar to the right.

Opening for: Alzheimer Scotland & Breast Cancer Campaign Scotland

Edinburgh, Midlothian & West Lothian

7 CRAIGENTINNY TELFERTON ALLOTMENTS

Telferton Road, off Portobello Road, Edinburgh EH7 6XG
The Gardeners of Craigentinny and Telferton
E: callotments@gmail.com

Established in 1923 and celebrating our centenary, this independent allotment site is a tranquil and charming space, hidden away in a built-up area, where the local community benefit from growing their own vegetables and fruit. Come and enjoy tea, home baking and a chat with our friendly plot-holders.

Open: Sunday 23 July, 2pm - 5pm, admission £4.00, children free.

Directions: Park on Telferton Road. Buses 15, 26, 45.

Opening for: Craigentinny Telferton Allotments

8 DEAN GARDENS

Edinburgh EH4 1QE
Dean Gardens Management Committee

Nine acres of semi-woodland garden with spring bulbs on the steep banks of the Water of Leith in central Edinburgh. Founded in the 1860s by local residents, the Dean Gardens contain part of the great structure of the Dean Bridge, a Thomas Telford masterpiece of 1835. Lawns, paths, trees, and shrubs with lovely views to the weir in the Dean Village and to the St Bernard's Well. There is also a children's play area.

Open: Sunday 4 June, 2pm - 5pm, admission £5.00, children free.

Directions: Entrance at Ann Street or Eton Terrace.

Opening for: Macmillan Cancer Support

9 DR NEIL'S GARDEN

Duddingston Village EH15 3PX
Dr Neil's Garden Trust
E: info@drneilsgarden.co.uk
W: www.drneilsgarden.co.uk

A wonderful, secluded, landscaped garden on the lower slopes of Arthur's Seat including conifers, heathers, alpines, a physic garden, herbaceous borders and ponds.

Open: Saturday/Sunday, 6/7 May, 2pm - 5pm, admission £5.00, children free.

Directions: Park at the kirk car park on Duddingston Road West and then follow signposts through the manse garden.

Opening for: Dr. Neil's Garden Trust

Edinburgh, Midlothian & West Lothian

10 **ESKBANK VILLAGE GARDENS**
23 Lasswade Road, Eskbank EH22 3EE
The Gardeners of Eskbank

A trail offering a range of varied gardens, large and small.
Trail start and plant sale will be at **23 Lasswade Road** EH22 3EE (Kate Fearnley & Maruska Greenwood): A third of an acre, with beautiful mature planting including a range of trees, rhododendrons and azaleas. Bearded irises and peonies are a feature of early summer. Bees and insects encouraged with lots of colour, small pond full of wildlife. We grow vegetables and fruit and garden organically, making our own compost and leaf mold.
18 Dundas Road EH22 3EL (Edward and Mary McMillan): Detached bungalow with south-facing front lawn bordered by trees, shrubs and seasonal flowers. Rear garden has trees, shrubs, a rose border, ornamental pond, summer house, greenhouse and vegetable plot, fruit trees and bushes; also a small, secluded 'Japanese' garden.
20 Dalhousie Road (NEW) EH22 3AL (Kenneth Hyslop): Productive veg and flowers.
5 Melville Terrace (NEW) EH22 3AR (Annette Henderson): This small walled garden is hidden away within a Victorian terrace with the only access a garden gate, and is shaded by trees. A mix of shade tolerant David Austin roses, geraniums, tree peonies and hydrangeas are the mainstay.
61 Eskbank Road EH22 3BU (Tim Rideout): A little of the Western Cape in Scotland. Moderate sized garden with a rich variety of plants. I have a connection with Cape Town after living there for ten years so put much effort into growing Western Cape plants, including *Widdringtonia cedarbergensis*, a CITES Red Book species and some of the only examples in the Northern Hemisphere.
We hope other gardens will join us – please check the website.

Open: Saturday 17 June, noon - 5pm, admission £7.00, children free. Tickets and trail maps available from 23 Lasswade Road. Maps can also be downloaded from Scotland's Gardens Scheme website. Vintage teas (charged separately) at 5 Melville Terrace.

Directions: Lothian Buses 3, 49, 140. Borders bus X95. Train: to Eskbank Station, 15m walk. Car: from A7 take A768 (Lasswade Road) towards Dalkeith. Number 23 is on the right, after Larkfield Road, middle of three white houses. From Dalkeith take A768 from Justinlees roundabout, number 23 is on the left, after Dundas Crescent. Street parking unrestricted.

Opening for: Deaf Children's Society Of East Scotland, One Dalkeith & Dalkeith Guerrilla Gardeners

11 **FALCON BOWLING & TENNIS CLUB**
84 Newbattle Terrace, Edinburgh EH10 4SE
Miles Weaver
E: fbtc.social@outlook.com

Falcon Bowling & Tennis Club celebrates its 25th anniversary as a community managed club in 2023. When the club obtained its lease from the City Council they acquired a garden established before 1817 (according to Kirkwood's 1817 map of Morningside), surrounding the bowling green and three tennis courts, which is maintained by its members. Prominent features of the garden are its flowering cherry trees and over 200 roses. Other plants have been introduced including varieties of buddleias, hebes and rhododendrons and four different varieties of abutilons. The garden, hidden from view behind a high wall, provides a peaceful oasis in our busy city. Among our members are many non-playing members who come simply to relax or picnic with friends. Why not come and see for yourself.

Open: Sunday 9 July, 2pm - 5pm, admission £4.00, children free.

Edinburgh, Midlothian & West Lothian

Directions: From Morningside: go past the Dominion Cinema for about 3-4 minutes pass turning for both Falcon Gardens and Eden Lane, see green gates on your right. Buses 5, 11, 16, 23, 36, 41.

Opening for: St Columba's Hospice Care

12 **GREENTREE**

18 Green Hill Park, Edinburgh EH10 4DW
Alison Glen

A rare opportunity to appreciate a mature garden which, with the exception of one magnificent old copper beech tree, is completely planted and created by its owner Alison Glen. Designed with an artist's appreciation of form, this woodland garden shelters a large collection of rhododendrons. There are many beautiful specimen trees and shrubs including *Hoheria glabrata, Halesia carolina* and several magnolia species. The garden is fully wheelchair accessible and there are several ways to move through it; from the Japanese-inspired stream garden presided over by a mature *Pinus wallichiana* at one end, to the newly developed borders at the other.

Open: Sunday 7 May, 10am - 5pm, admission £5.00, children free.

Directions: Buses 11, 16, 15, 23, 5. By car: from the east – Chamberlain Road, Strathearn Road, from the north – Morningside Road, from the west – Colinton Road.

Opening for: Alzheimer Scotland

13 **HUNTER'S TRYST**

95 Oxgangs Road, Edinburgh EH10 7BA
Jean Knox
T: 07708 653584 E: jean.knox@blueyonder.co.uk

Well-stocked and beautifully designed, mature, medium-sized town garden comprising herbaceous and shrub beds, lawn, fruit and some vegetables, water features, seating areas, trees and an example of cloud pruning. This is a wildlife-friendly garden that has been transformed from a wilderness 39 years ago and continues to evolve. In 2017 two raised beds were added to the front garden. This hidden treasure of a garden was featured on *The Beechgrove Garden* in June 2015 and on *The Instant Gardener* in June 2016. We were unable to open in 2021 due to serious house damage, so it is particularly exciting to be able to welcome everybody back.

Open: Sunday 4 June, 2pm - 5pm. Also open by arrangement 1 April - 30 September. Admission £5.00, children free.

Directions: From Fairmilehead crossroads head down Oxgangs Road to Hunter's Tryst roundabout and it's the last house on the left. Buses 4, 5, 27, 400. The bus stop is at Hunter's Tryst and the garden is opposite.

Opening for: St Columba's Hospice Care & Lothian Cat Rescue

Edinburgh, Midlothian & West Lothian

14 KEVOCK GARDEN
16 Kevock Road, Lasswade EH18 1HT
David and Stella Rankin
E: stella@kevockgarden.co.uk
W: www.kevockgarden.co.uk

This wonderful hillside garden has magnificent views over the North Esk Valley. Its steep slope creates a range of different habitats with a wide diversity of plants, ranging from those that love hot, sunny conditions to those that prefer the cool, damp places near the pond and woodland glades. Mature specimen trees, rhododendrons, azaleas and unusual shrubs are underplanted with many rare woodland plants. Lawns have been relaid, surrounding borders have been planted, and there is a new rock garden. Kevock Garden has featured in many magazine articles and gardening programmes.

Open: by arrangement 1 January - 31 December, admission £5.00, children free. Please email to arrange. Individuals and couples are welcome as well as groups.

Directions: Kevock Road lies to the south of the A678 Loanhead/Lasswade Road. Five minutes from the city bypass Lasswade Junction and on the 31 Lothian Bus route to Polton/Bonnyrigg Road.

Opening for: Fischy Music

15 MAGGIE'S EDINBURGH

Western General Hospital, Crewe Road, Edinburgh EH4 2XU
Maggie's Centre
W: www.maggies.org

At Maggie's we believe that gardens can have an amazing, positive effect on health and well-being. Each of our centres has a beautiful garden designed alongside the building to ensure a strong connection between the outside and inside. The garden was designed by Emma Keswick and has been adapted to grow and flourish alongside two new extensions. The walled garden and statue gardens create a connection with nature and the ever-changing seasons. Emma's planting design ensures the garden has year-round colour and creates a calming transition away from the hospital. The garden is fully accessible for all with enclosed spaces cleverly interspersed with more open areas with longer views.

Open: Sunday 16 July, 11am - 4pm, admission £5.00, children free. Homemade teas and plants for sale. There will also be guided tours of the Maggie's Centre available.

Directions: Maggie's is situated behind Ward 1 in the grounds of the Western General Hospital near the Crewe Road entrance to the hospital. Lothian Buses: 19, 19A, 28, 28B, 29, 37, 37A, 38; First Bus: 129. Parking available within the grounds. Follow parking signs on the day.

Opening for: Maggie's

Edinburgh, Midlothian & West Lothian

16 **MEADOW PLACE**
19 Meadow Place EH9 1JR
Jan Wilson
T: 0131 229 8316 E: janwilson1920@gmail.com

The secret garden of Meadow Place is the walled garden of a Georgian house that was built in 1816. The owner has been tending the garden for 47 years and the garden is now patios, pots and flower beds rather than the lawn and roses of yesteryear. The planting is a mixture of trees, shrubs and herbaceous flowers.

Open: Sunday 18 June, 2pm - 5pm, admission £5.00, children free.

Directions: The garden is down the lane off Roseneath Terrace. Look for the brown garage door. Buses 24, 41.

Opening for: Maggie's

17 **MORAY PLACE AND BANK GARDENS**
Edinburgh EH3 6BX
The residents of the Moray Feu

Join us to celebrate the gardens of the Moray Feu in their spring and summer colours.
Bank Gardens Nearly six acres of secluded wild gardens with lawns, trees and shrubs with banks of bulbs down to the Water of Leith and stunning views towards Dean Bridge.
Moray Place Private garden of three-and-a-half acres in the Georgian New Town is framed by the polygon of Moray Place, and is laid out with shrubs, trees and flower beds offering an atmosphere of tranquility in the city centre.

Open: Sunday 21 May, 2pm - 5pm, admission £5.00, children free. There will be tea, coffee and home baking.

Directions: Bank Gardens: Enter by the gate at the top of Doune Terrace. **Moray Place:** Enter by the north gate in Moray Place.

Opening for: Euan Macdonald Centre for Motor Neurone Disease Research

18 **NEWLISTON**
Kirkliston EH29 9EB
Mr and Mrs R C Maclachlan
T: 0131 333 3231 E: newliston@gmail.com

A well preserved 18th-century parkland/designed landscape rather than a garden as such. Full of mature rhododendrons and azaleas, fine vistas and allées of trees. The walk around the woods and lake is a carpet of wild garlic and bluebells in the spring. The wood to the east of the house is in the pattern of the Union Jack, best appreciated by standing in the centre where all the radiating paths meet. The house, designed by Robert Adam, is also open.

Open: 3 May - 4 June (not Mondays & Tuesdays), 2pm - 6pm. Admission £5.00, children free.

Directions: Four miles south of the Forth Road Bridge, entrance off the B800.

Opening for: CHAS

Edinburgh, Midlothian & West Lothian

 19 REDCROFT
23 Murrayfield Road, Edinburgh EH12 6EP
James and Anna Buxton
T: 0131 337 1747 E: annabuxtonb@aol.com

Redcroft is a mature walled garden surrounding an attractive Arts and Crafts house. It is a hidden haven off a busy road with a variety of different features and habitats: old shrubberies, an orchard, a rockery, a pond, and a large lawn with contrasting longer grass. It is well maintained with many clipped shrubs – some of them quite unusual – and some cloud pruning. Early May is very colourful with rhododendrons and many other flowering shrubs and wall plants, and the greenhouse is full of tender plants. There will be tulips in pots and many other spring bulbs. Children and buggies are very welcome and there will be plenty of activities. We hope older children will enjoy our treehouse. Dogs on leads welcome.

Open: Saturday/Sunday, 13/14 May, 2pm - 5pm, admission £6.00, children free. There will be a bumper SGS PLANT SALE.

Directions: Murrayfield Road runs north from Corstorphine Road to Ravelston Dykes. There is easy free parking available. Buses 12, 26, 31, get off at Murrayfield Stadium. Bus 38 goes up Murrayfield Road.

Opening for: St Salvador's Scottish Episcopal Church: Edinburgh: Food Initiative

 20 RICCARTON MAINS HOUSE
Currie EH14 4AR
Mr and Mrs Michael Reid Thomas
E: ricmains@gmail.com

A large garden (developed from scratch over the last 50 years) divided into sections and terraces, giving interest and colour throughout the year, from spring bulbs and blossom to herbaceous borders and roses in the summer. There is a small wood with some interesting trees plus a pond and small orchard with vegetables.

Open: Sunday 2 July, 2pm - 5pm, admission £6.00, children free.

Directions: A71 from Edinburgh; follow directions for Heriot Watt University and the entrance to the garden is on the east side of the roundabout. Lothian Buses 45, 25 and 34.

Opening for: St Salvador's Scottish Episcopal Church: Edinburgh: Food Bank

 21 RIVALDSGREEN HOUSE
48 Friars Brae, Linlithgow EH49 6BG
Dr Ian Wallace
T: 07801 855146 E: ianwjw1940@gmail.com

Mature two-acre garden with lovely mixed herbaceous, rose, and tree planting.

Open: Sunday 18 June, 2pm - 5pm, admission £5.00, children free.

Directions: From the west end of the High Street turn into Preston Road, after crossing the canal turn left into Priory Road and at the T junction turn left down Friars Brae. There is car parking available.

Opening for: St John Scotland

Edinburgh, Midlothian & West Lothian

22 STOCKBRIDGE GARDENS
Garden trail runs between Logie Green Gardens EH7 4HE and Royal Circus Gardens
South EH3 6SS
Gardeners of Stockbridge
E: JW.homeoffice@gmail.com

Visit some of the surprising horticultural delights behind the discrete terraces of Stockbridge and enjoy homemade refreshments in a classic Georgian pleasure garden. Bringing fresh air and wildlife into the heart of the city, the collection provides lots of creative solutions to urban gardening with year-round interest through a mix of seasonal planting and structural evergreens which the gardeners will be on hand to talk about.

Open: Sunday 25 June, noon - 4:30pm, admission £8.00, children free. Tickets and route maps available at both ends. Refreshments at Royal Circus Gardens South. Plants for sale at Logie Green Gardens. See Scotland's Gardens Scheme website for up-to-date details.

Directions: Buses 23 and 27 to Dundas Street and Canonmills, 8 to Rodney St and Canonmills, 36 to Hamilton Place and Broughton Rd, 29 to Royal Circus.

Opening for: Shelter Scotland & Médecins Sans Frontières

23 SUNTRAP GARDEN
43 Gogarbank Edinburgh EH12 9BY
Robert Gillan & David Gillan-Reid
T: 07720 379248 E: robbie.gillan@gmail.com
W: www.suntrapgarden.com

Suntrap is a three-acre south-facing garden at Gogarbank, Edinburgh. It was started in 1957 when nearing the completion of Millbuies House (at the bottom of the garden), Scottish philanthropist George Boyd Anderson began to plant out the large garden area surrounding it. He intended the site to have an educational function and planted a series of small gardens to illustrate to others what could be achieved in a small space. The current owners have spent the last ten years restoring both Suntrap House and the award winning Millbuies House and are now, with a dedicated team of gardeners, nurturing the garden back to life. Features include informal borders and small gardens, a large glasshouse with mature palms and other tropical plants; greenhouse, potting shed and doocot, a large pond and a sunken garden with ferns and perennials.

Open: Saturday/Sunday, 8/9 July, 2pm - 5pm, admission £6.00, children free.

Directions: Several bus and tram routes to the Gyle shopping centre, where you can take a taxi to Suntrap. For Satnav and Google Maps please use postcode EH12 9BY.

Opening for: Alzheimer Scotland

Fife

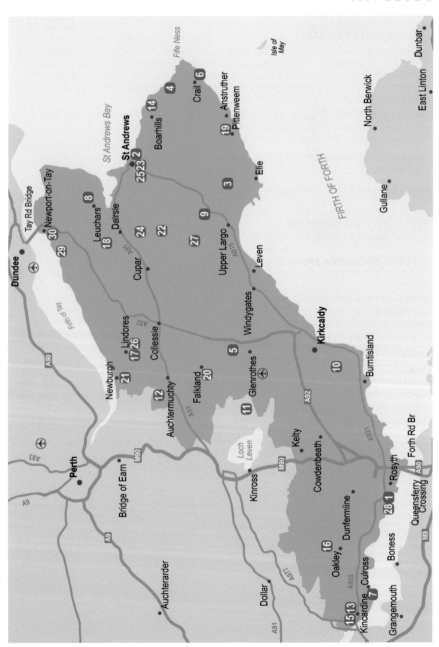

Fife

OUR VOLUNTEER ORGANISERS

District Organisers:	David Buchanan-Cook	Helensbank, 56 Toll Road, Kincardine FK10 4QZ
	Julia Young	South Flisk, Blebo Craigs, Cupar KY15 5UQ
Area Organisers:	Alison Aiton	Craigview Cottage, Blebo Craigs KY15 5UQ
	Clare Ansell	Coul House, Maree Way, Glenrothes KY7 6NW
	Pauline Borthwick	96 Hepburn Gardens, St Andrews KY16 9LP
	Lorna Duckworth	The Old Coach House, Dunbog KY14 6JF
	Catherine Erskine	Cambo Farmhouse, Kingsbarns KY16 8QD
	Barbara Pickard	Straiton Farmhouse, Balmullo KY16 0BN
	Fay Smith	37 Ninian Fields, Pittenweem KY10 2QU
District Photographers:	Carolyn Bell	carolynmbell@gmail.com
	Mike Bell	docmike@hotmail.co.uk
Treasurer:	David Buchanan-Cook	Helensbank, 56 Toll Road, Kincardine FK10 4QZ

GARDENS OPEN ON A SPECIFIC DATE

Coul House	Check the website for date
Dunimarle Castle, Balgownie West, Culross	Saturday/Sunday, 25/26 February
Lindores House, by Newburgh	Saturday, 25 February
Millfield Garden, Millfield House, Falkland, Fife	Saturday/Sunday, 25/26 February
St Andrews Botanic Garden Spring Fair, Canongate, St Andrews	Saturday, 8 April
Cambo Spring Plant & Garden Market, Kingsbarns	Saturday, 15 April
Teasses Gardens, near Ceres	Sunday, 30 April
South Flisk, Blebo Craigs, Cupar	Sunday, 30 April
Greenhead Farmhouse, Greenhead of Arnot, Leslie	Sunday, 7 May
The Garden with the Dragon, 2, Upper Wellheads, Limekilns	Saturday, 13 May
Kenlygreen House, Boarhills, St Andrews	Tuesday, 16 May
The Garden with the Dragon, 2, Upper Wellheads, Limekilns	Saturday, 20 May
The Tower, 1 Northview Terrace, Wormit	Sunday, 21 May
Balcarres, Colinsburgh	Sunday, 21 May
Kirklands, Saline	Sunday, 21 May
The Garden with the Dragon, 2, Upper Wellheads, Limekilns	Saturday, 27 May
20 Brucehaven Crescent, Limekilns	Saturday/Sunday, 27/28 May
South Flisk, Blebo Craigs, Cupar	Sunday, 28 May
Lindores House, by Newburgh	Sunday, 28 May
Earlshall Castle, Leuchars	Sunday, 28 May
Kincardine's Gardens – Great and Small, Kincardine Village	Sunday, 11 June
Gilston House, By Largoward, Leven	Wednesday, 14 June
Newburgh – Hidden Gardens, Newburgh	Sunday, 25 June
The Tower, 1 Northview Terrace, Wormit	Sunday, 25 June
Earlshall Castle, Leuchars	Sunday, 25 June
Crail: Gardens in the Burgh, Crail	Saturday/Sunday, 8/9 July

Fife

Lucklaw House, Logie, Cupar	Friday, 14 July
Greenhead Farmhouse, Greenhead of Arnot, Leslie	Sunday, 17 September
SGS Autumn Plant Sale at St Andrews Botanic Garden, St Andrews	Sunday, 8 October

GARDENS OPEN REGULARLY

Glassmount House, by Kirkcaldy	1 April - 30 September
Willowhill, Forgan, Newport-on-Tay	15 & 17 April and 13 & 15 May (Saturday/Sunday/Monday) and 17 & 19 June and 22 July - 26 August (Saturday & Monday)

GARDENS OPEN BY ARRANGEMENT

Harthill, Reediehill Farm, Auchtermuchty	2 January - 31 October
Madeira, Grangemuir, Pittenweem	1 February - 30 September (Tuesday, Thursday & Friday)
Swallows Rest, Lindores	1 March - 31 October
South Flisk, Blebo Craigs, Cupar	1 April - 30 June
The Tower, 1 Northview Terrace, Wormit	1 April - 1 October
46 South Street, St Andrews	1 April - 31 July
Kirklands, Saline	1 April - 30 September
Rosewells, Baldinnie, Ceres	1 April - 30 September
Willowhill, Forgan, Newport-on-Tay	10 April - 31 August
Helensbank House, Kincardine	1 June - 30 September
Lucklaw House, Logie, Cupar	15 July - 31 July

Willowhill

Fife

1

20 BRUCEHAVEN CRESCENT

Limekilns KY11 3JJ
Mrs Patricia Durie
T: 07513 293737 E: patriciadurie@googlemail.com

Petite cottage garden with large borders, formal and informal paths, and a tropical greenhouse featuring a large collection of carnivorous plants. Quirky artwork pops out from various corners of the garden. Multiple seating areas give idyllic views of the colourful borders. Highlights of the garden include a selection of roses, iris, peonies, clematis, hostas, ferns, hardy and tropical orchids, flowering trees, carnivorous plants, succulents, aroids and many more unusual plants.

Open: Saturday/Sunday, 27/28 May, 2pm - 5pm, admission £5.00, children free.

Directions: Enter the village from Dunfermline road, turn left at Upper Wellheads then another left onto Brucehaven Crescent, garden is on the left. Note – on 27 May the garden opens jointly with the Garden with the Dragon, also in Limekilns.

Opening for: Friends of Bandrum Nursing Home SCIO

2

46 SOUTH STREET

St Andrews KY16 9JT
Mrs June Baxter
T: 01334 474995

Renowned town garden in medieval long rig, with orchard underplanted with wildflowers and bulbs. Many unusual flowering shrubs will be looking their best. Roses and other climbers clothe the surrounding high walls. Shrub roses planted in a delightful central parterre fill the air with scent. An historic and unique feature in St Andrews, but also a wonderfully planted space where different styles of planting complement the range of plants used. Historic doocot.

Open: by arrangement 1 April - 31 July, admission £6.00, children free.

Directions: Access and parking information on request.

Opening for: Friends of Craigtoun

Balcarres © Angus Blackburn

Fife

3 BALCARRES
Colinsburgh KY9 1HN
Lord and Lady Balniel
T: 01333 340205 (Estate Office)

Balcarres House has been owned by the Lindsay family since the late 16th century and each generation has made their mark on the house and gardens. The formal gardens with their magnificent yew hedges and terraces were laid out by Sir Coutts Lindsay in the 1870s. Since then other changes have been made but the largest impact has come from the late Lady Crawford. She has been the inspiration for the garden and the driving force of much of what has been created in the past fifty years. The gardens come into their own in early summer with the Rose Garden in full bloom with a variety of Hybrid Teas and climbing roses such as Blairi II, Shropshire Lad & Lady Hillingdon. Herbaceous borders are bursting into life with a variety of geranium, astrantia, viola, oriental poppies and aquilegia. The Woodland & Chapel Walks will also be at their best with many different hostas, smilacina, and other diverse plants, shrubs and trees. Enjoy the walks to the Sawmill Pond planting, the Den and the Balcarres Craig. This year, Balcarres will be opening the Garden in support of the RNLI in Anstruther. We are particularly aiming the opening towards children and families. The RNLI will be arranging a Lifeboat Treasure Hunt throughout the garden and all the children will need to keep an eye out for "Stormy Sam" the Station Mascot! There will also be Water Safety demonstrations in the RNLI Gazebo together with a number of kids' activities.

Open: Sunday 21 May, 2pm - 5pm, admission £6.00, children free.

Directions: Half-a-mile north of Colinsburgh off A942. Bus to Colinsburgh.

Opening for: RNLI: Anstruther

4 CAMBO SPRING PLANT & GARDEN MARKET
Kingsbarns KY16 8QD
Trustees of Cambo Heritage Trust
T: 01333 451040 E: hello@camboestate.com
W: www.cambogardens.org.uk

Pop in to Cambo to freshen up your garden for spring. We will have a unique selection of plants and bulbs from visiting nurseries, garden goods and local crafts to browse. Outdoor cafe open all day. Gardens, woodlands and play area to visit.
National Plant Collection: Galanthus.

Open: Saturday 15 April, 11am - 4pm, admission £3.00, children free.

Directions: A917 between Crail and St Andrews.

Opening for: Cambo Heritage Trust

5 COUL HOUSE
Coul House, Maree Way, Glenrothes KY7 6NW
Dean & Clare Ansell
T: 07525 791277 E: Clareansell5@gmail.com

A hidden gem, Coul garden lies within the grounds of Coul House, an imposing B-listed Victorian farmhouse which dates back to circa 1875. A mix of hydrangeas, roses, rhododendron and wisteria are contained in this ever-evolving amateur garden. The garden has more recently been redesigned with hard landscaping and includes a small pond. Come and take a walk around and enjoy a cup of tea and home baking.

Open: see website for open dates.

Fife

Directions: From the A92, follow signs for Pitcairn

Opening for: Juvenile Diabetes Research Foundation Limited & Glenrothes & District Foodbank

6 CRAIL: GARDENS IN THE BURGH
Crail KY10 3TT
Gardeners of Crail

Take an enjoyable stroll around this quintessential East Neuk village and explore its many beautiful gardens. These include gardens in varied styles and planting schemes – cottage, historic, plantsman's and bedding. The stunning coastal location presents some challenges for planting but also allows for a great range of more tender species to flourish.

Open: Saturday/Sunday, 8/9 July, 1pm - 5pm, admission £6.00, children free. Tickets and maps are available on the day from Crail Museum and participating gardens

Directions: Approach Crail from either St Andrews or Anstruther on the A917. Parking available in Marketgate.

Opening for: Crail Community Partnership

7 DUNIMARLE CASTLE
Balgownie West, Culross KY12 8JN
George Fleming
T: 07713 629040 E: castledunimarle@gmail.com
W: www.dunimarlecastle.co.uk

Dunimarle Castle sits on the outskirts of the historic village of Culross, surrounded by 52 acres of formal gardens, meadows and woodlands. Entering the grounds from the rose arch on the main road, you will find the imposing Victorian gothic-style chapel, beautifully framed by the striking tulip tree and rhododendrons. Follow the path up towards the castle to the Italianate yew-lined terrace with its south-facing wall, home to a growing collection of grapes and other fruiting plants. The Bastion Garden provides a perfect backdrop to the original Georgian part of the castle with its colourful borders and trees. A stroll up the once grand "North Drive" takes you past specimen monkey puzzle trees sandwiched between dramatic redwoods and rhododendrons.
Champion Trees: Tulip Tree, Cedar, Monkey Puzzle, Redwood.

Open: Saturday/Sunday, 25/26 February, 10am - 4pm for Snowdrops and Winter Walks, admission by donation (recommended £5)

Directions: Situated on the B9037 to the west of Culross, approximately 500 yards from the village. Parking is available in the village's west car park. From there, follow the coastal path west to the Rose Arch.

Opening for: West Fife Woodlands Group

Fife

8 EARLSHALL CASTLE
Leuchars KY16 0DP
Paul and Josine Veenhuijzen
T: 01334 839205

Topiary gardens designed by Sir Robert Lorimer in the 1890s. The grounds also include a rose garden, croquet lawn, vegetable garden, orchard, park and wooded area.

Open: Sunday 28 May, 2pm - 5pm. Also open Sunday 25 June, 2pm - 5pm. Admission £6.50, children free. Due to grass areas and steps, the garden is not fully wheelchair accessible. Dogs only on leads please!

Directions: On Earlshall Road, three-quarters of a mile east of Leuchars Village (off A919).

Opening for: Leuchars St Athernase Parish Church (Sunday 28 May) & The Royal Scots Regimental Trust (Sunday 25 June)

9 GILSTON HOUSE
By Largoward, Leven KY8 5QP
Mr and Mrs Edward Baxter
T: 07754 857729 E: catherine@cathbrown.com
W: www.eastneukestates.co.uk

Large garden with mixed borders and mature trees in a beautiful park with wild flower meadow and woodland surrounding an early 19th-century house. Older, established, well-loved shrubs sit with abundant new planting of trees and perennials. Pink birches stand with sorbus *pink pagoda* above our attempt at matrix planting of grasses, foxgloves and verbascums. Acid-loving plants thrive here too with meconopsis on repeat throughout our deep borders which can be admired from a seat close by. Lots of startlingly bright azaleas. Enjoy your tea on the main terrace by our house alongside the central rectangle of catmint, wild swan anemones and sedums with their beautiful dusty dark purple leaves. Beyond the borders around the house, two different directions; a walled garden where Hebridean sheep graze, a Victorian pond cleared and reconfigured (inspired by Charles Jenks) but really work in progress! A short walk through the woods will take you to our pond (used for curling) and with an 1899 boathouse recently restored; the edges around planted with bulbs and wet-loving plants. Far reaching views everywhere.

Open: Wednesday 14 June, noon - 5pm, admission £6.00, children free.

Directions: 15 mins by car from St Andrews on A915 (buses from Leven and St Andrews request stop) one hour north of Edinburgh.

Opening for: Royal Highland Education Trust

10 GLASSMOUNT HOUSE
by Kirkcaldy KY2 5UT
Peter, James and Irene Thomson
T: 01592 890214 E: mcmoonter@yahoo.co.uk

Densely planted walled garden with surrounding woodland. An A-listed sundial, Mackenzie & Moncur greenhouse and historical doocot are complemented by a number of newer structures. Daffodils are followed by a mass of candelabra and cowslip primula, meconopsis and *Cardiocrinum giganteum*. Hedges and topiary form backdrops for an abundance of bulbs, clematis, rambling roses and perennials, creating interest through the summer into September. The garden is now extending beyond the walls, with new areas of naturalistic planting blending the boundary between the surrounding fields and the woodland.

Fife

Open: 1 April - 30 September, 2pm - 5pm, admission £6.00, children free.

Directions: From Kirkcaldy, head west on the B9157. Turn left immediately after the railway bridge on the edge of town. Follow the single track road for one-and-a-half miles and cross the crossroads. Glassmount House is the first turning on your right.

Opening for: Parkinsons UK

 ## 11 GREENHEAD FARMHOUSE
Greenhead of Arnot, Leslie KY6 3JQ
Malcolm and Maggie Strang Steel
T: 01592 840459

The south-facing garden contains a variety of spring bulbs – daffodils, erythroniums, aconites and tulips – and there is also a daffodil walk. The main garden has herbaceous borders. A well-stocked polytunnel is used to augment the fruit and vegetable garden.

Open: Sunday 7 May, 2pm - 5pm. Also open Sunday 17 September, 2pm - 5pm. Admission £6.00, children free.

Directions: A911 between Auchmuir Bridge and Scotlandwell.

Opening for: Scotland's Charity Air Ambulance (Sunday 7 May) & SSAFA Forces Help (Sunday 17 September)

 ## 12 HARTHILL
Reediehill Farm, Auchtermuchty KY14 7HS
Nichola and John Fletcher
T: 01337 828369 E: info@nicholafletcher.com
W: www.nicholafletcher.com

Harthill enjoys a tranquil setting in the Ochil hills just above Auchtermuchty with beautiful views and, if you are lucky, sightings of the herd of stunning pure white deer who also live there. The garden, of approximately one acre, offers a large flower garden, vegetables and fruit, two separate wild gardens planted with specimen trees, a lochan and a small woodland. Spring-time treats (late May to early June) are our meconopsis and primula beds with woodland plants at their best. Summer offers herbaceous interest including a pergola dripping with roses and a large mound with grasses, thalictrum and many very large plants. Autumn colours are in the trees and shrubs, with grasses and cyclamen through to early winter.

Open: by arrangement 2 January - 31 October, admission by donation.

Directions: Find 'Reediehill Deer Farm' on Google maps. Continue 50 metres up the drive then turn LEFT at HARTHILL sign. Continue over the cattle grid up the unsurfaced drive till you reach Harthilll house. Directions can be emailed.

Opening for: The Tim Stead Trust

Fife

13 HELENSBANK HOUSE
Kincardine FK10 4QZ
David Buchanan-Cook and Adrian Miles
T: 07739 312912 E: Helensbank@aol.com
W: www.helensbank.com

Hidden away from public view, this is an 18th-century walled garden, with main feature a Cedar of Lebanon, reputedly planted in 1750 by the sea captain who built the house. The tree is registered as a 'Notable Tree' and while it provides challenges for planting, in terms of shade and needle fall, the microclimate it provides has encouraged the owners' passion for pushing boundaries and growing unusual and exotic plants. Distinctive garden 'rooms' in part of the garden comprise a perennial blue and white cottage garden, a formal rose garden and an Italian double courtyard with citrus trees in pots. A 'hot' courtyard contains exotics including varieties of banana, acacia, iochroma, impatiens, melianthus and brugmansia. A shaded walk along the bottom of the garden leads to a Japanese themed area including a pagoda. A large glasshouse hosts various exotic and climbing plants. The garden has well over a hundred roses, including the National Collection of Portland roses. These are best viewed from mid June to early July.
National Plant Collection: Portland Roses.
Champion Trees: The garden has a 'notable' Cedar of Lebanon, the second largest in Fife.

Open: by arrangement 1 June - 30 September, admission £6.00, children free. There is an annual garden charity concert on the first Sunday of August. Details will be updated on this and the Helensbank website nearer the time. Tickets (£17.50, concessions £15.00 including wine and canapes) can be reserved via emailing helensbank@aol.com.
Helensbank is also open on Sunday 11 June under the Kincardine's Gardens opening – see separate listing.

Directions: The garden is down a lane off the main Toll Road. *SGS* signs.

Opening for: Scottish Veterans Residences

14 KENLYGREEN HOUSE
Boarhills, St Andrews KY16 8PT
Victoria Kilgour

Kenlygreen House was built in the 1790s, when many of the trees seen now were planted. The bluebells form a wonderful carpet to these ancient trees, which have since been interspersed with more recent planting. Recently the garden has become the home of a medicinal herb practice which incorporates the diverse herbs in the woodland area with newly planted beds closer to the house.
Champion Trees: Ancient sorbus and cherry.

Open: Tuesday 16 May, 11am - 4pm, admission £6.00, children free.

Directions: The entrance to the garden is directly off the A917 St Andrews to Crail road, which is on the 95 bus route. From St Andrews continue past the turning into Boarhills, after going over a small bridge turn immediately left through two stone gateposts, up a tarmacked drive. The main road bears sharp right at this point.

Opening for: The Herb Society

Fife

15 KINCARDINE'S GARDENS – GREAT AND SMALL

Kincardine Village FK10
Kincardine Gardeners
T: 07739 312912 E: Helensbank@aol.com

To mark the start of Kincardine's Gala week, a number of gardens – great and small – are opening in aid of local charities. Full details of all gardens taking part will be updated on the SGS website listing but will include Helensbank House, Dunimarle Castle (see separate listings) and the Grow West Fife community garden in the walled garden of Blair Castle. National Plant Collection: Portland Roses.
Champion Trees: Helensbank House has a 'notable' Cedar of Lebanon, the second largest in Fife; Dunimarle Castle has a number of exceptional ancient trees.

Open: Sunday 11 June, 11am - 4pm, admission £6.00, children free. Tickets and maps can be purchased from Helensbank House and also from the Kincardine Community Centre (KCC) where teas will be available. Teas and refreshments will also be available from the Grow West Fife garden.

Directions: Parking will be available at the Kincardine Community Centre from where most local gardens will be within easy walking distance. A minibus shuttle service will provide transport from there to and from Blair and Dunimarle Castles.

Opening for: Kincardine Community Association, Kincardine Children's Gala & Grow West Fife (SCIO)

16 KIRKLANDS

Saline KY12 9TS
Peter and Gill Hart
T: 07787 115477 E: peter@kirklandsgarden.co.uk
W: www.kirklandsgarden.co.uk

Kirklands, built in 1832, has been the Hart family home for 45 years. Over the years we have reinstated the walled garden from a paddock and constructed terraces with raised beds. There are 18 espalier apple trees against the walls and box hedging with a display of tulips. The woodland garden starts with snowdrops and bluebells, then rhododendrons, trilliums, fritillaries, meconopsis, erythroniums and candelabra primulas follow. The rockery displays dwarf rhododendrons and azaleas. The herbaceous borders reach their peak in the summer. The bog garden by the Saline Burn is home to giant *Gunnera manicata*. Over the bridge we have 20 acres of woodland with a pathway by the burn. To keep the grandchildren occupied, Peter built a tree house, climbing frame and rope swing, though we hope they will take an interest in gardening too!

Open: Sunday 21 May, 2pm - 5pm. Also open by arrangement 1 April - 30 September. Admission £6.00, children free.

Directions: Junction 4, M90, then B914. Parking in the centre of the village, then a short walk to the garden. Limited disabled parking at Kirklands.

Opening for: Saline & District Heritage Society

Fife

17 LINDORES HOUSE
by Newburgh KY14 6JD
Robert and Elizabeth Turcan & John and Eugenia Turcan
T: 01337 840369

Situated between Lindores House and Lindores Loch, and with stunning views over the loch, the garden has been developed by the current owners over the last 45 years. It now includes extensive lochside and woodland walks with banks of snowdrops, leucojum, hostas, gunnera manicata, primula, astilbes, crocuses, fritillaria, spring and autumn cyclamen, hellebores and a notably impressive collection of trilliums. As well as the much older established trees – and in particular the splendid 17th century ewe (believed to be the largest in Fife which you can actually walk inside) there are more recent plantings of interesting specimen trees and shrubs. The herbaceous beds are mainly laid out formally around the old tennis court overlooking the loch. There is a one-acre walled garden, mainly used for growing fruit and vegetables, and a new garden in front of the recently converted stable building is under construction.

Open: Saturday 25 February, 11am - 2pm for Snowdrops and Winter Walks. Also open Sunday 28 May, 2pm - 5pm. Admission £6.00, children free.

Directions: Off A913 two miles east of Newburgh. Bus from Cupar.

Opening for: Lindores Parish Church: Newburgh Wellbeing Choir (Saturday 25 February) & Diocese Of St Andrews Dunkeld & Dunblane General Fund: St Ninian's RC Church, Cupar (Sunday 28 May)

18 LUCKLAW HOUSE
Logie, Cupar KY15 4SJ
Kate and Robert Campbell
E: katie.elliott@btopenworld.com

Large country garden set on a challenging north facing slope that drops steeply down to a burn, backed by woodland. The planting around the house is grassy and naturalistic, leading to mixed borders planted for scent, roses and a woodland garden. Also a small experimental tea garden (camellia sinensis). There are some rougher areas of the garden so sturdy footwear is advised!

Open: Friday 14 July, noon - 5pm. Also open by arrangement 15 July - 31 July. Admission £6.00, children free.

Directions: From A92, take turning signposted *Logie* for two miles up the hill. From A914, follow signpost to *Logie at Thai Teak*, turning right at top of hill. Please park on the verge outside the garden wall.

Opening for: Médecins Sans Frontières

19 MADEIRA
Grangemuir, Pittenweem KY10 2RB
Tara Macdonald
T: 07867 798746 E: tara@madeirainfife.com
W: www.madeirainfife.com

Madeira is a wonderful, ten-acre eco garden with a Victorian walled garden at its centre. We have an orchard and vegetable garden, pretty paths through woodland and plenty of bluebells and snowdrops. We don't use chemicals and fully support wildlife and the habitat they live in; the bee garden and our wilding areas are just two examples. The garden is a work in progress and we are continually creating spaces and fun things for kids to enjoy e.g. our dragons' den, Viking shelter, rope swings and more. We grow our own vegetables and love turning our fruit

Fife

into juices, jellies, jams and ice-cream. We'd be delighted to show you round or let you wander and enjoy.

Open: by arrangement 1 February - 30 September (Tuesday, Thursday & Friday), admission £6.00, children free. Open for Snowdrops & Winter Walks

Directions: Take the bus to Pittenween and walk up Charles Street, past the recycling centre and we are 400 metres up on the left.

Opening for: SGS and Beneficiaries

 ## 20 MILLFIELD GARDEN

Millfield House, Falkland, Fife KY15 7BN
Sarah & Aaron Marshall
T: 07584 620534

Millfield is set on the edge of the beautiful and historic village of Falkland. Falkland Gardening Group is developing a snowdrop trail in the village. Millfield has a walled garden, bulb meadows, woodland paths, all with snowdrops. There are also over 100 different snowdrop varieties set around the driveway area at waist height, for ease of viewing! The garden also houses a selection of hellebores and winter flowering shrubs.

Open: Saturday/Sunday, 25/26 February, 11am - 3pm for Snowdrops and Winter Walks, admission £6.00, children free.

Directions: From the A912 turn into the village, travel straight past the central fountain. Follow the road until it makes a sharp left – Millfield is straight ahead.

Opening for: Chest Heart & Stroke Scotland

 ## 21 NEWBURGH – HIDDEN GARDENS

Newburgh KY14 6AH
Gardeners of Newburgh

Hidden behind the 18th-century facades of Newburgh High Street and surrounding streets lie a jumble of wonderful old gardens, some of them dating back centuries. Many have spectacular views of the Tay Estuary. We are opening for the fourth time and, as before, the gardens will include a mixture of those which have opened previously together with some gardens opening in 2023 for the first time. Those previously opened will have been developed considerably and, as before, there will be a wide mix of flowers, vegetables, herbaceous borders, orchards and a fair few hens and ducks!

Open: Sunday 25 June, noon - 5pm, admission £6.00, children free. Newburgh sits on a hill. In addition, access to some gardens is via narrow closes and vennels. As such, disabled access to some gardens may be restricted.

Directions: On the A913 between Perth and Cupar. There is a car park at each end of the town, with tickets and teas available nearby.

Opening for: Newburgh Community Trust

Fife

22 ROSEWELLS
Baldinnie, Ceres KY15 5LE
Birgitta and Gordon MacDonald
E: g.macdonald54@hotmail.co.uk

Rosewells, designed by the garden owners, has developed over the last 25 years. It started as a one-and-a-half acre, overgrown paddock. The design is based on the texture and foliage of trees and shrubs to create year-round interest. In spring and summer, colour and scent become increasingly important. In spring, highlights are around 55 magnolias and rhododendrons, many of which are chosen for their foliage. Other highlights include flowering cornus, trillium, fritillaries, erythroniums, peonies, roses, ferns and acers. There have been a number of developments in recent years. More winding paths have been developed creating wildlife friendly areas. There is a new lavender walk which leads to a covered seating area at the bottom of the garden.

Open: by arrangement 1 April - 30 September, admission £6.00, children free.

Directions: B940 between Pitscottie and Peat Inn, one mile from Pitscottie. Rosewells is the ochre-coloured house.

Opening for: Save the Children UK

23 ST ANDREWS BOTANIC GARDEN SPRING FAIR
Canongate, St Andrews, Fife KY16 8RT
St Andrews Botanic Garden
T: 01334 461200 E: info@standrewsbotanic.org
W: standrewsbotanic.org

This spring open day will feature egg painting and chocolate egg making activities, picnic lunches and Spring walks featuring the garden's impressive collection of rhododendrons, magnolias and other spring-flowering gems – and there will be some other surprises. The original Botanic Garden was founded by the University of St Andrews in 1889 in the precincts of St Mary's College. Originally a small garden, it now covers 18.5 acres and not only provides a wonderful space in which to relax and enjoy its beauty and atmosphere, but is also a scientific garden for teaching and research.
Champion Trees: A number of rare species.

Open: Saturday 8 April, 10am - 4pm, admission by donation.

Directions: The garden is located on Canongate and is a 10/15 minute walk from the centre of St Andrews. Follow the signs from the town down Viaduct walk, which is a shared path for bikes and walkers. The 99C bus route goes past the garden and takes five minutes from the bus stop in St Andrews. The nearest train station is Leuchars on the 99 bus route. There is a free car park at the garden.

Opening for: Donation to SGS

Fife

24 SOUTH FLISK
Blebo Craigs, Cupar KY15 5UQ
Mr and Mrs George Young
T: 01334 850859 E: southfliskgarden@gmail.com
W: www.standrewspottery.co.uk

The spectacular views to Perthshire and Angus, and the large flooded quarry full of fish (and the occasional otter) and planted with impressive marginals, make this garden very special. Flights of old stone steps, cliffs, boulders, exotic ferns and mature trees form a backdrop for carpets of primroses, bluebells, spring bulbs and woodland plants like trilliums, camassia, meconopsis and colourful primulas, with rhododendrons in flower from March until July. In front of the house is a charming, mature walled garden with traditional cottage-garden planting. Next to the house is the St Andrews Pottery where George will be demonstrating his pottery skills for those who need a break from the garden! New for 2023, a water garden with a stream running through it.

Open: Sunday 30 April & Sunday 28 May, 11am - 5pm. Also open by arrangement 1 April - 30 June. Admission £6.00, children free.

Directions: Six miles west of St Andrews off the B939 between Strathkinness and Pitscottie. There is a small stone bus shelter opposite the road into the village and sign saying *Blebo Craigs*. See map on our website. Bus to Blebo Craigs.

Opening for: Médecins Sans Frontières

25 SGS AUTUMN PLANT SALE AT ST ANDREWS BOTANIC GARDEN
St Andrews KY16 8RT
St Andrews Botanic Garden

For a third year, the famous Fife Autumn Plant Sale returns to its new home at the Botanic Garden in St Andrews. In addition to a fabulous selection of bare root and potted plants, all grown locally, watch the SGS website for updates on an exciting selection of local stall holders and other activities being planned for the day. The Botanic Garden will be open from 10am until 4pm with free entry and a range of activities throughout the day. For more details about the Garden itself, please see the Spring Fair entry. Champion Trees: A number of rare species.

Open: Sunday 8 October, noon - 3pm, plant sale admission £3.00, children free. Plant donations – large and small – will be extremely welcome on the Friday and Saturday preceding the sale. For delivery details please contact Julia Young – southfliskgarden@gmail.com – or David Buchanan-Cook – Helensbank@aol.com.

Directions: The garden is located on Canongate and is a 10/15 minute walk from the centre of St Andrews. Follow the signs from the town down Viaduct walk, which is a shared path for bikes and walkers. The 99C bus route goes past the garden and takes five minutes from the bus stop in St Andrews. The nearest train station is Leuchars on the 99 bus route. There is a free car park at the garden.

Opening for: St Andrews Botanic Garden Trust

Fife

26 SWALLOWS REST

Lindores KY14 6JD
Stuart & Elaine Ingram
T: 07703 435055 E: Elaine.ingram@icloud.com

The current owners moved in at the beginning of 2011 to a garden of grass and weeds. Since then, beds have been hand-dug, a slope filled with dwarf conifers and heathers, a pond and small stream made, and step-over fruit trees planted. The garden also hosts many perennials, shrubs, trees and acid-loving plants. Over 50 varieties of narcissus prolong spring interest, along with many hellebores and rhododendrons.

Open: by arrangement 1 March - 31 October, admission £6.00, children free.

Directions: 2 miles east of Newburgh on the A913 past Den of Lindores, on the left, house with navy wooden door.

Opening for: SGS and Beneficiaries

27 TEASSES GARDENS

near Ceres KY8 5PG
E: events@teasses.com
W: www.teasses.com

The season at Teasses erupts in colour in April with vibrant tulip blooms punctuating the verdant green of fresh perennials in the walled garden. Meander through our 'Millennium Wood' to witness a mass of Spanish Bluebells and early flowering rhododendrons. In the open spaces enjoy the lingering blooms of 'Pheasant Eye' *Narcissus, Narcissus* , 'Thalia' and fragrant *Narcissus* , 'Bridal Crown'.

Open: Sunday 30 April, 10am - 4pm, admission £6.00, children free.

Directions: Between Ceres and Largo. Access via farm entrance on Woodside Road.

Opening for: Donation to SGS

28 THE GARDEN WITH THE DRAGON

2, Upper Wellheads, Limekilns KY11 3JQ
Mr and Mrs Duncan Philp
T: 01383 872047 E: df.philp@btinternet.com

A quirky coastal garden hidden behind a walled plot. Scatterings of California poppies, bluebells and a varied mix of annuals and perennials with a small clear pond. Different themes blend in the garden, all overseen by a majestic dragon sculpture perched on a tree.

Open: Saturday 13 May, Saturday 20 May & Saturday 27 May, 2pm - 5pm, admission £5.00, children free.

Directions: Take the A985 from Rosyth or Kincardine and follow directions for Limekilns and Charlestown. The No.6 bus from Dunfermline bus station on the hour.
Note – on 27 May the garden opens jointly with 20 Brucehaven Crescent, also in Limekilns.

Opening for: The Queen's Nursing Institute Scotland

Fife

29 **THE TOWER**
1 Northview Terrace, Wormit DD6 8PP
Peter and Angela Davey
T: 01382 541635 M: 07768 406946 E: adavey541@btinternet.com

Situated four miles south of Dundee, this one-acre Edwardian landscaped garden has panoramic views over the River Tay. Set on a hill, a series of paths meander around ponds and a small stream, rockeries featuring hellebores and low-level planting, a curved lawn and larger borders. Original woodland paths lead to a granite grotto with a waterfall pool. At the rear of the house the vegetable garden features raised beds made from granite sets. The garden is colourful throughout the summer, with many architectural plants accentuating the clever hard landscape design.

Open: Sunday 21 May & Sunday 25 June, 1pm - 5pm. Also open by arrangement 1 April - 1 October. Admission £6.00, children free.

Directions: From B946 park on Naughton Road outside Spar shop and walk up path on left following signs.

Opening for: Brain Tumour Research

30 **WILLOWHILL**
Forgan, Newport-on-Tay DD6 8RA
Eric Wright and Sally Lorimore
T: 01382 542890 E: e.g.wright@dundee.ac.uk
W: www.willowhillgarden.weebly.com

An evolving three-acre garden. The house is surrounded by a series of mixed borders designed with different vibrant colour combinations for effect all season. Spectacular mix of roses, herbaceous perennials and annuals planted through the wide borders are a highlight in mid to late summer. A new 'no dig' 160-foot border in shades of white, blue, purple and pale yellow created in 2019/2020. Come and see! April and May for late spring bulbs and flowers; June and July for roses and high summer colour; August for late summer colour.

Open: Saturday/Sunday/Monday 15 - 17 April and 13 - 15 May 1 - 5pm. Then open Saturday/ Monday 17/19 June, and Saturday/Monday 22 July - 26 August 1 - 5pm. Also open by arrangement 10 April - 31 August. Admission £6.00, children free. The plant stall includes a lovely selection from the garden. Visitors are welcome to bring their own refreshments and picnic in the garden. A season ticket for all these dates, and by arrangement, is £20 plus p&p and admits the ticket holder plus guest. It comes with a limited edition of the Willowhill Garden Guide: 35 pages of beautiful photographs with descriptions of key garden features and plantings. A **season ticket** with booklet is a perfect gift for garden lovers for a birthday or at Christmas and do treat yourself too! Season tickets are available online at **bit.ly/3fNntpj** or by post (cheque for £23 payable to Scotland's Garden Scheme) from S. Lorimore, Willowhill, Forgan, Newport-on-Tay, Fife DD6 8RA.

Directions: One-and-a-half miles south of Tay Road Bridge. Take the B995 to Newport off the Forgan roundabout. Willowhill is the first house on the left-hand side next to West Friarton Farm Strawberry Shed.

Opening for: Rio Community Centre: Newport-on-Tay

Glasgow & District

Sponsored by

Investec

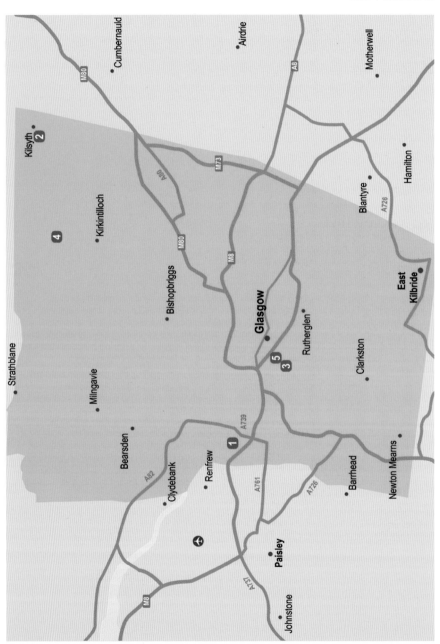

Glasgow & District

OUR VOLUNTEER ORGANISERS

District Organiser: Heidi Stone   E: info@scotlandsgardens.org

Area Organisers: Caroline Anderson
                            Ian Angus
                            Hilda Kelly
                            Jim Murray
                            Anne Murray

Treasurer: Vivien Pritchard

GARDENS OPEN ON A SPECIFIC DATE

Kilsyth Gardens, Allanfauld Road	Sunday, 28 May
The Gardens of Milton of Campsie, Milton of Campsie	Sunday, 18 June
Horatio's Garden, National Spinal Unit, Queen Elizabeth University Hospital, Govan Road, Glasgow	Sunday, 2 July
Strathbungo Garden, March Street, Glasgow	Sunday, 9 July

GARDENS OPEN REGULARLY

The Hidden Gardens, 25a Albert Drive, Glasgow	2 January – 31 December (not Monday)

GARDENS OPEN BY ARRANGEMENT – BOOK A VISIT WITH THE GARDEN OWNER

Kilsyth Gardens, Allanfauld Road	1 April - 31 August

Could you open your garden?

We would love to have more gardens in the Glasgow area.
Find out how to join.
scotlandsgardens.org/open-your-garden/

Glasgow & District

1 HORATIO'S GARDEN

National Spinal Unit, Queen Elizabeth University Hospital, Govan Road, Glasgow G51 4TF
Horatio's Garden
E: sallie@horatiosgarden.org.uk
W: Horatiosgarden.org.uk

Carefully created by acclaimed garden designer and RHS Judge, James Alexander-Sinclair, Horatio's Garden Scotland opened in 2016 and supports patients affected by spinal cord injury from across the whole of Scotland, their loved ones and NHS staff. The gardens provide peaceful, yet vibrant, horticultural havens. Horatio's Garden Scotland features a woodland garden awash with striking seasonal blooms and framed by a beautiful collection of Betula pendula trees, as well as artfully planted borders, courtyard garden, gorgeous garden room, fruitful glasshouse and much more. There's plenty to explore in this thoughtful, therapeutic garden; one which rarely opens to the public and is unusually nestled right in the heart of a Greater Glasgow & Clyde NHS hospital.

Open: Sunday 2 July, 2pm - 5pm, admission £7.00, children free.

Directions: From the east or west of the city: on the M8 motorway to Junction 25, follow signs for the *Clyde Tunnel* (A739) for three-quarters of a mile, then follow signs for the *Queen Elizabeth Hospital*. Turn left into Govan Road and the hospital is on the left. From north of the River Clyde: go through the Clyde Tunnel (A739) and follow signs for the hospital. Please look at our website for the hospital estate map for directions to the garden and available parking.

Opening for: Horatio's Garden

2 KILSYTH GARDENS

Allanfauld Road G65 9DE
Mr George Murdoch, Mr and Mrs Alan Patrick
T: 07743 110908 E: alan.patrick3@googlemail.com

Aeolia Allanfauld Road, Kilsyth G65 9DE (Mr George Murdoch): A third-of-an-acre woodland garden developed since 1960 and designed to have something in flower every month of the year. The garden contains a large variety of mature specimen trees and shrubs, maples, primulas, hardy geraniums and herbaceous plants. Spring bulbs provide early colour and lilies and dahlias provide late season interest. There are a couple of small ponds for wildlife, two greenhouses and a fruit production area. The owner is a member of the *Scottish Rhododendron Society* and has a collection of over 100 specimens, some grown from seed. Areas of the garden are often under development to provide something new to see and provide material for the extensive plant sale, which is all home grown.

Blackmill Allanfauld Road, Kilsyth G65 9DE (Mr and Mrs A Patrick): Across the road from Aeolia is Blackmill through which the Garrel Burn flows. The garden includes the magnificent seven-metre waterfall with its ever-changing moods throughout the year. On one side of the property, on the site of an old water-powered sickle mill, is an acre of mature specimen trees, rhododendrons and shrubs with an ornamental pond and a rock pool built into the remains of the mill building. Across the burn there is a further two acres of woodland glen with paths along the waterside offering glimpses of the many cascading waterfalls. A large area of wildflowers has been newly introduced alongside the burn. A micro-hydro scheme is on view, along with many different examples of dry stone walls. Visitors remark on the sense of tranquility and peace they experience in the garden and appreciate the works of art created from repurposed stone and salvaged material.

Open: Sunday 28 May, 2pm - 5pm. Also open by arrangement 1 April - 31 August. Admission £6.00 children free. Tea, coffee and box of home baked cakes £3.00, children £1.00. Cash payment or card payments welcome. By arrangement openings for parties of six or more. WC available but not for disabled.

Glasgow & District

Directions: Turn off the A803 into Parkburn Road up to the crossroads (parking attendant will advise on parking). The 89 bus Glasgow – Kilsyth has a stop at the crossroads a couple of minutes walk to the gardens. The nearest station is Croy, then take the bus 147 or 344 to Kilsyth.

Opening for: Charity to be confirmed

Kilsyth Gardens, Blackmill

Glasgow & District

3   STRATHBUNGO GARDEN
March Street, Glasgow G41 2PX
Frank Burns
W: facebook.com/strathbungogarden

Nestled behind Glasgow's busy main road artery to the Southside, you will happen upon a hidden walled terrace garden which marks the historical boundary to Strathbungo. It's an unexpected cottage-style city garden, showing how a piece of ground can be turned into a lovely colourful space for all the occupants of the terrace to enjoy. Inventive container planting is a key feature of this distinct urban retreat, which holds year-round interest. There is a range of fruit trees, some of which are trained as minarettes and stepovers. Why not visit Strathbungo Garden on Facebook and see what's been happening in the garden over the past months?

Open: Sunday 9 July, 2pm - 5pm, admission £4.00, children free.

Directions: From the south take the M74 to Junction 1A Polmadie. Turn left onto Polmadie Road, then turn right at the next traffic lights onto Calder Street. Proceed to Nithsdale Drive, then turn left into March Street where ample parking can be found. From the north take the M8 and join the M74, turn right into Polmadie Road at Junction 1A.

Opening for: ALVO Rural South Lanarkshire

The Gardens of Milton of Campsie, 18 James Boyle Square

4   THE GARDENS OF MILTON OF CAMPSIE
Milton of Campsie G66 8EA
The Gardeners of Milton Campsie
T: 07958 760169

18 James Boyle Square Milton of Campsie G66 8JN (Hugh and Vivian Pritchard): Developed from scratch a few years ago, this peaceful, colourful garden holds a wide variety of perennial plants as well as hanging baskets, a well-stocked greenhouse and summer bedding plants, all of which can be grown by anyone who loves gardening.
2 Kirton Crescent Milton of Campsie G66 8DP (Mr and Mrs McFarlane): This very pretty garden has been created in the style of a cottage garden with lots of colourful traditional cottage plants and a greenhouse; it's a really great example of what can be achieved in a small garden.
56 Lochiel Drive Milton of Campsie G66 8EU (James and Ann Pert): A small garden with a variety of plants in the north-facing front garden, with herbs and geraniums under the balcony made from recycled scaffold boards by the garden owner.
Attadale, 31 Birdston Road Milton of Campsie G66 8BX (Ian and Helen McCulloch): A Victorian garden with lovely rockeries to the front and leading to the rear, where there are borders with flowers and ferns, also a raised pond and seating areas.

Glasgow & District

Marengo Cottage, 8 Campsie Road Milton of Campsie G66 8EA (Angela Welsh): A small garden with many quirky features, it contains fruit trees, a vegetable patch, paths between flower and fauna beds, a small pond and if you can spot him, a topiary rabbit.
Milton of Campsie Community Garden Campsie Road G66 8EU (Gardens of Milton of Campsie): The community garden is the creation of one man covering roughly an acre of hillside beside the Glazert water. A small beach where there are otters and kingfishers, memorial gardens, various bespoke seating make this an unmissable garden.
Willow Cottage 11 Lochiel Drive Milton of Campsie G66 8EU (Glynis and Sarah Ainsworth): The garden has evolved over many years and attracts lots of wildlife. It is our hope that we have created a welcoming space that intrigues, delights and inspires all who visit.

Open: Sunday 18 June, 1am - 5pm, admission £7.00, children free. Dogs on a lead welcome in some gardens. Plant sale and teas are at Campsie Church.

Directions: From Glasgow, Kirkintilloch, Bishopbriggs Bus number X85, 89, 88. By road B757, SatNav using postcode G66 8EU and follow SGS yellow road signs. There is free parking at the church and at other various signposted sites.

Opening for: CHAS & Multiple Sclerosis Society

5 **THE HIDDEN GARDENS**
25a Albert Drive, Glasgow G41 2PE
The Hidden Gardens Trust
T: 0141 433 2722 E: info@thehiddengardens.org.uk
W: thehiddengardens.org.uk

Celebrating its 20 years anniversary in 2023, the multi-award winning Gardens have been designed to reflect the legacy of this historic site as well as the ever-changing character and needs of the local area. The north to south borders echo the layout of the site when it was a nursery in the 1800s, supplying trees and shrubs to major gardens in Scotland, whilst the retained tramlines and the chimney reflect its industrial past. A number of artworks are integrated into the overall design, for example Alec Finlay's Xylotheque, a library of wooden books detailing 17 native Scottish trees. This work will be decommissioned in 2024, so it is the last opportunity to view it. The Hidden Gardens is an independent charity offering learning and social activities and opportunities for the whole community to participate in its development. It is a calm, green space where you can relax away from the busy city streets: take a meditative walk along the square route path around the formal lawn; brush past the aromatic herb border; admire the white wall border with its herbaceous plantings and espalier fruit trees; stroll through the wildlife area; connect with nature in the woodland glade; and enjoy the naturalistic planting of the grassy or wild flower meadows or buy some young plants propagated here. Volunteer-led guided tours are available to book during most of the year, for free.

Open: April – October open Tuesday – Saturday (10am – 5pm) and 12noon -5pm on Sundays. November – March we are open Tuesday – Friday (10am – 4.30pm) and on Saturday and Sunday (12noon - 3pm). Closed on Mondays and selected public holidays. Check the garden's website for up to date details and one-off events.

Directions: Free street parking on surrounding streets is available. The Gardens are accessible by public transport; the 3, 4, 5, 6, 7, 38, 57 and 59 buses take you within walking distance; enter through Tramway (after 12pm) or from Pollokshaws Road and follow the green line painted on the ground to find the garden gates. Trains to Pollokshields East station are every 15 mins from Glasgow Central Station. At the top of the stairs at Pollokshields East station turn right and enter the Gardens through Tramway (off Albert Dr) or walk to end of street, turn right and enter via the back yard (off Pollokshaws Rd)

Opening for: Donation to SGS

Inverness, Ross, Cromarty & Skye

Sponsored by

Investec

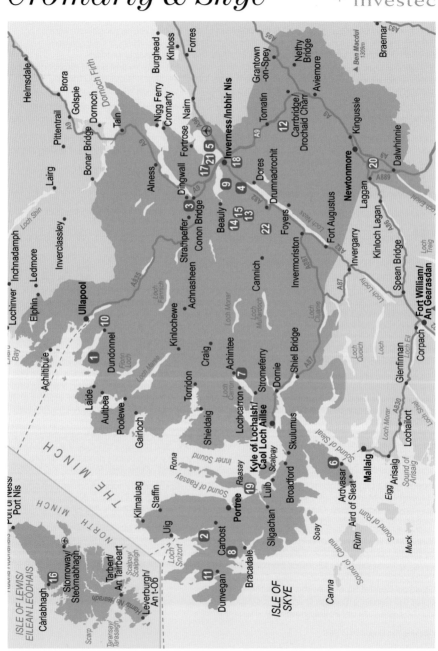

Inverness, Ross, Cromarty & Skye

OUR VOLUNTEER ORGANISERS

District Organiser:	Lucy Lister-Kaye	House of Aigas, Aigas, Beauly IV4 7AD E: info@scotlandsgardens.org
Area Organiser:	Emma MacKenzie	Glenkyllachy, Tomatin IV13 7YA
Treasurer:	Sheila Kerr	Lilac Cottage, Struy, By Beauly IV4 7JU

GARDENS OPEN ON A SPECIFIC DATE

Dundonnell House, Little Loch Broom, Wester Ross	Saturday, 15 April
Dundonnell House, Little Loch Broom, Wester Ross	Thursday, 1 June
Old Allangrange, Munlochy	Sunday, 18 June
House of Aigas and Field Centre, by Beauly	Sunday, 25 June
7 Braes of Conon, Conon Bridge	Sunday, 9 July
2 Durnamuck, Little Loch Broom, Wester Ross	Sunday, 16 July
Kiltarlity Gardens, Kiltarlity,	Sunday, 16 July
Ar Dachaigh, Redhill Farm, Allanfearn, Inverness	Sunday, 23 July
Dundonnell House, Little Loch Broom, Wester Ross	Saturday, 29 July
House of Aigas and Field Centre, by Beauly	Sunday, 30 July
Old Allangrange, Munlochy	Sunday, 13 August
2 Durnamuck, Little Loch Broom, Wester Ross	Saturday, 19 August

GARDENS OPEN REGULARLY

Oldtown of Leys Garden, Inverness	1 January - 31 December (not Thursdays & Fridays 1 May - 31 Oct)
Highland Liliums, 10 Loaneckheim, Kiltarlity	1 January - 31 December
Raasay Walled Garden, Isle of Raasay	1 January - 31 December
Abriachan Garden Nursery, Loch Ness Side	1 February - 30 November
Armadale Castle, Gardens & Museum,, Sleat, Isle of Skye	1 April - 31 October
Dunvegan Castle and Gardens, Isle of Skye	1 April - 15 October
Attadale, Strathcarron	1 April - 31 October
Glenkyllachy, Tomatin	1 April - 31 October (Mondays & Tuesdays)
Leathad Ard, Upper Carloway, Isle of Lewis	1 May - 30 September (not Sundays)
Balmeanach House, Balmeanach, nr Struan, Isle of Skye	1 May - 2 October
5 Knott, Clachamish, Portree, Isle of Skye	2 June - 30 September (Mondays, Fridays & Sundays)
Torcroft, Balnain, Glenurquhart	3 June - 27 August (Saturdays & Sundays)

Inverness, Ross, Cromarty & Skye

GARDENS OPEN BY ARRANGEMENT – BOOK A VISIT WITH THE GARDEN OWNER

Ar Dachaigh, Redhill Farm, Allanfearn, Inverness	1 January - 31 December
Old Allangrange, Munlochy	1 January - 31 December
House of Aigas and Field Centre, by Beauly	1 April - 31 October
Leathad Ard, Upper Carloway, Isle of Lewis	1 April - 30 April
Berryfield House, Lentran, Inverness	1 April - 1 September
Dundonnell House, Little Loch Broom, Wester Ross	1 April - 31 October
Glenkyllachy, Tomatin	1 April - 31 October
Torcroft, Balnain, Glenurquhart	1 April - 30 September
The Lookout, Kilmuir, North Kessock	1 June - 31 August (not Saturdays)
5 Knott, Clachamish, Portree, Isle of Skye	1 June - 30 September
2 Durnamuck, Little Loch Broom, Wester Ross	1 July - 30 September
Shanvall, Glentruim, Newtonmore	22 July - 31 August

House of Aigas

Inverness, Ross, Cromarty & Skye

 2 DURNAMUCK
Little Loch Broom, Wester Ross IV23 2QZ
Will Soos and Susan Pomeroy
T: 01854 633761 E: sueandwill@icloud.com. You can also find us on Facebook.

Our garden is south-east facing on the edge of Little Loch Broom. It is a coastal plantsman's garden with a rich mix of herbaceous borders, trees and shrubs, vegetables, drystone wall planting, South African/Mediterranean plants, a wild meadow and stunning views. Many of the plants have been collected from all over the world, and growing them has provided obvious challenges but with a pleasing outcome. Featured in 2019 entries in *Gardens Illustrated, Homes & Gardens* and *Beechgrove*. Entry in the *English Garden* magazine in September 2020. A wood and stone Wee Garden Hut accommodation is available for garden passionate people, it is small and compact but very beautiful in its own garden. Enquiries to sueandwill@icloud.com.

Open: Sunday 16 July and Saturday 19 August, 11am - 4pm. Also open by arrangement 1 July - 30 September. Admission £5.00, children free. Teas by donation.

Directions: On the A832, between Dundonnell and Ullapool, take the turning along the single-track road signed *Badcaul*, continue to the egg shack, turn right, go to the bottom of the hill and 2 Durnamuck is the house with the red roof. There is parking down by the house if needed.

Opening for: Fauna & Flora International

 5 KNOTT
Clachamish, Portree, Isle of Skye IV51 9NZ
Brian and Joyce Heggie
T: 01470 582213 E: jbheggie@hotmail.co.uk
W: www.knottskye.co.uk

An informal, organic garden on a gently sloping half-acre site. Perimeter hedging has enabled a sheltered and tranquil oasis to be created. Winding paths meander through the densely planted borders filled with a diverse range of perennials, annuals and shrubs. There is also a vegetable area with raised beds and a large polytunnel. A developing wild flower meadow with sea loch views leads onto a sheltered bay and a shoreside walk to the headland. There are regular sightings of seals, otters, sea eagles and harbour porpoises. Garden seating in several locations. The garden is situated in an easily reached, particularly quiet and scenic area of Skye.

Open: 2 June - 30 September (Monday, Friday & Sunday), 2pm - 5pm. Also open by arrangement 1 June - 30 September. Admission £4.00, children free.

Directions: From Portree, take the A87 to Uig/Dunvegan. After approximately three miles, take the A850 towards Dunvegan. Six miles on, pass the *Treaslane* sign. Turn right on the bend at the signpost for *Knott*.

Opening for: Crossroads Care Skye & Lochalsh

Inverness, Ross, Cromarty & Skye

3 | 7 BRAES OF CONON
Conon Bridge IV7 8AX
Mr Nigel Stanton

A beautifully designed garden created by a professional nurseryman. Nigel Stanton moved to the Highlands in 2014. The garden needed imported local topsoil and a lot of manure. Now, seven years later, with the help of raised beds and paved paths, the fruits of his endeavours are a delight. Specialities include magnificent delphiniums, rampant sweet peas and subtly blended roses.

Open: Sunday 9 July, 2pm - 5pm. Admission £5.00, children free.

Directions: Coming into Conon Bridge on the A862 from Muir of Ord, turn right into the Braes of Conon, and follow the road signs to No. 7. From Dingwall, take the A835 towards Tore at the Maryburgh roundabout, then turn first right towards Conon Bridge, and follow the signs.

Opening for: Highland Hospice: Aird branch

7 Braes of Conon

4 | ABRIACHAN GARDEN NURSERY
Loch Ness Side IV3 8LA
Mr and Mrs Davidson
T: 01463 861232 E: info@lochnessgarden.com
W: www.lochnessgarden.com

This is an outstanding garden with over four acres of exciting plantings with winding paths through native woodlands. Seasonal highlights include snowdrops, hellebores, primulas, meconopsis, hardy geraniums and colour-themed summer beds. Views over Loch Ness.

Inverness, Ross, Cromarty & Skye

Open: 1 February - 30 November, 9am - 5pm, admission £3.00, children free. Open for Snowdrops in the spring.

Directions: On the A82 Inverness/Drumnadrochit road, about eight miles south of Inverness.

Opening for: Highland Hospice

5 AR DACHAIGH
Redhill Farm, Allanfearn, Inverness IV2 7JA
Mrs Tina Ross
T: 07920 803410 E: tinaross463@hotmail.co.uk

This sloping garden has stunning views towards Kessock Bridge, the Black Isle, and the Great Glen. The site is very exposed and over the last four years a lot of time and effort has been spent erecting hedging and fences to create shelter for numerous well stocked flower beds in various planting styles. There are two ponds, five decking areas, a secret nook, a large greenhouse and a large display of plants in pots.

Open: Sunday 23 July, 2pm - 5pm. Also open by arrangement 1 January - 31 December. Admission £4.00, children free. Homemade teas £4.00.

Directions: Ar Dachaigh is to be found on a farm directly off the A96, four-and-a-half miles east of Inverness. From Inverness head east along the A96. Shortly after the turn off for Alturlie, there is a turn off on the left with an old telephone box – this is the drive for Ar Dachaigh. From the east: Once you have passed the Balloch junction, the turn off for the garden will be on your right-hand side at the old telephone box. PLEASE TAKE CARE as this is a busy stretch of the A96, and there are no filter lanes. There is a railway crossing on the drive, but this will be staffed on the day.

Opening for: Teenage Cancer Trust

Ar Dachaigh

Inverness, Ross, Cromarty & Skye

6   ARMADALE CASTLE, GARDENS & MUSEUM

Armadale, Sleat, Isle of Skye IV45 8RS
Clan Donald Lands Trust
T: 01471 844305 E: office@armadalecastle.com
W: https://www.armadalecastle.com/

Armadale Castle Gardens sit in a magnificent setting on the southern tip of the Isle of Skye, with sweeping views over the Sound of Sleat to the mountains of Knoydart. The estate was once the seat of the Macdonalds of Sleat and is now run by a charitable trust. Visitors can enjoy 40 acres of historic woodland gardens featuring 19th century specimen trees and exotic shrubs. Formal lawns, tranquil ponds and colourful herbaceous borders are set around the romantic ruins of Armadale Castle. There's also an adventure playground, café and fascinating museum telling the story of the Highlands & Islands through the eyes of Clan Donald.

Open: 1 April - 31 October, 9:30am - 5:30pm, admission details can be found on the garden's website.

Directions: On the A851, close to the Armadale Ferry terminal and approximately 30 minutes drive from the Skye Bridge. Local buses from Broadford; or train to Mallaig then 25 minutes ferry to Armadale (CalMac ferries). The garden is a 10-minute walk from there.

Opening for: Donation to SGS

7   ATTADALE

Strathcarron IV54 8YX
Mr Ewen Macpherson
T: 01520 722603 E: info@attadalegardens.com
W: www.attadalegardens.com

The Gulf Stream, surrounding hills and rocky cliffs create a microclimate for 20 acres of outstanding water gardens, old rhododendrons, unusual trees and a fern collection in a geodesic dome. There is also a sunken fern garden developed on the site of an early 19th-century drain, a waterfall into a pool with dwarf rhododendrons, sunken garden, peace garden and kitchen garden. Other features include a conservatory, Japanese garden, sculpture collection and giant sundial.

Open: 1 April - 31 October, 10am - 5pm, admission £10.00, children free. Seniors £8.00.

Directions: On the A890 between Strathcarron and South Strome.

Opening for: Highland Hospice

8   BALMEANACH HOUSE

Balmeanach, nr Struan, Isle of Skye IV56 8FH
Mrs Arlene Macphie
T: 01470 572320 E: info@skye-holiday.com
W: www.skye-holiday.com

Very much a plantsman's garden, begun in the early 1990s after a third-of-an-acre of croft land was fenced. A shelter belt now permits a plethora of diverse plants in exuberant herbaceous borders, which give nectar and pollen to keep the buzzing and fluttering going until autumn, plus rockeries and raised beds. Native trees rub shoulders with more exotic ornamental varieties, providing a canopy for shade-loving plants and nesting sites for the many birds who make the garden their home. A small pond in a sunken garden; a large pond divided in two by a path over a culvert and a bog garden, give scope for marginal and moisture-loving plants. Meandering pathways lead through a small bluebell wood, an arbour garden, shrubbery and a

Inverness, Ross, Cromarty & Skye

small birch wood, full of azaleas and rhododendrons. Plenty of seating throughout provides an invitation to sit, relax and enjoy the garden and stunning scenery beyond.

Open: 1 May - 2 October, 11am - 4pm, admission £4.00, children free. No teas on Saturdays and Sundays.

Directions: A87 to Sligachan, turn left and Balmeanach is five miles north of Struan and five miles south of Dunvegan.

Opening for: Scottish SPCA & Redwings

Attadale

 9 ## BERRYFIELD HOUSE
Lentran, Inverness IV3 8RJ
Lynda Perch-Nielsen
T: 01463 831346 M: 07547 960341 E: lyndazpn@gmail.com

An open garden of trees and bushes with views across the Beauly Firth to Ben Wyvis. There are large swathes of bulbs: crocus, dogtooth violets and heritage daffodils. A three-acre wildflower meadow with meandering paths adjoins the garden giving interest until the start of autumn foliage and crocus.

Open: by arrangement 1 April - 1 September, admission by donation.

Directions: Halfway between Inverness and Beauly on the A862. From Inverness, four-and-a-quarter miles on the left from crossing over the Clachnaharry railway bridge. From Beauly, one-and-a-quarter miles on the right from The Old North Inn.

Opening for: Action Medical Research

Inverness, Ross, Cromarty & Skye

10 **DUNDONNELL HOUSE**
Little Loch Broom, Wester Ross IV23 2QW
Dundonnell Estates
T: 07789 390028 E: sueandwill@icloud.com

Camellias, magnolias and bulbs in spring, rhododendrons and laburnum walk in this ancient walled garden. Exciting planting in new borders gives all year colour, centred around one of the oldest yew trees in Scotland. A new water sculpture, midsummer roses, recently restored unique Victorian glass house, riverside walk, arboretum – all in the valley below the peaks of An Teallach.
Champion Trees: Yew and Holly.

Open: Saturday 15 April, Thursday 1 June and Saturday 29 July, 2pm - 5pm. Also open by arrangement 1 April - 31 October. Admission £5.00, children free. Teas only available in June.

Directions: Turn off the A835 at Braemore on to the A832. After 11 miles take the Badralloch turn for a half-mile.

Opening for: The Linda Norgrove Foundation & The Greenpeace Environmental Trust

Dundonnell House

Inverness, Ross, Cromarty & Skye

11 **DUNVEGAN CASTLE AND GARDENS**
Isle of Skye IV55 8WF
Hugh Macleod of Macleod
T: 01470 521206 E: info@dunvegancastle.com
W: www.dunvegancastle.com

Any visit to the Isle of Skye is incomplete without enjoying the wealth of history and horticultural delights at award-winning 5* Dunvegan Castle & Gardens, now an RHS partner garden. The five acres of formal gardens began life in the 18th century. In stark contrast to the barren moorland and mountains which dominate Skye's landscape, the Castle's Water Garden, Round Garden, Walled Garden and woodland walks provide an oasis for an eclectic mix of flowers, exotic plants, shrubs and specimen trees, framed by shimmering pools fed from waterfalls. After visiting the Water Garden with its ornate bridges and islands replete with colourful plants along the riverbanks, wander through the elegant formal Round Garden. The Walled Garden, formerly the Castle's vegetable garden, now has a diverse range of plants and flowers completing the attractive features, including a water lily pond, garden museum, 17th century lectern sundial, glass house and the 'Dunvegan Pebble', a rotating 2.7 ton Carrara marble sculpture. The informal areas of the garden are kept wild to encourage wildlife, creating a more natural aesthetic framed by the coastal scenery. The present Chief, Hugh MacLeod, and his dedicated team of gardeners, continue to build on this unique legacy for future generations to enjoy.

Open: 1 April - 15 October, 10am – 5.30pm (last entry 5pm); open for snowdrops days in February. Please check website for further details and admission rates. Catering available from MacLeod Tables Cafe in the car park.

Directions: One mile from Dunvegan village, 23 miles west of Portree. Follow the signs for *Dunvegan Castle.*

Opening for: Donation to SGS

12 **GLENKYLLACHY**
Tomatin IV13 7YA
Mr and Mrs Philip Mackenzie
E: emmaglenkyllachy@gmail.com

In a magnificent Highland glen, at 1200 feet above sea level, Glenkyllachy offers a glorious garden of shrubs, herbaceous plants, rhododendrons, trees and spectacular views down the Findhorn River. There are some rare specimens and a recently planted arboretum. Rhododendrons and bulbs flower in May/June, herbaceous plants bloom through July/August with glorious autumn colours in September and October. Original sculptures and a Highgrove-inspired wall provide year-round interest. Featured on *Beechgrove* in 2018. We took advantage of Lockdown in 2020 to re-assess existing plant schemes and create new borders and paths. We have also extended the garden with a 'wild area' blending the garden into the beautiful birch and juniper natural hillside.

Open: 1 April - 31 October (Monday & Tuesday), 10am - dusk. Also open by arrangement 1 April - 31 October. Admission £5.00, children free.

Directions: Turn off the A9 at Tomatin and take the Coignafearn/Garbole single-track road down the north-side of the River Findhorn, there is a cattle grid and gate on the right 500 yards AFTER the humpback bridge and the sign to *Farr.*

Opening for: Marie Curie

Inverness, Ross, Cromarty & Skye

13 HIGHLAND LILIUMS
10 Loaneckheim, Kiltarlity IV4 7JQ
Neil and Frances Macritchie
T: 01463 741365 E: accounts@highlandliliums.co.uk
W: www.highlandliliums.co.uk

Highland Liliums is a working retail nursery with spectacular views over the Beauly valley and Strathfarrar hills. A wide selection of home-grown plants are available including alpines, ferns, grasses, herbaceous, herbs, liliums, primulas and shrubs.

Open: 1 January - 31 December, 9am - 5pm, admission free. Also open as part of Kiltarlity Gardens, on Sunday 16th July.

Directions: Signposted from Kiltarlity village, which is just off the Beauly to Drumnadrochit road (A833), approximately 12 miles from Inverness.

Opening for: Donation to SGS

14 HOUSE OF AIGAS AND FIELD CENTRE
by Beauly IV4 7AD
Sir John and Lady Lister-Kaye
T: 01463 782443 E: info@aigas.co.uk
W: www.aigas.co.uk

The House of Aigas has a small arboretum of named Victorian specimen trees and modern additions. The garden consists of extensive rockeries, herbaceous borders, ponds and shrubs. Aigas Field Centre rangers lead regular guided walks on nature trails through woodland, moorland and around a loch.
Champion Trees: Douglas fir, Atlas cedar and *Sequoiadendron giganteum*.

Open: Sundays 25 June and 30 July, 2pm - 5pm. Also open by arrangement 1 April - 31 October. Admission £5.00, children free. Homemade Teas £5.00.

Directions: Four-and-a-half miles from Beauly on the A831 Cannich/Glen Affric road.

Opening for: Highland Hospice: Aird branch

15 KILTARLITY GARDENS
Kiltarlity IV4 7JH
Sheila Ross, Neil and Frances Macritchie
T: 01463 741365 E: accounts@highlandliliums.co.uk

Aird View 30a Camault Muir, Kiltarlity IV4 7JH (Sheila Ross): The garden at Aird View offers a mix of borders, a water feature, an arbour and a newly added herbaceous border. There are also fruit trees and vegetable beds. Vintage tractors on display.
Highland Liliums 10 Loaneckheim, Kiltarlity IV4 7JQ (Neil and Frances Macritchie): Highland Liliums is a working retail nursery with spectacular views over the Beauly valley and Strathfarrar hills. A wide selection of home-grown plants are available including alpines, ferns, grasses, herbaceous, herbs, liliums, primulas and shrubs.

Open: Sunday 16 July, noon - 5pm, admission £4.00, children free. Admission tickets are available at either garden. Homemade teas and discounted plants for sale at Highland Liliums.

Inverness, Ross, Cromarty & Skye

Directions: Aird View – take the A833 Beauly to Drumnadrochit road, pass Brockies Lodge. Turn right at the bus shelter and follow the single track road to the junction at the school. Turn left and go up the hill to the top, at the junction Aird View is on the right. Highland Liliums is signposted from *Kiltarlity village.*

Opening for: Highland Hospice: Aird branch

---

16 ## LEATHAD ARD

Upper Carloway, Isle of Lewis HS2 9AQ
Rowena and Stuart Oakley
T: 01851 643204 E: leathad.ard@gmail.com
W: www.leathadard.org.uk

A one-acre sloping garden with stunning views over East Loch Roag. It has evolved along with the shelter hedges that divide the garden into a number of areas giving a new view at every corner. With shelter and raised beds, the different conditions created permit a wide variety of plants to be grown. Features include herbaceous borders, cutting borders, bog gardens, grass garden, exposed beds, patios, a pond and vegetables and fruit grown both in the open ground and the Keder greenhouse. Some of the vegetables are grown to show standards.

Open: 1 May - 30 September (not Sundays), 10am - 6pm. Also open by arrangement 1 April - 30 April. Admission £5.00, children free.

Directions: On the A858 Shawbost-Carloway take the first right after the Carloway football pitch, and it is the first house on the right. By bus take the Westside circular bus, exit Stornoway and head for Carloway football pitch.

Opening for: British Red Cross

---

17 ## OLD ALLANGRANGE

Munlochy IV8 8NZ
J J Gladwin
T: 01463 811304 E: office@blackislegardendesign.com

There are two distinct areas to the garden – the three acre ornamental gardens that surround the house, linked by hedges and repeated shapes with key plants seeping from one area to another to visually connect them, and a five acre organic vegetable garden. The ornamental garden is a mix of formal shapes and loose planting. There are pleached lime hedges, lime lollipop pompoms, cloud pruning, box buttons, box cubes, pyrus mushrooms, beech and holly hedges, and then through and amongst and around are swathes of herbaceous perennials and grasses. In the vegetable garden, there is a large Keder greenhouse and agroecological methods including no-dig systems are used, along with agroforestry planting techniques and a forest garden. The main production area is laid out using permaculture design in the shape of the Celtic Triskele symbol. This represents the ethos of striving to create a balance of wildlife, productivity and beauty. New areas are developed each winter into an ever more cohesive whole.
Champion Trees: Yew and sweet chestnut.

Open: Sundays 18 June and 13 August, 2pm - 5pm. Also open by arrangement 1 January - 31 December. Admission £6.00, children free. Baking stall. Homemade teas £6.50. Groups by arrangement, minimum of 10 people.

Directions: From Inverness head four miles north on the A9, and follow the directions for *Black Isle Brewery.* Park up at the Brewery and walk down to the garden. Directions will be given in the shop.

Opening for: Charity to be confirmed

Inverness, Ross, Cromarty & Skye

18 OLDTOWN OF LEYS GARDEN

Inverness IV2 6AE
David and Anne Sutherland
T: 01463 238238 E: ams@oldtownofleys.com

Established in 2003, on the outskirts of Inverness, with views over the town, this large garden of three acres has year-round interest. Spring rhododendrons and azaleas, summer herbaceous plantings, autumn trees and shrubs and winter appeal from the conifers, evergreens and structures. Features include a rockery, ponds, musical instruments, a new stumpery and an area of prairie planting.

Open: 1 January - 31 December, daily – except 1 May - 31 October (not open Thursday & Friday), dawn – dusk, admission by donation.

Directions: Turn off southern distributor road (B8082) at Leys roundabout towards Inverarnie (B861). At the T junction turn right. After 50 metres turn right into Oldtown of Leys.

Opening for: Highland Hospice & Alzheimer Scotland

19 RAASAY WALLED GARDEN

Isle of Raasay IV40 8PB
Raasay Community
T: 07939 106426 E: raasaywalledgarden@gmail.com
W: Raasay.com/the-walled-garden-raasay

Situated behind Raasay House, a 10 minute walk from the Ferry Terminal, is the Category A listed Walled Garden. Visited by Boswell & Johnson in 1773, the garden suffered neglect before coming into community ownership. Ongoing restoration began in 2013 and the 1.43 acre garden now supplies vegetables, fruit, salad, herbs and cut flowers to the community and visitors. Features an orchard, rose beds, polytunnels, a fruit cage, wildflowers for pollinators and insects, and plenty of seats. We have a composting toilet for visitors' use. June to August provide the most colourful time and our main produce harvests take place from May to September. We run events during the year – please check our Facebook page for details. The garden isn't always staffed, so please contact us for further details.

Open: 1 January - 31 December, 9am - 7pm, admission by donation. Plants for sale occasionally, and vegetables once/twice weekly during the season.

Directions: Take the Calmac Ferry to Raasay (20 minute journey) from Sconser, between Broadford and Portree on the Isle of Skye. The garden is an easy walk from the terminal and there is plenty to do and see on foot, although cars can also cross.

Opening for: Donation to SGS

20 SHANVALL

Glentruim, Newtonmore PH20 1BE
George and Beth Alder
T: 01540 673213 E: beth.alder@yahoo.co.uk

The garden is two-thirds-of-an-acre at 900 feet above sea level, surrounding a 19th-century cottage. On the south side of the River Spey, it has lovely views of the Creag Dubh and Creag Meagaidh mountains. There are ruined buildings of an old township within the garden. To the south is a cottage garden of roses and perennials. Within a stone wall, there are fruit cages, a small orchard and organic vegetable beds which have been cultivated for about 200 years. The garden on the north slopes has trees, shrubs, herbaceous border, scree bed, wildflowers, and a pond, and is rich with wildlife, including woodpeckers and red squirrels.

Inverness, Ross, Cromarty & Skye

Open: by arrangement 22 July - 31 August, admission by donation. Teas included.

Directions: Shanvall is on the minor road running along the south side of the Spey, linking the A9 south of Newtonmore at Glentruim and the A889 at Catlodge. The garden gate is on the right about one-and-a-half miles from the A9. Further details on request.

Opening for: Laggan and Newtonmore Church of Scotland

 21 THE LOOKOUT
Kilmuir, North Kessock IV1 3ZG
David and Penny Veitch
T: 01463 731489 E: david@veitch.biz

A three-quarter-acre, elevated coastal garden, with incredible views over the Moray Firth, which is only for the sure-footed. This award-winning garden, featured on the *The Beechgrove Garden*, has been created out of a rock base with shallow pockets of ground, planted to its advantage to encourage all aspects of wildlife. There is a small, sheltered courtyard, raised bed vegetable area, pretty cottage garden, scree and rock garden, rose arbour, rhododendrons, flowering shrubs, bamboos, trees and lily pond with waterside plants.

Open: by arrangement 1 June - 31 August (not Saturday), admission £4.00, children free. Teas available on request £6.00 per head. Dogs are not allowed.

Directions: From Inverness, take the North Kessock left turn from the A9, and third left at the roundabout to go on the underpass, then sharp left onto Kilmuir Road. From Tore, take the slip road for North Kessock and immediately right for Kilmuir. Follow signs for *Kilmuir* (three miles) until you reach the shore. The Lookout is near the far end of the village with a large palm tree in front, surrounded by gravel.

Opening for: Alzheimer's Research UK

 22 TORCROFT
Balnain, Glenurquhart IV63 6TJ
Barbara Craig
E: barbaramcraig@gmail.com

This garden is about three-quarters of an acre on a hillside overlooking Loch Meiklie in Glen Urquhart. It is a wild garden, with its own character and style. There are weeds and cardamine for the orange-tip butterflies, but most of all there are plants in profusion from acer, anemone and astrantia to veronicastrum, verbascum, weigela and water lilies. A natural stream comes into the garden and meanders into various small ponds. In the spring there are masses of bog primula of all types and colours. There is a fern bed, a rockery, herbs, wooded area, a stumpery and another pond nearby.

Open: 3 June - 27 August (Saturday & Sunday), 2pm - 5pm. Also open by arrangement 1 April - 30 September. Admission £3.00, children free.

Directions: From Inverness turn right at Drumnadrochit and go towards Cannich. After four miles, sign *Balnain*, there is a very sharp right-hand bend with a high retaining wall on the right. At the end of the wall take the turning to the right signposted *Torcroft Lodges*.

Opening for: Munlochy Animal Aid & Ripple Effect

Kincardine & Deeside

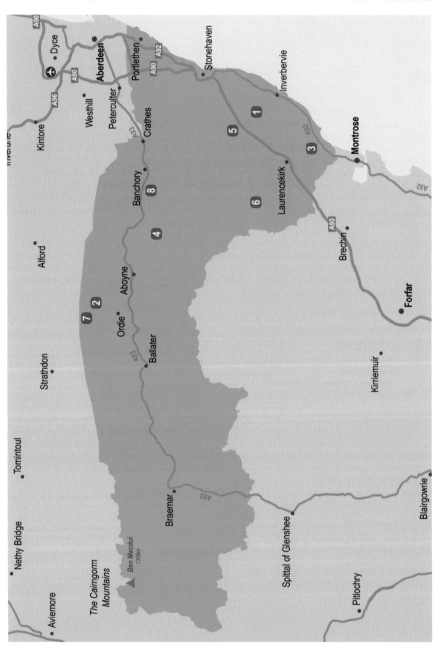

Kincardine & Deeside

OUR VOLUNTEER ORGANISERS

District Organisers:	Catherine Nichols	Westerton Steading, Dess, Aboyne AB34 5AY
	Julie Nicol	Cedarwood Lodge, Rhu-Na-Haven Road, Aboyne AB34 5JB
		E: info@scotlandsgardens.org
Area Organisers:	Wendy Buchan	Inneshewen, Dess, Aboyne AB34 5BH
	Gavin Farquhar	Ecclesgreig Castle, St Cyrus DD10 0DP
	Tina Hammond	Sunnybank, 7 Watson Street, Banchory AB31 5UB
	Liz Inglesfield	2 Earlspark Circle, Bieldside, Aberdeen AB15 9BW
	David & Patsy Younie	Bealltainn, Ballogie, Aboyne AB34 5DL
Treasurer:	Michael Buchan	Inneshewen, Dess, Aboyne AB34 5BH

GARDENS OPEN ON A SPECIFIC DATE

Ecclesgreig Castle, St Cyrus	Sunday, 5 March
Inchmarlo Retirement Village Garden, Inchmarlo, Banchory	Sunday, 21 May
Finzean House, Finzean, Banchory	Sunday, 28 May
Glensaugh, Glensaugh Lodge, Fettercairn, Laurencekirk	Sunday, 4 June
Arbuthnott House Gardens, Arbuthnott House, Laurencekirk	Sunday, 11 June
Douneside House, Tarland	Sunday, 9 July
Hopewell, Tarland	Sunday, 16 July
Glenbervie House, Drumlithie, Stonehaven	Sunday, 6 August
Glensaugh, Glensaugh Lodge, Fettercairn, Laurencekirk	Sunday, 27 August

GARDENS OPEN BY ARRANGEMENT – BOOK A VISIT WITH THE GARDEN OWNER

Glenbervie House, Drumlithie, Stonehaven	1 May - 15 September

Kincardine & Deeside

 1 ARBUTHNOTT HOUSE GARDENS
Arbuthnott House, Laurencekirk AB30 1PA
Chris and Emily Arbuthnott
W: arbuthnotthouse@gmail.com

Arbuthnott House is the seat of the Viscount of Arbuthnott, whose family have lived here since 1190. The five-acre garden was laid out in the 17th century and comprises a walled garden with some 1920s Arts and Crafts planting. Thought to be one of the oldest gardens in Scotland, it runs down a steep south-facing slope that is divided by three main broadwalks which run horizontally and are intercepted with diagonal pathways. The vegetables and soft fruit are contained within beds which are bound by topiary, herbaceous borders, rose beds and long beds for cut flowers.

Open: Sunday 11 June, 2pm - 5pm, admission £10.00, children free. Admission price includes teas.

Directions: Located at the heart of Arbuthnott Estate, just off the B967 Inverbervie to Fordoun. Three miles off the A90.

Opening for: RNLI

 2 DOUNESIDE HOUSE
Tarland AB34 4UD
The MacRobert Trust
W: www.dounesidehouse.co.uk

Join our Garden Summer Fair at Douneside – the former home of Lady MacRobert, who developed these magnificent gardens in the early to mid-1900s. Ornamental borders, an Arts and Crafts themed terraced garden and water gardens surround a spectacular infinity lawn overlooking the Deeside hills. The walled garden houses a large ornamental greenhouse and supplies organic fruit, vegetables, herbs and cut flowers to Douneside House which is a multi-award winning hotel. All areas of the garden will be open and there will be music, ice-cream stall, children's activities, local craft and produce stalls and more...

Open: Sunday 9 July, noon - 4pm, admission £7.50, concessions £5.00, children free.

Directions: On the B9119 towards Aberdeen. Tarland one mile.

Opening for: Perennial

 3 ECCLESGREIG CASTLE
St Cyrus DD10 0DP
Mr Gavin Farquhar
T: 01224 214301 E: enquiries@ecclesgreig.com
W: www.ecclesgreig.com

Ecclesgreig Castle, Victorian Gothic on a 16th-century core, is internationally famous as an inspiration for Bram Stoker's *Dracula*. The snowdrop walk (over 150 varieties of snowdrops) starts at the castle, meanders around the estate, along woodland paths and the pond, ending at the garden. In the Italian balustraded gardens, there is a 140-foot-long herbaceous border, classical statues and stunning shaped topiary with views across St Cyrus to the sea. Started from a derelict site, development continues. Also to be found in the grounds is the ancient well of St Cyrus.

Open: Sunday 5 March, 1pm - 4pm for Snowdrops and Winter Walks, admission £5.00, children free.

Kincardine & Deeside

Directions: *Ecclesgreig* will be signposted from the A92 Coast Road and from the A937 Montrose/Laurencekirk Road.

Opening for: Girlguiding Montrose District

---

4 ### FINZEAN HOUSE

Finzean, Banchory AB31 6NZ
Mr and Mrs Donald Farquharson

Finzean House was the family home of Joseph Farquharson, the Victorian landscape painter, and the garden was the backdrop for several of his paintings. The garden has lovely views over the historic holly hedge to the front of Clachnaben. There is a spring woodland garden, extensive lawns with herbaceous and shrub borders and a working cut-flower garden for late summer, alongside a recently restored pond area. A new vegetable garden was created in 2020. The garden is opening earlier in late May this year so that visitors have a chance to enjoy the many azaleas and rhododendrons.

Open: Sunday 28 May, 2pm - 5pm, admission £5.00, children free.

Directions: On the B976, South Deeside Road, between Banchory and Aboyne.

Opening for: The Forget-Me-Not Club

---

5 ### GLENBERVIE HOUSE

Drumlithie, Stonehaven AB39 3YA
Mr and Mrs A Macphie

The nucleus of the beautiful present-day house dates from the 15th century with additions in the 18th and 19th centuries. There is a traditional Scottish walled garden on a slope with roses, herbaceous and annual borders along with fruit and vegetables. One wall is taken up with a Victorian-style greenhouse with many species of pot plants and climbers including peach and figs. A woodland garden by a burn is punctuated with many varieties of plants, primula to name but one.

Open: Sunday 6 August, 2pm - 5pm, admission £5.00, children free. Also open by arrangement 1 May - 15 September, apply in writing. Please note some steep pathways and tree roots can make walking difficult in places. Gravel pathways are not accessible for electric wheelchairs. Please no dogs.

Directions: Drumlithie one mile. Garden is one-and-a-half miles off the A90.

Opening for: Scotland's Charity Air Ambulance

Kincardine & Deeside

 6 **GLENSAUGH**
Glensaugh Lodge, Fettercairn, Laurencekirk AB30 1HB
Donald and Sue Barrie

The twenty year development of the hillside garden at Glensaugh, with its fine outlook over the Howe of the Mearns, continues as lawn evolves into wild flower meadow and borders are replanted. Trees, species rhododendrons and other shrubs provide year round interest while herbaceous planting extends colour into the autumn. Yew hedges and well-placed natural stone give structure in the lower garden where a productive kitchen garden and polytunnel exist alongside informal borders and a sunken pond.

Open: Sunday 4 June & Sunday 27 August, 1:30pm - 4:30pm. Admission £5.00, children free. No teas, but you are welcome to bring a picnic.

Directions: Three miles north of Fettercairn. Turn right off the B974 at Clatterin Brig and follow minor road signed *Drumtochty* for half a mile, then turn right into Glensaugh Farm. Follow beech avenue from the steading to Glensaugh Lodge.

Opening for: Kincardine And Deeside Befriending

 7 **HOPEWELL**
Tarland AB34 4XD
Mr Anthony de Winton

Located near Tarland, with stunning views of the surrounding countryside, the gardens at Hopewell Lodge have been developed as an integral part of the surrounding farm by the current owner over the last fifty years. Adjacent to the house is a one acre formal garden with parterre, plus an area of wildflowers with an arbour presently under construction. The wider grounds encompass fifteen acres of woodland gardens created under sustainable woodland management policies, complete with four lochans and wildlife flight ponds, along with many hundreds of trees and rhododendrons – all planted by the owner. Paths crisscross through the woods allowing delightful walks and the opportunity to view a variety of wildlife.

Open: Sunday 16 July, 1:30pm - 5pm, admission £5.00, children free. Car park is approximately half a mile from the formal garden. Stout footwear required.

Directions: On entering Tarland from the Aboyne direction, take the road left just before the bridge signposted *Logie Coldstone*. After one mile turn right on road signposted *Migvie* and *Tillypronie*. Proceed for a further mile. Home Farm is on your left where parking will be available.

Opening for: The Salvation Army

Kincardine & Deeside

8 INCHMARLO RETIREMENT VILLAGE GARDEN

Inchmarlo, Banchory AB31 4AL
Skene Enterprises (Aberdeen) Ltd
T: 01330 826242 E: info@inchmarlo-retirement.co.uk
W: www.inchmarlo-retirement.co.uk

Beautiful five-acre woodland garden filled with azaleas and rhododendrons beneath ancient Scots pines, Douglas firs and silver firs (some over 140 feet tall). Also beeches, rare and unusual trees including pindrow firs, Pere David's maple, Erman's birch and a mountain snowdrop tree. The Oriental Garden features a Karesansui, a dry slate stream designed by Peter Roger, a *RHS Chelsea* gold medal winner. The Rainbow Garden, within the keyhole-shaped purple *Prunus cerasifera* hedge, has been designed by Billy Carruthers of Binny Plants, an eight-times gold medal winner at Gardening Scotland and a regular at the RHS Chelsea Flower Show.

Open: Sunday 21 May, 1:30pm - 4:30pm, admission £5.00, children free.

Directions: From Aberdeen via North Deeside Road on the A93, one mile west of Banchory turn right at the main gate to the Inchmarlo Estate.

Opening for: Alzheimer Scotland & The Forget-Me-Not Club

Glensaugh

Kirkcudbrightshire

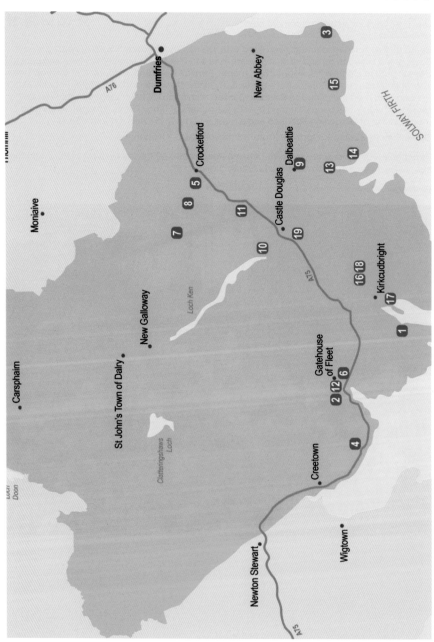

Kirkcudbrightshire

OUR VOLUNTEER ORGANISERS

District Organisers:	Julian Stanning	Seabank, Merse Road, Dalbeattie DG5 4QH
	Theodora Stanning	Seabank, Merse Road, Dalbeattie DG5 4QH
		E: info@scotlandsgardens.org
Area Organisers:	May Lockhart	25 Victoria Park, Kirkcudbright DG6 4EN
	Norman McClure	142 Cotton Street, Castle Douglas DG7 1DG
	Lesley Pepper	Anwoth Old Schoolhouse DG7 2EF
	George Thomas	Savat, Meikle Richorn, Dalbeattie DG5 4QT
Media Volunteer	Alison Forrest	Conifers, Rockcliffe, Dalbeattie DG5 4QF
District Photographer:	Stuart Littlewood	stu@f8.eclipse.co.uk
Treasurer:	Russell Allan	Braeburn, 6 Barcloy Mill, Dalbeattie DG5 4QL

GARDENS OPEN ON A SPECIFIC DATE

Danevale Park, Crossmichael	Sunday, 19 February
The Limes, Kirkcudbright	Sunday, 26 March
3 Millhall, Shore Road, Kirkcudbright	Sunday, 16 April
Threave Garden, Castle Douglas	Monday, 1 May
Cally Gardens, Cally Avenue, Gatehouse of Fleet	Sunday, 7 May
Arbigland House, Kirkbean, Dumfries	Sunday, 14 May
The Limes, Kirkcudbright	Sunday, 21 May
Brooklands, Crocketford	Sunday, 21 May
Corsock House, Corsock, Castle Douglas	Sunday, 28 May
Seabank, The Merse, Rockcliffe	Sunday, 11 June
Southwick House, Southwick	Sunday, 2 July
Dalbeattie Community Allotments Association, Port Road, Dalbeattie	Sunday, 16 July
Crofts, Kirkpatrick Durham, Castle Douglas	Sunday, 23 July
Kings Grange House, Castle Douglas	Sunday, 30 July
Cally Gardens, Cally Avenue, Gatehouse of Fleet	Sunday, 13 August
3 Millhall, Shore Road, Kirkcudbright	Sunday, 3 September

GARDENS OPEN BY ARRANGEMENT – BOOK A VISIT WITH THE GARDEN OWNER

The Limes, Kirkcudbright	1 January - 31 December
Barholm Castle, Gatehouse of Fleet	1 January - 31 December
Stockarton, Kirkcudbright	1 January - 31 December
Brooklands, Crocketford	1 February - 28 February
Danevale Park, Crossmichael	13 February - 25 February
Anwoth Old Schoolhouse, Anwoth, Gatehouse of Fleet	15 February - 15 November
Luckie Harg's, Anwoth, Gatehouse of Fleet, Castle Douglas	1 March - 30 September
3 Millhall, Shore Road, Kirkcudbright	1 March - 31 October

Kirkcudbrightshire

GARDENS OPEN BY ARRANGEMENT – BOOK A VISIT WITH THE GARDEN OWNER
Continued

Corsock House, Corsock, Castle Douglas	1 April - 30 June
Savat, Meikle Richorn, Dalbeattie (Friday - Monday)	1 April - 31 October (Friday - Monday)
The Waterhouse Gardens at Stockarton, Kirkcudbright	1 May - 30 September
Brooklands, Crocketford	1 May - 30 September
Seabank, The Merse, Rockcliffe	8 June - 4 July
Kings Grange House, Castle Douglas	15 July - 13 August

Kings Grange House

Kirkcudbrightshire

 1 ### 3 MILLHALL
Shore Road, Kirkcudbright DG6 4TQ
Mr Alan Shamash
T: 01557 870352 E: shamash@freeuk.com

Impressive five-acre garden with a large collection of mature shrubs, including over 200 rhododendron species, many camellias, perennials, over 300 hydrangeas and many rare Southern Hemisphere plants. The garden has several interesting paths and is on a hillside running along the rocky shore of the Dee Estuary in Kirkcudbright Bay.

Open: Sunday 16 April & Sunday 3 September, 2pm - 5pm. Also open by arrangement 1 March - 31 October. Admission £5.00, children free.

Directions: On the B727 between Kirkcudbright and Borgue on the west shore of the Dee Estuary. Parking at Dhoon Beach public car park, about three miles south of Kirkcudbright. There is a five-minute walk to the house. Please note there will be no vehicular access to 3 Millhall and all visitors should park at Dhoon Beach and walk up to the property.

Opening for: Kirkcudbright Hospital League Of Friends & Alzheimer's Research UK

3 Millhall

2 ### ANWOTH OLD SCHOOLHOUSE
Anwoth, Gatehouse of Fleet DG7 2EF
Mr and Mrs Pepper
T: 01557 814444 E: lesley.pepper@btinternet.com

Two acres of delightful cottage-style gardens behind the old schoolhouse and cottage in a picturesque setting opposite Anwoth Old Church (in ruins) and graveyard. Much of the garden provides an excellent habitat for wildlife, with winding paths alongside a burn, informally planted with unusual woodland perennials and shrubs. Wildlife pond, fish pond, rock garden, vegetable garden, wildflower area and viewpoint.

Open: by arrangement 15 February - 15 November, admission by donation.

Directions: Driving west on the A75, take the Anwoth turn off about half a mile after Gatehouse of Fleet. Anwoth Church is about half a mile along the road and Anwoth Old Schoolhouse is a little further along, opposite Anwoth Old Church (in ruins).

Opening for: Dogs for Good

Kirkcudbrightshire

3 ARBIGLAND HOUSE

Kirkbean, Dumfries DG2 8BQ
Alistair Alcock and Wayne Whittaker
T: 01387 880764 E: alcockalistair@gmail.com
W: www.arbiglandhouseandgardens.co.uk

Arbigland House is an Adam-style 18th-century mansion surrounded by 24 acres of woodland gardens running down to a beach on the Solway Firth. The gardens date from the 18th century but the more formal areas were developed in the late 19th and early 20th centuries and are currently undergoing a programme of restoration and development. There are 200 year-old trees lining the Broad Walk which runs down to the Solway and a huge variety of rhododendrons and azaleas. Within the woodland are a range of features including a stream-fed lake and a Japanese garden, with a more formal sundial garden and sunken rose garden, all in the process of renewal. Amongst these are a diverse collection of mature trees and shrubs.

Open: Sunday 14 May, 2pm - 5pm, admission £5.00, children free. Teas at John Paul Jones Museum. Short tours available of the principal rooms of the House.

Directions: Take the A710 to Kirkbean. In the village turn off towards Carsethorn and, after 200 yards, turn right and follow signs to *John Paul Jones Cottage*. After a mile or so, turn left at the T junction through white gates and down the drive through ornamental gates to Arbigland House.

Opening for: Absolute Classics

4 BARHOLM CASTLE

Gatehouse of Fleet DG7 2EZ
Drs John and Janet Brennan
T: 01557 840327 E: barholmcastle@gmail.com

Barholm Castle, a 16th-century tower, was restored from a ruin in 2006. The gardens surrounding the tower have been mostly developed from scratch and are now mature. There is a recently extended walled garden, with a gate designed by the artist blacksmith Adam Booth; a courtyard garden; a wooded ravine with huge hybrid rhododendrons from Benmore; a pond and a large fernery with over 100 varieties of fern, including very large tree ferns; a large Victorian-style greenhouse filled with succulents and tender perennials; and a large open garden with island beds of shrubs and perennials and a pond. Directly around the castle are rockeries and shrub borders. Views over Wigtown Bay are magnificent. The garden is planted for year-round colour, from February, when the castle ravine is a river of snowdrops, to October, when autumn colour is splendid.

Open: by arrangement 1 January - 31 December, including for Snowdrops and Winter Walks, admission £5.00, children free.

Directions: Off the A75 at the Cairn Holy turn off, fork right three times up a steep narrow road for half-a-mile.

Opening for: Home-Start Wigtownshire

5 BROOKLANDS

Crocketford DG2 8QH
Mr and Mrs Robert Herries
T: Gardener, Holly: 07534 573529

Large old walled garden with a wide selection of plants, including some interesting shrubs and climbers and a kitchen garden. Mature woodland with many established rhododendrons and azaleas, and carpeted with snowdrops in February.

Kirkcudbrightshire

Open: Sunday 21 May, 2pm - 5pm (Teas will be weather dependent). Also open by arrangement 1 February to 28 February, for Snowdrops, and 1 May to 30 September. A minimum of four adults for by arrangement openings. Admission £5.00, children free.

Directions: Turn off the A712 Crocketford to New Galloway Road one mile outside Crocketford at the Gothic gatehouse (on the right travelling north).

Opening for: SGS and Beneficiaries

 ## 6 CALLY GARDENS
Cally Avenue, Gatehouse of Fleet DG7 2DJ
Kevin Hughes
T: 01557 815228 E: info@callygardens.co.uk
W: www.callygardens.co.uk

Cally Gardens and specialist Plant Centre is a treasure trove of rare and exotic hardy plants gathered worldwide. The towering 18th-century walls of the former kitchen and pleasure garden of Cally House provide shelter for informal gardens created by the famous plant collector Michael Wickenden. Plantsman Kevin Hughes took ownership in 2018 and has since brought his own large collection of magnolias, daphnes and trilliums and has also expanded on many existing plant taxa, notably paeonia, meconopsis and nerines. As an ecologist and environmentalist, Kevin has adopted a philosophy of gardening with wildlife and is creating a new grassland planting whilst making the entire garden pesticide free with notable increases in biodiversity.

Open: Sunday 7 May and Sunday 13 August, 10am - 5pm. Admission £5.00, children free.

Directions: From Dumfries take the Gatehouse of Fleet turning off the A75, follow the B727 and turn left through the Cally Palace Hotel gateway from where the gardens are well signposted. A regular bus service will stop at the end of Cally Drive if requested.

Opening for: WWF-UK

 ## 7 CORSOCK HOUSE
Corsock, Castle Douglas DG7 3DJ
The Ingall family
T: 01644 440250 E: jingall@hotmail.com

Corsock House garden includes an amazing variety of designed landscape, from a strictly formal walled garden, through richly planted woodlands full of different vistas, artfully designed water features and surprises to extensive lawns showing off the Bryce baronial mansion. This is an Arcadian garden with pools and temples, described by Ken Cox as 'perhaps my favourite of Scotland's many woodland gardens'.

Open: Sunday 28 May, 2pm - 5pm. Also open by arrangement 1 April - 30 June. Admission £5.00, children free.

Directions: Off the A75, Dumfries is 14 miles, Castle Douglas is ten miles, Corsock Village is half-a-mile on the A712.

Opening for: Corsock & Kirkpatrick Durham Church Of Scotland

Kirkcudbrightshire

8 CROFTS

Kirkpatrick Durham, Castle Douglas DG7 3HX
Mrs Andrew Dalton
T: 01556 650235 E: jenniedalton@mac.com

Victorian country-house garden with mature trees, a walled garden with fruit and vegetables and glasshouses, hydrangea garden and a pretty water garden. Delightful woodland walk, colourfully planted with bog plants, and a stream running through.

Open: Sunday 23 July, 2pm - 5pm, admission £5.00, children free.

Directions: A75 to Crocketford, then three miles on the A712 to Corsock and New Galloway.

Opening for: Corsock & Kirkpatrick Durham Church Of Scotland

9 DALBEATTIE COMMUNITY ALLOTMENTS ASSOCIATION
Port Road, Dalbeattie DG5 4AZ
Dalbeattie Community Allotments Association
T: 01556 612208

Dalbeattie Community Allotments Association was formed in 2008 and the site was officially opened in August 2010. A local landowner has leased the land for 25 years at £1 per year, initially providing for 47 plots. The initial results were so successful that the area is now increased to provide for 81 productive plots where local residents can grow their own fruit, vegetables and flowers. Come and enjoy a stroll around the site, chat to members or relax in one of the community areas with a cup of tea. Information will be available and photos of the development of the site will be on display.

Open: Sunday 16 July, 2pm - 5pm, admission £3.00, children free.

Directions: The allotment site can be found on the Dalbeattie bypass (A710) next to Craignair Health Centre.

Opening for: Dalbeattie Community Initiative

Seabank

Kirkcudbrightshire

10 DANEVALE PARK

Crossmichael DG7 2LP
Mrs Pam Fitton
T: 01556 670223 E: pamfitton@outlook.com

First opening for snowdrops in 1951, these mature grounds have a wonderful display of snowdrops as well as aconites and many other wildflowers. Walks through the woods and alongside the River Dee make this a memorable afternoon. We will have snowdrops for sale and home-made teas in the house.

Open: Sunday 19 February, noon - 4pm, and also open by arrangement 13 February - 25 February, for Snowdrops and Winter Walks. Admission £5.00, children free. By arrangement opening for a minimum of 4 adults.

Directions: On the A713 two miles from Castle Douglas and one mile short of Crossmichael.

Opening for: Crossmichael Community Trust SCIO

11 KINGS GRANGE HOUSE

Castle Douglas DG7 3EU
Christine and Peter Hickman
T: 07787 535889

An extensive garden surrounded by mature trees and shrubberies, with views to the south west over the surrounding countryside. Originally Victorian, the garden is being restored by the present owners with a colourful variety of herbaceous mixed borders, beds and rockeries, mainly to the front of the house. There are banks of daffodils and a carpet of white narcissus in the lawns and around the pergola in springtime.

Open: Sunday 30 July, 2pm - 5pm. Also open by arrangement 15 July - 13 August. Admission £5.00, children free.

Directions: Take the B794 north off the A75, two miles east of Castle Douglas. Kings Grange House is approximately one mile on the left.

Opening for: RNLI & Marie Curie

12 LUCKIE HARG'S

Anwoth, Gatehouse of Fleet, Castle Douglas DG7 2EF
Drs Carole and Ian Bainbridge
T: 01557 814141 E: luckiehargs@btinternet.com

A new and developing garden on the outskirts of Gatehouse of Fleet. A rock and spring herbaceous garden of around an acre, with a wide range of alpines, Himalayan and New Zealand plants, shrubs and small trees. There is a rock garden, modern crevice gardens, troughs, a large alpine house and bulb frame. New boulder, scree and stumpery beds, a pond and a woodland area are being developed. Small productive vegetable and fruit garden, plus a bluebell bank in May.

Open: by arrangement 1 March - 30 September, admission £5.00, children free.

Directions: From Gatehouse High Street, turn north onto Station Road, immediately west at the Fleet Bridge by The Ship Inn. After almost one mile turn left signed to *Anwoth Old Church*. Luckie Harg's is the first on the right after 400 yards. The nearest bus stop is on Gatehouse High Street, walk about 15 minutes to Luckie Harg's.

Opening for: Scottish Rock Garden Club

Kirkcudbrightshire

13 SAVAT

Meikle Richorn, Dalbeattie DG5 4QT
George Thomas
T: 01556 612863 Mob. 07866 392150 E: georgethomas6@icloud.com

A generally informal garden of about two-thirds of an acre with mature trees, exposed
Dalbeattie granite and winding paths. The garden houses a unique summerhouse, artist Sue
Thomas's studio and a greenhouse. Planting caters for sun to shade and dry to very moist, with
shrubs – including rhododendrons, herbaceous and minimal summer bedding with an eye to
keeping maintenance requirements to a minimum! There is a paved area around the house in
which there are two water features, and may display potted plants.

Open: by arrangement 1 April - 31 October, admission £5.00, children free. (Fridays to Mondays
inclusive)

Directions: Leave Dalbeattie along the A710 south towards Kippford. After about 1.7 miles pass
Gorsebank on the left and 200 yards further on turn right into a large lay-by. Enter the lane
marked with cul de sac signs and proceed straight ahead along the paved road for about 500
yards. Limited parking is available at the property entrance. Savat is the sixth house on the left.

Opening for: SGS and Beneficiaries

14 SEABANK

The Merse, Rockcliffe DG5 4QH
Julian and Theodora Stanning
T: 01556 630244

This one-and-a-half-acre garden extends to the high water mark with westerly views across
a wildflower meadow to the Urr Estuary, Rough Island and beyond. The house is flanked by
raised beds, and overlooks a cottage-style garden; peripheral plantings of mixed shrubs
and perennials are interspersed with spring bulbs and summer annuals for all-year-round
interest. There is a greenhouse with a range of succulents and tender plants. To the rear of the
property is a new walled garden stocked with top and soft fruit, perennial vegetables (sea kale,
asparagus and globe artichokes), a range of annual vegetables and flower borders. A further
greenhouse is used for tomatoes and cucumbers, and has peaches growing against the back
wall. A plantswoman's garden with a range of interesting and unusual plants.

Open: Sunday 11 June, 2pm - 5pm. Also open by arrangement 8 June - 4 July. Admission £5.00,
children free.

Directions: Park in the public car park at Rockcliffe. Walk down the road about 50 yards towards
the sea and turn left along The Merse, a private road. Seabank is the sixth house on the left.

Opening for: Marie Curie: DG5 Group

15 SOUTHWICK HOUSE

Southwick DG2 8AH
Mr and Mrs R H L Thomas

The extensive gardens at Southwick House comprise three main areas. The first is a traditional
formal walled garden with potager and large glasshouse producing a range of fruit, vegetables
and cutting flowers. Adjacent to this is a hedged formal garden with herbaceous, shrub and
rose beds centred around a lily pond, with roses being a notable feature. Outwith the formal
gardens there is a large water garden with two connected ponds with trees, shrubs and lawns
running alongside the Southwick Burn.

Kirkcudbrightshire

Open: Sunday 2 July, 2pm - 5pm, admission £5.00, children free.

Directions: On the A710 near Caulkerbush. Dalbeattie seven miles, Dumfries 17 miles.

Opening for: Loch Arthur

---

16 ### STOCKARTON
Kirkcudbright DG6 4XS
Lt Col and Mrs Richard Cliff
T: 01557 330430

This garden was started in 1995 by Carola Cliff, a keen and knowledgeable plantswoman, and contains a collection of unusual shrubs and small trees, which are growing well. Her aim has been to create different informal gardens around a Galloway farm house, leading down to a lochan. Above the lochan there is a sweet cottage, used for holiday retreats, with its own interesting garden. In 1996 a three-acre arboretum was planted as a shelter belt and it now contains some rare oak trees.

Open: by arrangement 1 January - 31 December, admission £5.00, children free.

Directions: On the B727 Kirkcudbright to Gelston Road. Kirkcudbright three miles, Castle Douglas seven miles.

Opening for: Loch Arthur

Stockarton © Stuart Littlewood

Kirkcudbrightshire

17 THE LIMES

Kirkcudbright DG6 4XD
David and Carolyn McHale
E: carolyn.mchale@btinternet.com

This one-and-a-quarter acre plantswoman's garden has a variety of different plant habitats: woodland, dry sunny gravel beds, rock garden, crevice garden and mixed perennial and shrub borders. There is also a large productive vegetable garden. The McHales like to grow most of their plants from seed obtained through various international seed exchanges. You can expect to see a large number of unusual and exciting plants. The garden is full of colour with an abundance of spring flowers in March, and in late May and early June the meconopsis should be at their best. Hardy cyclamen are a big favourite and one species or another is in flower in almost every month of the year. Winter is a good time to admire their varied leaf forms.

Open: Sunday 26 March & Sunday 21 May, 2pm - 5pm. Also open by arrangement 1 January - 31 December. Admission £5.00, children free.

Directions: In Kirkcudbright go straight along St Mary Street towards Dundrennan. The Limes is on the right, about half a mile from the town centre crossroads, on the edge of the town.

Opening for: Friends Of Kirkcudbright Swimming Pool

The Limes

18 THE WATERHOUSE GARDENS AT STOCKARTON

Kirkcudbright DG6 4XS
Martin Gould & Sharon O'Rourke
T: 01557 331266 E: waterhousekbt@aol.com
W: www.waterhousekbt.co.uk

One acre of densely planted, terraced, cottage-style gardens attached to a Galloway cottage. Three ponds surround the oak-framed eco-polehouse, The Waterhouse. Climbing roses, clematis and honeysuckles are a big feature as well as a pond-side walk. There are over 50 photos on their website. Featured on *The Beechgrove Garden* in 2007.

Kirkcudbrightshire

Open: by arrangement 1 May - 30 September, admission £5.00, children free.

Directions: On the B727 Kirkcudbright to Gelston/Dalbeattie road. Kirkcudbright is three miles and Castle Douglas is seven miles.

Opening for: Loch Arthur

 19 **THREAVE GARDEN**
Castle Douglas DG7 1RX
National Trust for Scotland
T: 01556 502 575 E: threave@nts.org.uk
W: www.nts.org.uk/visit/places/threave-garden

The Threave SGS 'Open Day' is a one-day event at the home of the School of Heritage Gardening which will offer the opportunity to gain advice and ideas from people who have innovated, transformed and developed these fine gardens and to take tours of the garden and glasshouses. Food and drink will be available from Threave's catering team.
Champion Trees: *Acer platanoides* 'Princeton Gold'; *Carpinus caroliniana*; X *Cuprocyparis leylandii* 'Picturesque' and a further 25 Scottish Champion Trees.

Open: Monday 1 May, 10am - 5pm, admission £5.00, children free.

Directions: Off the A75, one mile west of Castle Douglas.

Opening for: The National Trust for Scotland: School of Gardening Heritage

Threave © Malcolm Ross

Lanarkshire

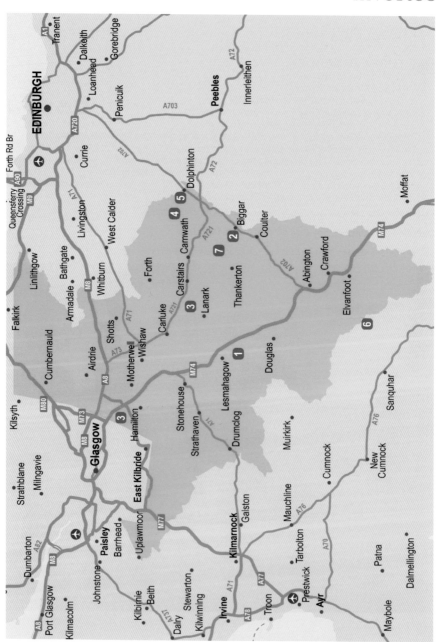

Lanarkshire

OUR VOLUNTEER ORGANISERS

District Organiser:	Vanessa Rogers	1 Larkspur Way, Carluke, Lanarkshire ML8 5TD E: info@scotlandsgardens.org
Area Organiser:	Nicky Eliott Lockhart	Stable House, Cleghorn Farm, Lanark ML11 7RW
District Photographer:	Alistair McNeill	57 Sherifflats Road, Thankerton ML12 6PA
Treasurer:	Sheila Munro Tulloch	Castlegait House, Lanarkshire ML10 6FF

GARDENS OPEN ON A SPECIFIC DATE

Cleghorn, Stable House, Cleghorn Farm, Lanark	Sunday, 5 March
Biggar Open Gardens, High Street Biggar	Sunday, 4 June
Meadowhead, Dolphinton, West Linton	Sunday, 11 June
Little Sparta, Stonypath, Dunsyre	Tuesday, 27 June
Little Sparta, Stonypath, Dunsyre	Tuesday, 4 July
The Walled Garden, Shieldhill, Quothquan, Biggar	Sunday, 30 July
Little Sparta, Stonypath, Dunsyre	Tuesday, 29 August
Little Sparta, Stonypath, Dunsyre	Tuesday, 5 September

GARDENS OPEN BY ARRANGEMENT – BOOK A VISIT WITH THE GARDEN OWNER

Old Manse Wild Garden, Old Manse, Wanlockhead, Biggar	1 April - 31 October
Auchlochan Walled Garden, New Trows Road, Lesmahagow	19 June - 30 October
The Walled Garden, Shieldhill, Quothquan, Biggar	1 July - 31 August

Lanarkshire

1 AUCHLOCHAN WALLED GARDEN
New Trows Road, Lesmahagow, Lanarkshire ML11 0GS
MHA Auchlochan Garden Village
T: 01555 893592 E: auchlochan.enquiries@mha.org.uk

The Walled Garden at Auchlochan Garden Village was created at the turn of the century as a kitchen garden to service Auchlochan House. The garden, which is located within 50 acres of landscaped parkland with a small lochan, has evolved over the years and now has interesting mixed planting within a traditional framework. Around every corner you will find a mass of summer colour with lots of lovely shaded seating areas from which to appreciate the wide variety of plants on offer. The central walkway is of particular note. Adjacent to the garden is a large lily pond offering picturesque views of the terraces beyond.

Open: by arrangement 19 June - 30 October, admission £5.00, children free.

Directions: Exit the M74 at Junction 9 and follow signs to *Lesmahagow Village*. Once on the High Street take New Trows Road, opposite the Bank of Scotland, keep on this road for two miles. Follow the brown tourist signs to *Auchlochan Garden Village*.

Opening for: MHA Auchlochan

Auchlochan Walled Garden

2 BIGGAR OPEN GARDENS
High Street Biggar ML12 6DH
The Gardeners of Biggar Town

This year Biggar is opening its gardens earlier in the season to showcase late spring/early summer gardens. With six new gardens and two that have opened before to enjoy, the easily-walked route is centred on the northern end of the town. Once again we have an eclectic mix including three very different little gems to be found behind the High Street: the garden of an award-winning authority on *Meconopsis*, an impressive contemporary garden, a delightful cottage garden developed on a budget, as well as two larger gardens filled with interest and surprises, one of which is the perfect location to enjoy a homemade tea.

Lanarkshire

Open: Sunday 4 June, noon - 5pm, admission £6.00, children free. Ticket sales and plant stall will be in front of the Corn Exchange (clock tower) in the centre of Biggar.

Directions: Biggar is situated on the A702, 30 miles south of Edinburgh and 10 miles north of Junction 13 on the M74. Bus services to Biggar run from Lanark (routes 191 and 91) from Peebles (route 91) and from Edinburgh and Dumfries (route 101).

Opening for: BCAG

 3 CLEGHORN
Stable House, Cleghorn Farm, Lanark ML11 7RN
Mr and Mrs R Eliott Lockhart
T: 01555 663792 E: eliottlockhart.nicky@gmail.com
W: www.cleghornestategardens.com

Eighteenth-century garden gradually being returned to its former layout. Lawns with mature trees, shrubs, abundant snowdrops and a woodland walk along the valley, formed by 12th-century dams that were originally built to form fish ponds. The valley has been totally cleared in the last couple of years and the burn and snowdrops are now visible from both sides of the valley. Visitors are welcome to return when the daffodils are in flower.

Open: Sunday 5 March, 2pm - 4pm for Snowdrops and Winter Walks, admission by donation.

Directions: Cleghorn Farm is situated two miles north of Lanark off the A706.

Opening for: Marie Curie

Meadowhead © Alistair McNeill

Lanarkshire

4 LITTLE SPARTA
Stonypath, Dunsyre ML11 8NG
Laura Robertson
T: 07826 495677 E: contact@littlesparta.org.uk
W: www.littlesparta.org.uk

Little Sparta is Ian Hamilton Finlay's greatest work of art. Ian and Sue Finlay moved to the farm of Stonypath in 1966 and began to create what would become an internationally acclaimed garden across seven acres of a wild and exposed moorland site. Collaborating with stone carvers, letterers and other artists and poets, the numerous sculptures and artworks created by Finlay explore themes as diverse as the sea and its fishing fleets, our relationship to nature, classical antiquity, the French Revolution and the Second World War. Individual poetic and sculptural elements, in wood, stone and metal, are sited in relation to carefully structured landscaping and planting. Please note that there is a 700m uphill walk from the car park and livestock grazing in the fields. For visitors with limited mobility, it may be possible to book a space near the house; call the garden for details.

Open: Tuesday 27 June, Tuesday 4 July, Tuesday 29 August & Tuesday 5 September, 1pm - 4pm, admission £9.00, children £5.00. Last entry 3pm.

Directions: Check www.littlesparta.org.uk/visit/ for directions.

Opening for: Little Sparta Trust

5 MEADOWHEAD
Dolphinton, West Linton EH46 7AB
Andrew and Pam Taylor
E: pam.taylor1@btinternet.com

Water is a major feature of this eleven-and-a-half-acre garden with a lochan, river and many wildlife ponds. Wilderness areas provide valuable biodiversity with a wide variety of habitats for flora and fauna, including a family of swans. Many varieties of primula provide a mass of colour in the extensive bog garden, and the rhododendrons and azaleas will still be in bloom. A small parterre offers more formal seclusion. The walled garden's features include a terrace with two Italianate ponds and sitooteries and below, a further terrace with a grotto, leading to a gentle trough cascade which feeds a rill.

Open: Sunday 11 June, 2pm - 5pm, admission £5.00, children free. Stout shoes recommended. There will be a variety of activities for the young folk. Old and young alike will be fascinated by the live moths collected from the garden and presented by a local lepidopterist.

Directions: The garden can be found just off the A702 in the village of Dolphinton.

Opening for: Wateraid

6 OLD MANSE WILD GARDEN
Old Manse, Wanlockhead, Biggar ML12 6UR
Callum Gough
T: 07717 768324 E: oldmansewildgarden@gmail.com
W: www.facebook.com/The-Old-Manse-Wild-garden-179050766257960

Featured in *The Scotsman* and on *Border television*. It is recognised that gardening at 1530 feet is not easy, but this fascinating garden is exceptional. Extending to about one acre, it is divided into many intriguing and sometimes quirky rooms, each one very different from the next and hugely biodiverse. The owner has an interest in permaculture and the garden is dedicated to providing habitats for wildlife (the entire ecosystem for some species), in particular amphibians

Lanarkshire

and all types of insects including butterflies and bees. The garden is enjoyed all year round by people and wildlife alike.

Open: by arrangement 1 April - 31 October, admission £5.00, children free. Not suitable for visitors with limited mobility. Stout shoes recommended. In an area of great interest, the Museum of Lead Mining in Wanlockhead has a Mine and Visitors' Centre.

Directions: Leave the M74 at Junction 13 following signs to *Abington*, through the village signposted *Leadhills*. From the A76 Sanquhar/Thornhill road take the turn near Mennock signposted *Wanlockhead*. Buses available from Sanquhar and Lanark.

Opening for: WLMT Hidden Treasures Museum of Lead Mining

 7 ## THE WALLED GARDEN, SHIELDHILL
Quothquan, Biggar ML12 6NA
Mr and Mrs Gordon
T: 01899 221961 E: nicolagord@gmail.com

This 200-year-old walled garden was completely redesigned and planted in 2014/15 with contemporary features within a classic design. The garden incorporates a modern rill and banks of colour with perennial flowers in a variety of borders. The resident bees enjoy the large area of traditional meadow flowers as well as the rose garden planted with lavenders, salvias and stocks. Outside the wall you will find mature woodland including a giant sequoia and a wildlife pond. If you are interested in fruit and vegetables, take a look at the raised beds and the peach tree and vine in the greenhouse. There are many secluded spots around the garden to sit and enjoy a cup of tea and a homemade cake.

Open: Sunday 30 July, 2pm - 5pm. Also open by arrangement 1 July - 31 August. Admission £5.00, children free.

Directions: Turn off the B7016 between Biggar and Carnwath towards Quothquan. After about a mile, look for signs and turn right at the lodge.

Opening for: Médecins Sans Frontières

The Walled Garden, Shieldhill © Alistair McNeill

Moray & Nairn

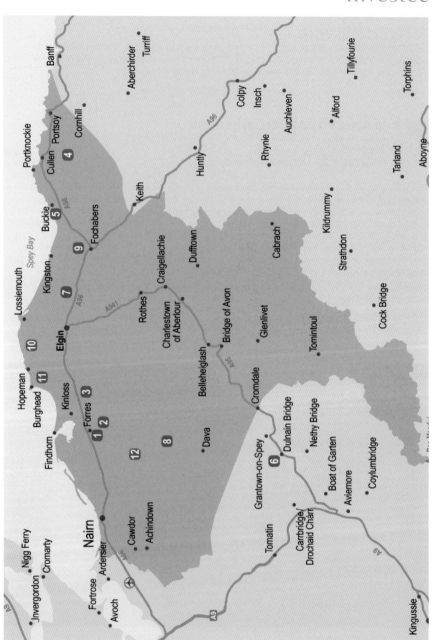

Moray & Nairn

OUR VOLUNTEER ORGANISERS

District Organiser:	James Byatt	E: info@scotlandsgardens.org
Area Organisers:	Michael Barnett	
	Lorraine Dingwall	
	David Hetherington	
	Gwynne Hetherington	
	Annie Stewart	
Treasurer:	David Barnett	

GARDENS OPEN ON A SPECIFIC DATE

Easter Laggan, Dulnain Bridge, Grantown-on-Spey	Saturday, 20 May
Glenernie, Glenernie House, Dunphail, Moray	Sunday, 4 June
Carestown Steading, Deskford, Buckie	Saturday, 10 June
Gordonstoun, Duffus, near Elgin	Sunday, 25 June
Haugh Garden, College of Roseisle	Sunday, 25 June
Cuthberts Brae, 84 Seatown, Buckie	Saturday/Sunday, 1/2 July
Glebe House, Main Street, Urquhart	Sunday, 9 July
A Trio of Gardens near Rafford, Rafford, Forres	Saturday, 22 July
Haugh Garden, College of Roseisle	Sunday, 30 July

GARDENS OPEN REGULARLY

Burgie Arboretum, Between Forres and Elgin	1 January - 31 December
Gordon Castle Walled Garden, Fochabers, Moray	2 January - 31 December
Logie House, Dunphail, Forres	1 April - 31 December

GARDENS OPEN BY ARRANGEMENT – BOOK A VISIT WITH THE GARDEN OWNER

10 Pilmuir Road West, Forres	25 January - 11 March
10 Pilmuir Road West, Forres	1 June - 1 September
Haugh Garden, College of Roseisle	1 June - 31 July

Moray & Nairn

 1 ### 10 PILMUIR ROAD WEST
Forres IV36 2HL
Mrs Lorraine Dingwall
T: 01309 674634 E: fixandig@aol.com

Plantswoman's small town garden with over 300 cultivars of hostas, an extensive collection of hardy geraniums together with many other unusual plants. Managed entirely without the use of artificial fertilisers or chemicals, the owner encourages hedgehogs, toads and wild birds to control slugs. In early spring there are approximately 150 named snowdrops to be seen, some of which are very rare.

Open: by arrangement 25 January - 11 March for Snowdrops and Winter Walks. Also open by arrangement 1 June - 1 September. Admission £5.00, children free. There is a well-stocked sales area.

Directions: From Tesco roundabout at Forres continue along Nairn Road. Take the first left onto Ramflat Road, then go right at the bottom and first left onto Pilmuir Road West.

Opening for: Macmillan Cancer Support

 2 ### A TRIO OF GARDENS NEAR RAFFORD
Rafford, Forres IV36 2RT
Susan & Howard Stollar, Joanna & Peter Taylor, Carol & Colin Shepherd
T: 07843 795053 E: mcstollars@gmail.com

Three charming neighbouring gardens close to Forres. There are connecting gates between the gardens, allowing visitors to roam and explore the unique character of each. You will find lots of interesting features to inspire you with new ideas, as well as places to just sit and relax. You may also enjoy meeting friends, old and new over a cuppa and some home baking.

An-Grianan Rafford, Forres IV36 2RT (Susan and Howard Stollar): Delightful, four-acre garden. There are beautiful herbaceous borders which will appeal to the beginner and connoisseur alike; a herb area and rockery, as well as a mature orchard, organic vegetable garden and polytunnel which supply the owners, neighbours and friends with fresh food all year round. Enjoy a tranquil walk through semi-mature woodland and enjoy the abundant birdsong and the sight of the wild flowers growing freely in the meadow and wooded areas.
Balnagreine: The 'Orchard' (NEW) Rafford, Forres IV36 2RT (Joanna and Peter Taylor): Some thirty-five years ago, the 'orchard' of Balnagreine was simple grazing land: the 'Line-side Field' – farmed by Marcassie, on the north side of the Dallas Dhu road, all the way from Redhill to the old Rafford Station and the railway bridge on the Dava Way. An-Grianan was the first house to be built. Balnagreine was next. The new owners planted many trees; willows and standards near the house, with shrubs and fruit trees. The 'orchard', however, has been allowed to become a resurgent area of native woodland, lightly managed and a home for bees, hares, deer, badger, red squirrel and a multitude of birds. Within the fenced area, you will find most Scottish native species – plus one wee group of small trees that we just cannot identify! We hope you will enjoy a meander through the trees while you are here.
Southview (NEW) Rafford, Forres IV36 2RT (Carol and Colin Shepherd): Southview is set in two acres of mixed woodland and has been established over the last nine years. There is a good mix of conifers, rhododendrons and fruit trees. This leads onto a beautifully maintained raised bed of heathers, rock roses and azaleas, all of which surround a patio sitting area which has a colourful display of herbaceous plantings to provide colour throughout the summer and autumn.

Open: Saturday 22 July, 11am - 4pm, admission £5.00, children free. Teas (home baking) and plant stall at An-Grianan.

Directions: Head out of Forres on St Leonards Road towards Rafford. In Lower Rafford, take the sharp right for Dallas Dhu Distillery. Parking is available at Balnagreine and An-Grianan, approximately three quarters of a mile along this road on the right.

Opening for: RNLI, Guide Dogs & Rangjung Yeshe Gomde Trust

Moray & Nairn

3 **BURGIE ARBORETUM**
Between Forres and Elgin IV36 2QU
Hamish Lochore
T: 01343 850231 E: hamish@burgie.org

A rare opportunity to see a sizeable woodland garden/arboretum in its infancy. It has a good collection of rhododendrons, Sorbus, alder, birch and Tilia but also includes many unusual trees from around the world. The arboretum is zoned into geographic areas and species type. It includes a Japanese Garden, bog garden, bog wood, loch and quarry garden. First created in 2005 and is ongoing. Most plants are grown from hand-collected seed and propagated in the Georgian greenhouse.

Open: 1 January - 31 December, 8am - 5pm, admission by donation.

Directions: A96 between Forres and Elgin. Four miles east of Forres. Six miles west of Elgin. Sign to *Burgie Mains* along the A96 is set in wrought iron decorated with horses and cattle. South off the main road and one mile to the Woodland Garden car park.

Opening for: Sandpiper Trust

4 **CARESTOWN STEADING**
Deskford, Buckie AB56 5TR
Cherie Timney-Gunn
T: 01542 841245 E: cherietg@sky.com

Carestown Steading is a sculptural garden which is spread over six acres. The garden has been created and developed over the past 35 years. It contains many features including a Knot Garden, a full-sized maze and a completed laburnum walk. The garden features Alice in Wonderland statues and there are many specimen trees including acers and a dawn redwood.

Open: Saturday 10 June, 11am - 4pm, admission £5.00, children free. Toilet facilities available. Parking in the field next to the house. Teas will be served in the Garden room.

Directions: East of B9018 Cullen/Keith (Cullen three miles, Keith nine-and-a-half miles). Follow SGS signs towards Milton and Carestown or use what3words.com/Perfectly.swing. beans

Opening for: Scottish Autism

Carestown Steading © James Byatt

Moray & Nairn

5 CUTHBERTS BRAE

84 Seatown, Buckie AB56 1JS
Elizabeth and Malcolm Schofield
T: 07878 486093 E: malcolmsgsp@gmail.com
W: www.instagram.com/cuthbertsbrae_garden

Gardeners' World Magazine, Readers' Garden of the Year 2020, Judges' Choice Winner. *'In the small seaside town of Buckie in the north east Moray Coast, what was once a wild hill, overgrown with brambles, has now been transformed into a beautiful colourful haven for all to admire.'* – Gardeners' World Magazine. The garden is sited on a steep hill with a small flat terrace with gravel garden wrapping around the house. The path then takes you down the bank into a terraced cottage garden that is a magnet for bees, butterflies and other wildlife. As you continue into the newer section of the garden you discover the greenhouse, rabbit enclosure and veg beds. *'This garden is a really good lesson in what you can achieve in inhospitable conditions with limited knowledge and money.'* – Alan Titchmarsh.

Open: Saturday/Sunday, 1/2 July, 2pm - 5pm, admission by donation.

Directions: Arriving from the Tesco road turn left at the Town Square. Take the next right. Use the car park at the *Seatown* sign. Follow the signage to our garden. The garden is a short walk (five minutes) from the Town Square.

Opening for: Scottish Association For Mental Health

6 EASTER LAGGAN

Dulnain Bridge, Grantown-on-Spey PH26 3NU
Rob and Julie Forrest

A garden under development, designed by Jens Nielsen. It has stunning views of the River Spey and the Cairngorm mountains and is a haven for wildlife, including red squirrels. Five acres in size, the garden consists of some formal lawns with herbaceous borders, newly created rockeries and drystone walls and the beginnings of a Japanese garden. A stream enters the garden and flows into a newly restored pond. The stream then winds its way through the garden back in to the surrounding fields. Gravel driveways allow some wheelchair access with assistance.

Open: Saturday 20 May, 2pm - 5pm, admission £5.00, children free.

Directions: From Grantown-on-Spey take the A95 towards Aviemore. Take the first turn signed to Dulnain Bridge, then turn immediately right on to the old road. Turn immediately left up the track signed to Easter Laggan. Parking is available in a paddock by the house.

Opening for: Parkinsons UK

7 GLEBE HOUSE

Main Street, Urquhart IV30 8LG
Melanie Collett
E: mel.collett2015@outlook.com

Early 19th-century formal walled garden of the former manse by Alexander Forteath, also incorporating a unique doocot in its construction of clay dab. The garden consists of colourful herbaceous borders within the walled garden and box hedge symmetry. A wide variety of roses together with an orchard and kitchen garden area to the south.

Open: Sunday 9 July, noon - 3pm, admission £5.00, children free.

Moray & Nairn

Directions: Off the main street in Urquhart, find the walled entrance at the end of the street. Follow parking signs.

Opening for: The Royal Air Force Benevolent Fund

8 GLENERNIE
Glenernie House, Dunphail, Moray IV36 2QH
Robert and Fiona Laing
T: 01309 611203 E: robert@glenernie.co.uk

A tranquil landscaped woodland garden set in the Dorbach river valley with garden, woodland and river walks. The garden, which includes some ornamental ponds, has been created over the last forty years and is planted with azaleas, rhododendrons, dogwoods and other shrubs set amongst both mature and younger specimen trees.

Open: Sunday 4 June, 2pm - 5pm, admission £5.00, children free.

Directions: Access is from the A940 Forres to Grantown on Spey road approximately ten miles south of Forres. Half-a-mile south of Edinkillie church on the right.

Opening for: Edinkillie Parish Church of Scotland

Glenernie

Moray & Nairn

9 GORDON CASTLE WALLED GARDEN

Fochabers, Moray IV32 7PQ
Angus and Zara Gordon Lennox
T: 01343 612317 E: info@gordoncastlescotland.com
W: www.gordoncastle.co.uk

At almost eight acres in size, Gordon Castle has one of the oldest and largest walled gardens in Britain. Lovingly restored to its former glory with a modern design by award-winning designer Arne Maynard, this beautiful garden is overflowing with vegetables, fruit, herbs, and cut flowers. The onsite cafe has a 'Plant, Pick, Plate' ethos using wonderful fresh produce grown in the garden. There is a children's natural play area and shop.

Open: 2 January - 31 December, 10am - 4pm, admission details can be found on the garden's website. The cafe is open from Wednesday to Sunday.

Directions: The main entrance is at the western end of the village of Fochabers, just off the A96, nine miles east of Elgin and 12 miles west of Keith.

Opening for: Donation to SGS

10 GORDONSTOUN

Duffus, near Elgin IV30 5RF
The Principal
E: principalpa@gordonstoun.org.uk
W: www.gordonstoun.org.uk

Gordonstoun is famous for educating the Royal family, but its history dates much further back and was the 18th century Georgian home of the first marquis of Huntly. The school gardens consist of formal herbaceous borders, an ornamental lake and an apple orchard. Visitors can take a self-guided tour of the extensive school grounds including the unique 'Round Square' former farm building (now boarding house) which has an unusual echo and can stroll down the 'silent walk' to the 17th century kirk where former students including members of the Royal Family would have worshipped. This is the only occasion when Gordonstoun opens its gates to the public.

Open: Sunday 25 June, 2pm - 5pm, admission £8.00, children free. Refreshments included in entry price.

Directions: Entrance off B9012, four miles from Elgin at Duffus village.

Opening for: SGS and Beneficiaries

11 HAUGH GARDEN

College of Roseisle IV30 5YE
Gwynne and David Hetherington
T: 01343 835790

Within our two acre garden, we have created four different areas. The mature woodland, with informal pond and 18th century farmhouse ruin, is filled with birdsong, insects and wildlife. Walks meander through early flowering snowdrops followed by hellebores, tulips and narcissi. Extensive herbaceous borders enclosing the lawns and orchard display vibrant colours. Various paths wind their way through young pine and birch woodland underplanted with shrubs and meadow areas. Lastly, our organic vegetable beds, soft fruit and polytunnel keep us almost self-sufficient all year round.

Open: Sunday 25 June and Sunday 30 July, 2pm - 5pm. Also open by arrangement 1 June - 31 July. Admission £5.00, children free. Home made teas and plants for sale.

Moray & Nairn

Directions: From Elgin take the A96 west, then the B9013 Burghead Road to the crossroads at the centre of College of Roseisle. The garden is on the right, enter from the Duffus Road. Car parking at the village hall off Kinloss road. Drop off and disabled parking is available at the house.

Opening for: CHAS & Alzheimer Scotland

 LOGIE HOUSE
Dunphail, Forres IV36 2QN
Alasdair and Panny Laing
E: panny@logie.co.uk
W: www.logie.co.uk

Originally a traditional formal garden, Logie House walled garden has been developed since 1991 with emphasis on trees, shrubs and hardy perennials, giving all-year-round interest. The meandering burn and dry stone walls support the creation of a wide variety of planting habitats from dry sunny banks to damp shady areas. Many of the unusual plants are propagated for sale in the Garden Shop at Logie Steading. Also features woodland and river walks.

Open: 1 April - 31 December, 10am - 5pm, admission details can be found on the garden's website.

Directions: Six miles south of Forres off the A940. Follow signs to *Logie Steading*.

Opening for: Donation to SGS

Logie House © James Byatt

Peeblesshire & Tweeddale

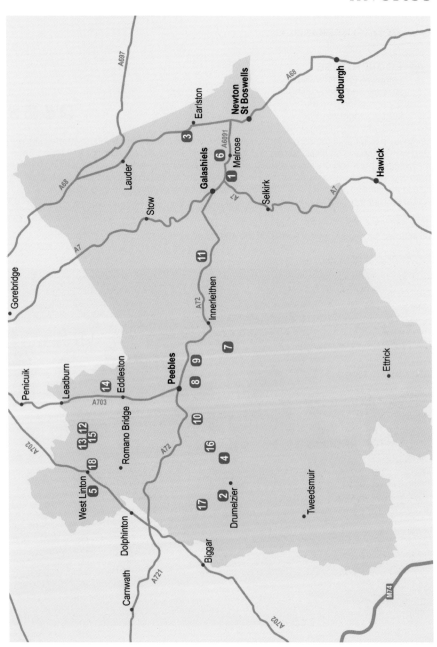

Peeblesshire & Tweeddale

OUR VOLUNTEER ORGANISERS

District Organiser:	Lesley McDavid	Braedon, Medwyn Road, West Linton EH46 7HA
		E: info@scotlandsgardens.org
Deputy District Organiser:	John Bracken	Gowan Lea, Croft Road, West Linton EH46 7DZ
Area Organisers:	Jennifer Barr	Allerly, Gattonside, Melrose TD6 9LT
	Jenny Litherland	Laidlawstiel House, Clovenfords TD1 1TJ
Treasurer:	Marie Gilmour	1 Kittlegairy Place, Peebles EH45 9LW

GARDENS OPEN ON A SPECIFIC DATE

Kailzie Gardens, Kailzie Gardens	Sunday, 5 March
Quercus Garden Plants, Whitmuir Farm, West Linton	Sunday, 28 May
Haystoun, Peebles	Sunday, 28 May
Stobo Japanese Water Garden, Stobo Farm, Stobo	Sunday, 4 June
The Potting Shed, Broughton Place, Broughton, Biggar	Wednesday, 7 June
Beechwood, Broughton, Peeblesshire	Wednesday, 7 June
Laidlawstiel House, Clovenfords, Galashiels	Wednesday/Thursday, 7/8 June
Lamancha Community Hub Plant Sale, Old Moffat Road, Lamancha	Sunday, 11 June
The Potting Shed, Broughton Place, Broughton, Biggar	Wednesday, 14 June
Beechwood, Broughton, Peeblesshire	Wednesday, 14 June
Carolside, Earlston	Sunday, 18 June
The Potting Shed, Broughton Place, Broughton, Biggar	Wednesday, 21 June
Beechwood, Broughton, Peeblesshire	Wednesday, 21 June
Gattonside Village Gardens, Gattonside	Sunday, 25 June
The Potting Shed, Broughton Place, Broughton, Biggar	Wednesday, 28 June
Beechwood, Broughton, Peeblesshire	Wednesday, 28 June
Glen House, Glen Estate, Innerleithen	Sunday, 2 July
The Potting Shed, Broughton Place, Broughton, Biggar	Wednesday, 5 July
Carolside, Earlston	Sunday, 16 July
Kailzie Gardens, Kailzie Gardens	Sunday, 23 July
West Linton Village Gardens, West Linton	Sunday, 30 July
Quercus Garden Plants, Whitmuir Farm, West Linton	Sunday, 20 August
Macbiehill Gardens, The Walled Garden, Macbiehill	Sunday, 20 August
Garvald West Linton Gardens, West Linton	Sunday, 3 September
Dawyck Botanic Garden, Stobo	Sunday, 8 October

Peeblesshire & Tweeddale

GARDENS OPEN REGULARLY

Kirkton Manor House, Peebles — 15 February - 12 July (Wednesdays)
Abbotsford, Melrose — 1 March - 30 November
Portmore, Eddleston — 5 July - 30 August (Wednesdays)

GARDENS OPEN BY ARRANGEMENT – BOOK A VISIT WITH THE GARDEN OWNER

Kirkton Manor House, Peebles — 15 February - 12 July
Garvald West Linton Gardens, West Linton — 1 March - 30 September (Wednesdays)
Beechwood, Broughton, Peeblesshire — 1 May - 31 October
The Potting Shed, Broughton Place, Broughton, Biggar — 1 May - 31 October
Portmore, Eddleston — 1 June - 31 August

Dawyck Botanic Garden © Kathy Henry

Peeblesshire & Tweeddale

1 ABBOTSFORD
Melrose TD6 9BQ
The Abbotsford Trust
T: 01896 752043 E: enquiries@scottsabbotsford.co.uk
W: www.scottsabbotsford.com

The garden was designed by Sir Walter Scott with advice from artists, architects and friends. It is a rare surviving example of a Regency garden layout and completely different from the English landscape garden style of Capability Brown. Scott's garden aims to provide a harmonious transition between the luxury and comfort of the interiors of the house with wonders of nature in the wider estate through a series of secluded, richly detailed and sheltered 'rooms'. In its day it would have showcased the latest plants discovered from around the globe, both in its borders and 'stove houses'. Regular tours are held exploring Scott's vision for the garden and the hidden meanings of its design. Check the Abbotsford website for details.

Open: 1 March - 30 November (March and November 10am - 4pm), (1 April - 31 October, 10am - 5pm). Admission details can be found on the garden's website.

Directions: Off the A6091 near Melrose. Buses X62 and 72 from Edinburgh and Peebles. Train from Waverley to Tweedbank. Minibus or one-mile walk from train station.

Opening for: Donation to SGS

2 BEECHWOOD
Broughton, Peeblesshire ML12 6HH
Susheila and James Gordon
T: 07810 837068 or 01899 830443 E: susheilarachan@gmail.com

An informal sculptor's garden adjacent to a mature woodland and pond. A well-planted stream runs through the garden. There are varied perennial meadows to encourage wildlife and provide forage for the resident bees, it also features many examples of the owners' artworks which are inspired by the natural world.

Open: 7 June - 28 June (Wednesday only), 2pm - 5pm. Also open by arrangement 1 May - 31 October. Admission £5.00, children free.

Directions: Approximately one mile south of Broughton take the B712 off the A701. Then first left turn onto unmade road.

Opening for: The Multiple Sclerosis Society of Great Britain and Northern Ireland

Peeblesshire & Tweeddale

3 **CAROLSIDE**
Earlston TD4 6AL
Mr and Mrs Anthony Foyle
T: 01896 849272 E: info@carolside.com
W: www.carolside.com

A traditional and romantic garden set in a beautiful 18th-century landscape, comprising lawns, shrubberies, mixed borders, a secret garden, winter garden, herb and hidden garden and an apple orchard of wild flowers. The oval walled garden contains herbaceous borders, fruits, vegetables, parterres and an historically important collection of roses. Carolside is best known for its roses, soft delicate herbaceous planting and design of rooms. Kenneth Cox in his book *Scotland for Gardeners* describes Carolside as 'one of Scotland's finest private gardens'. National Plant Collection: Pre-19th century *Rosa* Gallica.

Open: Sunday 18 June and Sunday 16 July, 11am - 5pm. Admission £6.00, children free. Dogs on leads in the park only.

Directions: One mile north of Earlston on the A68. Entrance faces south. Garden accessible by bus, ask to get off at Carolside gate.

Opening for: Marie Curie

Carolside

4 **DAWYCK BOTANIC GARDEN**
Stobo EH45 9JU
A Regional Garden of the Royal Botanic Garden Edinburgh
T: 01721 760254
W: www.rbge.org.uk/dawyck

Dawyck is a regional garden of the Royal Botanic Garden Edinburgh which had its 350th anniversary in 2020. Stunning collection of rare trees and shrubs. With over 300 years of tree planting, Dawyck is a world-famous arboretum with mature specimens of Chinese conifers, Japanese maples, Brewer's spruce, the unique Dawyck beech and sequoiadendrons from

Peeblesshire & Tweeddale

North America which are over 150 feet tall. Bold herbaceous plantings run along the burn. Range of trails and walks. Fabulous autumn colours.
National Plant Collection: *Larix* spp. and *Tsuga* spp.
Champion Trees: Numerous.

Open: Sunday 8 October, 10am - 5pm, admission details can be found on the garden's website.

Directions: Eight miles south-west of Peebles on the B712.

Opening for: Donation to SGS

---

 5 **GARVALD WEST LINTON GARDENS**
West Linton EH46 7HJ
Gardeners of Garvald
T: 01968 682211 E: info@garvaldwestlinton.org.uk
W: www.garvaldwestlinton.org.uk

Two contrasting organic gardens – a therapeutic flower and herb garden and a production-based Walled Garden. Our therapeutic garden in an enclosed woodland setting known as the Paradise Garden workshop – one of our five workshops providing day services for our residents and day service users. The Walled Garden, originally built as part of a large Victorian estate, is used for seasonal fruit and vegetable production. Through the garden door there is a stunning view over to Black Mount and White Hill.

Open: by arrangement 1 March - 30 September (Wednesday only). Snowdrops and Winter Walks in early March. Also open Sunday 3 September, 2pm - 5pm. Admission £5.00, children free.

Directions: About 17 miles south-west of Edinburgh off the A702. Take the right turn just before Dolphinton, signposted to *Garvald*. Bus 101 or 102. It is approximately a two-mile walk from the bus stop.

Opening for: Garvald West Linton Ltd

---

 6 **GATTONSIDE VILLAGE GARDENS**
Gattonside TD6 9NP
The Gardeners of Gattonside
T: 07500 869041 E: jenbarr@gmx.com

A group of varied village gardens situated on a south facing slope with views across the River Tweed to Melrose. Gattonside is known for its roses and early summer colours. Some new gardens and some old will be open this year.

Open: Sunday 25 June, 2pm - 5pm, admission £6.00, children free. Plant sale and teas available at the Village Hall.

Directions: Short walk from Melrose over the chain bridge. Twenty minute walk along the River Tweed from Tweedbank Railway station. By car access off A68, signposted *Gattonside*. Parking within the village.

Opening for: Tweed Valley Mountain Rescue

Peeblesshire & Tweeddale

7 **GLEN HOUSE**
Glen Estate, Innerleithen EH44 6PX
The Tennant family
T: 01896 830210 E: info@glenhouse.com
W: www.glenhouse.com

Surrounding the outstanding Scots Baronial mansion designed by David Bryce in the mid-19th century, Glen House gardens are laid out on shallow terraces overhanging the glen itself. It offers one of the loveliest designed landscapes in the Borders. The garden expands from the formal courtyard through a yew colonnade, and contains a fine range of trees, long herbaceous border and a pool garden with pergola, all arranged within the curve of slopes sheltering the house.

Open: Sunday 2 July, 1pm - 4pm, admission £5.00, children free.

Directions: Follow the B709 out of Innerleithen for approximately two-and-a-half miles. Right turn at signpost for *Glen Estate.*

Opening for: WFGA

8 **HAYSTOUN**
Peebles EH45 9JG
Mrs David Coltman

This seventeenth-century house (not open) has a charming walled garden with an ancient yew tree, herbaceous beds and vegetable garden. There is a wonderful burnside walk created since 1980, with azaleas and rhododendrons leading to a small ornamental loch (cleared in 1990) with stunning views up Glensax Valley.

Open: Sunday 28 May, 1:30pm - 5pm, admission £5.00, children free.

Directions: Cross the River Tweed in Peebles to the south bank and follow *Scotland's Gardens Scheme* sign for approximately one mile.

Opening for: Kingsmeadows Catering: The Peebles Food Foundation & Peebles Community Action Network

Haystoun © Kathy Henry

Peeblesshire & Tweeddale

9 KAILZIE GARDENS

Kailzie Gardens EH45 9HT
Susan and Steve Plag
T: 01721 720682
W: kailziegardens.com

Kailzie Gardens sits at the heart of the Tweed Valley just a mile east of Peebles occupying a beautiful position on the River Tweed. At its heart lies the stunning walled garden with plantings of many unusual shrubs, laburnum arches, an enchanting rose garden and spectacular herbaceous borders and one of the best examples of a Mackenzie and Moncur glasshouse still in existence, filled with fuschias, pelargoniums and exotics. The garden also features prize winning show vegetables. The surrounding woodlands have one of the best laid arboretums in Scotland, with champion trees and specimens (including the oldest Larch), providing 15 acres of captivating woodland and burnside walks and spectacular vistas. Champion Trees: Larch planted 1725.

Open: Sunday 5 March, 10am - 4pm for Snowdrops and Winter Walks. Also open Sunday 23 July, 10am - 4pm. Admission £5.00, children free (Sunday 5 March) and £6.50, children free (Sunday 23 July). See website for other opening times.

Directions: A mile east of Peebles on the B7062.

Opening for: Tweed Togs SCIO

10 KIRKTON MANOR HOUSE

Peebles EH45 9JH
Mrs Rosemary Thorburn
T: 01721 740220 E: rpthorburn@icloud.com

Kirkton Manor House has a delightful, three-acre, informal country garden set in the beautiful Manor Valley. It enjoys spectacular open views and calling curlews from its riverside position. Bluebells flank the impressive entrance leading to a new shrub border. Stone steps continue through to terraced slopes filled with bulbs, roses and hellebores providing height, interest and fragrance. Grass paths meander along the burn where blue and white camassia, meconopsis, and ligularia thrive in this sunny meadow environment. Later, in June, sisyrinchiums, irises, orchids and many flowering shrubs and roses are abundant. The natural woodland includes many interesting trees.

Open: 15 February - 12 July (Wednesdays only), 1pm - 4pm. Open on Wednesdays for Snowdrops and Winter Walks 15 February - 15 March. Also open by arrangement 15 February - 12 July. Individuals and small groups are welcome. Admission £5.00, children free.

Directions: Turn off the A72 west of Neidpath Castle, signposted to *Kirkton Manor*. After crossing the River Tweed, enter a garden gate which is a mile downhill, opposite a *Beware Horses* sign.

Opening for: SGS and Beneficiaries

Peeblesshire & Tweeddale

11 **LAIDLAWSTIEL HOUSE**
Clovenfords, Galashiels TD1 1TJ
Mr and Mrs P Litherland

Walled garden containing herbaceous border, fruit, and vegetables in raised beds. There are colourful rhododendrons and azaleas as well as splendid views down to the River Tweed.

Open: Wednesday/Thursday, 7/8 June, 2pm - 5pm, admission £5.00, children free.

Directions: On the A72 between Clovenfords and Walkerburn turn up the hill signposted for *Thornielee*. The house is on the right at the top of the hill.

Opening for: Young Lives vs Cancer

12 **LAMANCHA COMMUNITY HUB PLANT SALE**
Old Moffat Road, Lamancha EH46 7BD
Mike Madden
T: 07774 609547 E: hello@lamanchahub.org.uk

A small community garden with shrubs for year-round interest, and herbaceous and cottage garden borders. We are delighted to have the polytunnel to grow tomatoes and other produce for the cafe and the locals, plus plenty of space there to bring on plugs and seeds for our plant sales, and not least the roadside planters.

Open: Sunday 11 June, 10am - 1pm, admission by donation.

Directions: Three miles south of the Leadburn Junction on the A701.

Opening for: Lamancha Hub

13 **MACBIEHILL GARDENS**
The Walled Garden, Macbiehill EH46 7AZ
Simone Lyon
T: 07933 113067

Three very different gardens in the hamlet of Macbiehill which sits at some 1,000 feet above sea level, very exposed to the copious wind and rain.
The Walled Garden (NEW) A contemporary walled garden paved with multi-hued sandstone enlivened by plants in raised beds and containers, plus a variety of ceramic and large one-off sculptures.
Alderbank (NEW) Alderbank is a large garden containing a mix of wild flower meadows and trees, a herbaceous border and a productive area of fruit and vegetables. It is very much a family garden used by our children to explore nature and play.
Birchbrae (NEW) The house was built on this site by the owners in 2019 and thereafter the garden was created from rough moorland ground. The enrichment of the soil and planting became a 'lockdown project' in June 2021.

Open: Sunday 20 August, 2pm - 5pm, admission £5.00, children free.

Directions: From the A701 take the turning opposite the entrance to Whitmuir Farm, signposted *Macbiehill*. After the narrow bridge go uphill and take the first entrance on the left, signposted *Macbiehill Farm*. There will be signs to the gardens and parking at the far end of the driveway.

Opening for: Macmillan Cancer Support

Peeblesshire & Tweeddale

14 **PORTMORE**
Eddleston EH45 8QU
Mr and Mrs David Reid
T: 07825 294388
W: www.portmoregardens.co.uk

Lovingly created by the current owners over the past 30 years; the gardens surrounding the David Bryce-designed mansion house contain mature trees and offer fine views of the surrounding countryside. Large walled garden with box-edged herbaceous borders is planted in stunning colour harmonies, potager, rose garden, pleached lime walk and ornamental fruit cages. The Victorian glasshouses contain fruit trees, roses, geraniums, pelargoniums and a wide variety of tender plants. There is also an Italianate grotto and water garden with shrubs and *Meconopsis*. The woodland walks are lined with rhododendrons, azaleas and shrub roses. Starred in *Good Gardens Guide* and featured in Kenneth Cox's book *Scotland for Gardeners* and on *The Beechgrove Garden*.

Open: 5 July - 30 August (Wednesday only), 1pm - 5pm. Also open by arrangement 1 June - 31 August. Admission £6.00, children free. Self-service refreshments for Wednesday openings. Homemade cream teas for groups over 15 people by prior arrangement. Please consult the garden's website.

Directions: Off the A703 one mile north of Eddleston. Bus 62.

Opening for: Bauer Radio's Cash for Kids Charities (Scotland)

Portmore © Kathy Henry

Peeblesshire & Tweeddale

15   QUERCUS GARDEN PLANTS
Whitmuir Farm, West Linton EH46 7BB
Rona Dodds
T: 01968 660708 E: quercusgardenplants@gmail.com
W: www.quercusgardenplants.co.uk

We are a small, independent nursery growing and selling a wide range of happy, healthy plants propagated from our nursery gardens. At just under two acres, these gardens were started in 2015 to show visitors and customers what can be grown in our conditions here on a north-west-facing hill at 850 feet above sea level. Explore our herb garden, scented garden, wildlife garden, prairie-style garden, winter garden and all the other inspirational smaller borders. Our new woodland garden will be opening in Spring 2023. Many of the plants seen in the gardens are available to buy in the nursery.

Open: Sunday 28 May, 10am - 5pm and Sunday 20 August, 10am - 5pm. Admission by donation. A percentage of plant sales on these dates will be donated to Scotland's Garden Scheme and Breast Cancer Now. The 16mm narrow gauge garden railway will be running from 2pm. Garden books and succulents will be available for a donation.

Directions: On the A701, four miles south of the Leadburn junction or two miles north of West Linton.

Opening for: Breast Cancer Now

16   STOBO JAPANESE WATER GARDEN
Stobo Farm, Stobo EH45 8NX
E: enquiries@stobofarmestate.com

This is a mature, secluded woodland garden created in the early 1900s. Its most prominent feature is the constant presence of water that adds to the tranquility of the garden, beginning with the drama of a waterfall at its head through a cascade of ponds, punctuated along the way by stepping stones and bridges. The garden was brought to life when Japanese style was the height of fashion – hence its cherry trees, maples, and iconic Japanese lanterns, 'tea house' and humpback bridge. The azaleas and rhododendrons provide a spectacular display in the spring. Limited disabled access due to gravel paths and steps. Visitors are advised to wear appropriate footwear.

Open: Sunday 4 June, 2pm - 5pm, admission £5.00, children free.

Directions: Off the B712. (Peebles/Broughton road) via *Stobo Castle* entrance. Bus 91.

Opening for: Stobo and Drumelzier Church of Scotland & Scotland's Charity Air Ambulance

17   THE POTTING SHED
Broughton Place, Broughton, Biggar ML12 6HJ
Jane and Graham Buchanan-Dunlop
T: 01899 830574 E: buchanandunlop@btinternet.com

A one-acre garden begun from scratch in 2008, on an exposed hillside at 900 feet. It contains herbaceous plants, climbers, shrubs and trees – all selected for wind resistance and ability to cope with the poor, stony soil. There are usually fine views to the Southern Uplands.

Open: 7 June - 5 July (Wednesdays only), 11am - 5pm. Also open by arrangement 1 May - 31 October. Admission £5.00, children free.

Peeblesshire & Tweeddale

Directions: Signposted from the main A701 Edinburgh – Moffat Road, immediately north of Broughton village.

Opening for: Macmillan Cancer Support: Borders General Hospital

18 WEST LINTON VILLAGE GARDENS

West Linton EH46 7EW
West Linton Village Gardeners
T: 01968 660669 E: j.bracken101@gmail.com

A varied and interesting selection of gardens including two new ones: Bank House is an unusual and structured garden, designed over 30 years by a non-gardener (he was however, a 'spade monitor' at primary school). Another relatively new garden is built on a steep slope and includes raised beds with vegetables. Also included are a walled manse garden in a beautiful riverside setting and two gardening enthusiasts gardens in sheltered positions near the village centre. There is a decent woodland walk which is steep in places with steps, this area is left wild for nature.

Open: Sunday 30 July, 2pm - 5pm, admission £6.00, children free. Teas, tickets and plant sale at the New Church Hall in the centre of the village, which will be signposted.

Directions: About 15 miles south-west of Edinburgh, take the A701 or A702 and follow signs. Bus 101 or 102 to Gordon Arms Hotel.

Opening for: Ben Walton Trust & Borders General Hospital, Margaret Kerr Unit

Stobo Japanese Water Garden © Kathy Henry

Perth & Kinross

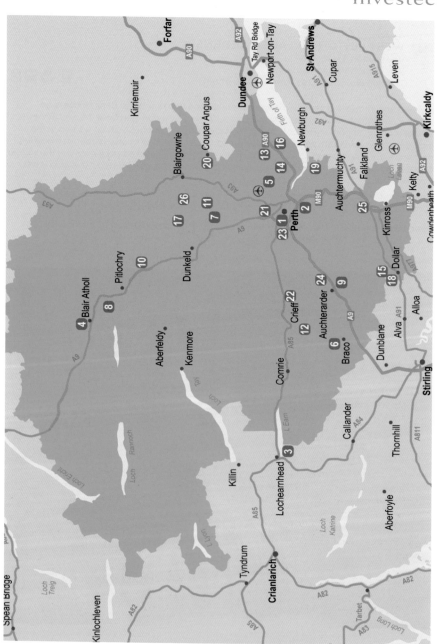

Perth & Kinross

OUR VOLUNTEER ORGANISERS

District Organiser:	Alex Lindsay	19 St Serfs Place, Auchterarder PH3 1QS E: info@scotlandsgardens.org
Area Organisers:	Gill Boardman	16, Acremoar Drive, Kinross KY13 8RE
	Jane Gallier	The Old Farmhouse, Dunning Road, Auchterarder PH3 1DU
	Henrietta Harland	Easter Carmichael Cottage, Forgandenny Road, Bridge of Earn PH2 9EZ
	Judy Norwell	Dura Den, 20 Pitcullen Terrace, Perth PH2 7EQ
	Kareen Robertson	2 The Orchard, Bridge of Earn PH2 9DX
	Fiona Stewart	7 Craigend Cottages, Craigend, Perth PH2 8PX
	Mary Jane Thompson	Mosspark House, Rumbling Bridge KY13 0QE
	Heather Wood	Mill of Forneth, Forneth, Blairgowrie PH10 6SP
District Photographers:	Carolyn Bell	carolynmbell@gmail.com
	Mike Bell	docmike@hotmail.co.uk
Treasurer:	Michael Tinson	Parkhead House, Parkhead Gardens, Burghmuir Road, Perth PH1 1JF

GARDENS OPEN ON A SPECIFIC DATE

Princeland House, Blairgowrie Road, Coupar Angus, Blairgowrie	Saturday/Sunday, 18/19 February
Cloan, by Auchterarder	Sunday, 19 February
Princeland House, Blairgowrie Road, Coupar Angus, Blairgowrie	Saturday/Sunday, 25/26 February
Scone Palace Garden, Perth	Sunday, 26 February
Princeland House, Blairgowrie Road, Coupar Angus, Blairgowrie	Saturday/Sunday, 4/5 & 11/12 March
Megginch Castle, Errol	Sunday, 16 April
Fingask Castle, Rait	Sunday, 23 April
Glendoick, Glencarse, Perthshire	Sunday, 7 May
The Steading at Clunie, The Steading	Sunday, 7 May
Cloan, by Auchterarder	Sunday, 14 May
Glendoick, Glencarse, Perthshire	Sunday, 14 May
The Abercairny Garden, Abercairny House, Crieff	Saturday/Sunday, 20/21 May
Glendoick, Glencarse, Perthshire	Sunday, 21 May
Cloan, by Auchterarder	Saturday/Sunday, 3/4 June
The Bield at Blackruthven, Blackruthven House, Tibbermore	Saturday, 3 June
Mill of Forneth, Forneth, Blairgowrie	Sunday, 4 June
36 Muirfield, Perth	Sunday, 11 June
Delvine, Murthly	Friday, 16 June
Muckhart Open Gardens, Coronation Hall, Pool of Muckhart, Dollar	Saturday/Sunday, 24/25 June
Blair Castle Gardens, Blair Atholl	Saturday, 1 July
Drummond Castle Gardens, Muthill, Crieff	Sunday, 6 August
Cloan, by Auchterarder	Sunday, 13 August

Perth & Kinross

GARDENS OPEN REGULARLY

Fingask Castle, Rait	23 January - 2 March (not Fridays, Saturdays & Sundays)
Braco Castle, Braco	1 February - 31 October
Blair Castle Gardens, Blair Atholl	1 April - 31 October
Glendoick, Glencarse, Perthshire	1 April - 31 May
Ardvorlich, Lochearnhead	29 April - 4 June
Bradystone House, Murthly	1 June - 10 August (Thursdays only)
The Abercairny Garden, Abercairny House, Crieff	1 June - 30 June

GARDENS OPEN BY ARRANGEMENT – BOOK A VISIT WITH THE GARDEN OWNER

Delvine, Murthly	3 January - 30 December
The Pond Garden, The Pond, Milnathort	1 February - 30 June
Bonhard House, Perth	1 April - 31 October
Hollytree Lodge, Muckhart, Dollar	1 April - 31 October
Craigowan, Ballinluig	9 April - 31 July
Mill of Forneth, Forneth, Blairgowrie	14 April - 21 April
Pitcurran House, Abernethy	1 May - 1 September
Carig Dhubh, Bonskeid, Pitlochry	1 May - 30 September
The Old Farmhouse, Dunning Road, Auchterarder	1 May - 30 June
7 Craigend Cottages, Craigend, Perth	15 May - 31 August
The Pond Garden, The Pond, Milnathort	1 August - 31 October

The Abercairny Garden © Richard Greenly Photography

Perth & Kinross

1

36 MUIRFIELD
Perth PH1 1JJ
Rob Mackay and Amanda Brown
T: 01738 636527 E: mackaybrownjoint@gmail.com

A small suburban garden with a Japanese theme. The garden was designed and planted in 2019 with the aim of being low maintenance and offering a fun and safe environment for children. The Japanese features include a stone lantern, a water bowl, the placing of rocks, raked gravel and a timber building. The planting includes prunus, acer, bamboo, hostas, ferns and flowering plants. Foliage and texture are important elements. Views of the distant hills are seen as an extension of the garden in the Japanese tradition.

Open: Sunday 11 June, 2pm - 5pm, admission £5.00, children free. Entrance includes tea/coffee.

Directions: Muirfield connects Muirend Road with Burghmuir Road. 36 Muirfield is the white bungalow near the junction with Muirend Road on the left-hand side as you travel up the hill. The 7b bus from Mill Street in the centre runs every 30 minutes, alight at Fairies Road just before the junction with Viewlands Road West. Go straight over the mini roundabout continuing along Fairies Road. At the next mini roundabout turn left into Muirend Road. Muirfield is the first turning on the right with number 36 the second house on the right. If coming by car please park on Muirend Road to avoid blocking neighbours' access.

Opening for: The Aiteal Trust

2

7 CRAIGEND COTTAGES
Craigend, Perth PH2 8PX
Fiona Stewart
T: 07468 303506 E: munro283@btinternet.com

This south-west facing garden has a sunny, open aspect with an extended landscape to the front and back. It is an informal cottage garden with a dedicated productive vegetable growing area including fruit bushes, dahlias and the lovely scent of sweet peas growing alongside. There are herbaceous borders with a colourful mix of flowers and shrubs many of which attract bees and butterflies. The soil is acid and so rhododendrons and pieris grow well. Also included are climbers such as clematis and honeysuckle, mixed hedges and a rose bed along with lawns, a productive greenhouse and a wildlife-attracting pond with beautiful water lilies.

Open: by arrangement 15 May - 31 August, admission £5.00, children free.

Directions: From Bridge of Earn follow the main street and drive north on the A912 for about one-and-a-half miles passing the Earn Cafe on your left. Craigend Cottages are on the main road on the left-hand side with number 7 at the Perth end of the row. From Tay Street in Perth follow the road to a mini-roundabout and go straight onto Shore Road which leads into Friarton Road. Turn left onto Edinburgh Road (A912) and continue with Craigclowan School on your right. Pass under two flyovers and Craigend cottages are immediately on your right.

Opening for: Alzheimer Scotland

Perth & Kinross

3 **ARDVORLICH**
Lochearnhead FK19 8QE
Mr and Mrs Sandy Stewart
T: 01567 830335

Beautiful hill garden featuring over 170 different species of rhododendrons and many hybrids, grown in a glorious setting of oaks and birches on either side of the Ardvorlich Burn. The paths are quite steep and rough in places and boots are advisable, especially when wet.

Open: 29 April - 4 June, 9am - dusk, admission £5.00, children free.

Directions: On South Loch Earn Road three miles from Lochearnhead, five miles from St Fillans.

Opening for: The Ghurka Welfare Trust

Ardvorlich

4 **BLAIR CASTLE GARDENS**
Blair Atholl PH18 5TL
Blair Charitable Trust
T: 01796 481207 E: office@blair-castle.co.uk
W: www.blair-castle.co.uk

Blair Castle stands as the focal point in a designed landscape of some 2,500 acres within a Highland estate. Hercules Garden is a walled enclosure of about nine acres recently restored to its original 18th-century design with landscaped ponds, a Chinese bridge, contemporary plantings, and an orchard of more than 100 fruit trees. The glory of this garden in summer is the herbaceous border, which runs along the 275 yard south-facing wall. A delightful sculpture trail incorporates contemporary and 18th-century sculpture as well as eight new works, letter-carving on stone from the *Memorial and Commemorative Arts* charity's 'Art and Memory Collection'. Diana's Grove is a magnificent stand of tall trees including grand fir, Douglas fir, larch and wellingtonia running along the Banvie Burn, with the 12th-century ruins of St Bride's Church on the far bank.

Open: Saturday 1 July, 9:30am - 4:30pm. Also open 1 April - 31 October, 9:30am - 4:30pm.

Perth & Kinross

Admission details can be found on the garden's website.

Directions: Off A9, follow signs to *Blair Castle, Blair Atholl.*

Opening for: Donation to SGS

5 BONHARD HOUSE
Perth PH2 7PQ
Stephen and Charlotte Hay
T: 07990 574570 E: stephenjohnhay@me.com

Traditional 19th-century garden of five acres approached through an avenue of magnificent oaks. Mature trees, six classified by the National Tree Register as 'remarkable', including a monkey puzzle, sequoias, Douglas fir and a variety of hollies. Reinstated and new herbaceous borders. Rhododendron and azalea beds. Recently planted spring and summer flowering meadow areas with a variety of fruit and nut trees. Beehive and a productive vegetable garden. A new larch arbour with climbing roses and clematis. Grass paths meander through a pond area with shrubs and mature trees. A pinetum with 25 different varieties. Garden emphasis on wildlife habitat as well as aesthetics. Resident red squirrels. Plentiful and varied birdlife.

Open: by arrangement 1 April - 31 October, admission £5.00, children free. Groups welcome to enquire.

Directions: On the A94 just under a mile north of Perth take the right turn, signed *Murrayshall Hotel.* After approximately one mile take the entrance right marked *Bonhard House,* at a sharp left turn. From Balbeggie turn left, signposted for *Bonhard,* one mile north of Scone. Turn right in a half-a-mile, pass any sign for *Bonhard Nursery,* and enter the drive at sharp right turn.

Opening for: Freedom from Fistula Foundation

6 BRACO CASTLE
Braco FK15 9LA
Mr and Mrs M van Ballegooijen
T: 01786 880437

A 19th-century landscaped garden with a plethora of wonderful and interesting trees, shrubs, bulbs and plants. An old garden for all seasons that has been extensively expanded over the last 33 years. The partly walled garden is approached on a rhododendron and tree-lined path featuring an ornamental pond. Spectacular spring bulbs, exuberant shrub and herbaceous borders and many ornamental trees are all enhanced by the spectacular views across the park to the Ochils. From snowdrops through to vibrant autumn colour, this garden is a gem. Look out for the embothrium in June, hoheria in August, eucryphia in September and an interesting collection of rhododendrons and azaleas with long flowering season.

Open: 1 February - 31 October, 10am - 5pm. February to early March for Snowdrops and Winter Walks. Admission £5.00, children free. No dogs please.

Directions: Drive for one-and-a-half miles from the gates at the north end of Braco Village, just west of the bridge on the A822. Parking at the castle is welcome.

Opening for: The Woodland Trust Scotland

Perth & Kinross

7 | BRADYSTONE HOUSE
Murthly PH1 4EW
Mrs James Lumsden
T: 01738 710308 E: pclumsden@me.com

A unique cottage garden converted from a derelict farm steading. Imaginative and abundant planting with interesting and unusual perennials, clematis, roses and shrubs. Small vegetable garden and orchard, meandering woodland walks and a duck pond. A garden oasis in which to sit and dream.

Open: 1 June - 10 August (Thursday only), 11am - 4pm, admission £5.00, children free. A good selection of interesting and unusual plants are available on a bountiful plant stall. Dogs on leads please.

Directions: From south/north follow the A9 to Bankfoot, then signs to *Murthly*. At the crossroads in Murthly take the private road to Bradystone.

Opening for: Scotland's Charity Air Ambulance

8 | CARIG DHUBH
Bonskeid, Pitlochry PH16 5NP
Jane and Niall Graham-Campbell
T: 01796 473469 E: niallgc@btinternet.com

'I don't know how Niall and Jane manage to grow their splendid meconopsis on the sand and rock of their garden but they do, most successfully.' In this stunning situation, when not admiring the views, you will find wonderful primulas, cardiocrinum and meconopsis, all interspersed between beautiful shrubs and other herbaceous plants. Look up and in July you will see roses flowering 40 feet up in the tree. This is a gem of a garden and you will be welcomed by Niall and Jane Graham-Campbell with all their expert knowledge.

Open: by arrangement 1 May - 30 September, admission £5.00, children free.

Directions: Take the old A9 between Pitlochry and Killiecrankie, turn west on the Tummel Bridge Road B8019, Carig Dhubh is three-quarters of a mile on the north side of the road.

Opening for: Earl Haig Fund Poppy Scotland

9 | CLOAN
by Auchterarder PH3 1PP
Neil Mitchison
T: 07958 155831 E: niall@fastmail.co.uk

Two acres of wild garden, with a wide variety of rhododendrons and azaleas, and an impressive collection of trees, including metasequoia, cryptomeria, *Acer cappadocicum*, *Sequoia sempervirens*, *Quercus robur* 'Filicifolia', liriodendron, several Japanese maples, magnificent beech and Scots pine trees, and extensive yew topiary; also an acre of walled garden with embothriums, *Acer griseum*, liquidambar, several sorbus varieties, parrotia and a large herbaceous border. Fine views of Strathearn from the front of the house.

Open: Sunday 19 February, 11am - 3pm for Snowdrops and Winter Walks. Also open Sunday 14 May, Saturday/Sunday, 3/4 June and Sunday 13 August, 10am - 5pm. Admission £4.00, children free.

Perth & Kinross

Directions: From the A823, just south of the A9, follow the small road heading north-east, signposted *Duchally*. Continue for approximately two-and-a-half miles, turn right at the sign *Coulshill*. Continue for just under half-a-mile. Follow the signs for *car parking*.

Opening for: Tiphereth Limited: Camphill Scotland

Cloan

Perth & Kinross

10 CRAIGOWAN
Ballinluig PH9 0NE
Ian and Christine Jones
T: 01796 482244 E: i.q.jones@btinternet.com

This is a specialist garden with a major collection of rhododendrons put together over the last 40 years; initially, mainly species from Glendoick following the plant hunting and discoveries of Peter Cox and the late Sir Peter Hutchison and others. In the last 20 years there have been added noteworthy hybrids sourced from Glendoick and the major English nurseries. Each year further additions are made and earlier introductions which have outgrown their original or secondary planting spot are moved to new locations. With growth rates tending to increase, this is a major exercise but the result is a constantly changing garden and more plants are developing into a spectacular presentation. Other plant types include magnolias, ornamental acers and a collection of unusual trees. There are areas of more formal beds where there is a large collection of meconopsis, lilies including cardiocrinum with roughly a hundred flowering each year. The rhododendron flowering period lasts from January to August but the best months are April, May and June. There is adjoining woodland which is being replanted with trees free of disease risk and with the larger rhododendrons which have outgrown the more formal areas. In June and July two large herbaceous borders give summer colour and interest.

Open: by arrangement 9 April - 31 July, admission £5.00, children free.

Directions: From the north or south of the A9 to Ballinluig junction. Follow sign for *Tulliemet* and *Dalcapon*. Pass the filling station and Ballinluig Hotel. Turn right following the *Tulliemet/ Dalcapon* sign; this is a steep narrow road so take care. About half-a-mile up the road take a left turning with fields on either side and Craigowan is the first house on the left about half-a-mile along. Park on paviours adjoining the house.

Opening for: LUPUS UK

11 DELVINE
Murthly PH1 4LD
Mr and Mrs David Gemmell
T: 07748 207647 E: gemmell.david@googlemail.com

The gardens and arboretum at Delvine cover about 20 acres. The old gardens are on the Inchtuthil plateau, leading down to the more recent garden and arboretum which is situated on a flood plain, flanked by oxbow lakes on each side. This is the place to visit for those who seek a remote and peaceful setting. As one proceeds in a westerly direction, one departs from the traditional and enters an area of great drifts of chimonobambusa and miscanthus grasses with water and wildlife in abundance. The walking is easy. This garden will appeal to those seeking the unusual and also for those with an adventurous spirit.

Open: Friday 16 June, 1pm - dusk. Also open by arrangement 3 January - 30 December. Admission £5.00, children free. Surfaces are level grass. Dogs on leads, please.

Directions: On the A984, seven miles east of Dunkeld, four miles south-west of Blairgowrie.

Opening for: ABF The Soldiers' Charity

Perth & Kinross

12 DRUMMOND CASTLE GARDENS

Muthill, Crieff PH7 4HN
Grimsthorpe & Drummond Castle Trust Ltd
T: 01764 681433
W: www.drummondcastlegardens.co.uk

Activities and events for a great family day out. The gardens of Drummond Castle were originally laid out in 1630 by John Drummond, second Earl of Perth. In 1830 the parterre was changed to an Italian style. One of the most interesting features is the multi-faceted sundial designed by John Mylne, Master Mason to Charles I. The formal garden is said to be one of the finest in Europe and is the largest of its type in Scotland.

Open: Sunday 6 August, 1pm - 5pm, admission details can be found on the garden's website.

Directions: Entrance two miles south of Crieff on Muthill road (A822).

Opening for: BLESMA

13 FINGASK CASTLE

Rait PH2 7SA
Mr and Mrs Andrew Murray Threipland
T: 01821 670777 ext 4 & 6 E: andrew@fingaskcastle.com
W: www.fingaskcastle.co.uk

Scotland's surrealist garden: spectacular topiary staggers across the garden bumping into stone globes, marble balls, statues and a figure of Alice (in Wonderland). Other literary and historical characters are scattered among the 17th-century pleasure gardens. Bonnie Prince Charlie and his father are said to have approached the castle up the long yew avenue known as 'The King's Walk'. A 15-minute walk takes you down to the dell beneath the castle and St Peter's Well – a stopping place for medieval pilgrims on their way to the bones of the saintly Queen Margaret at Dunkeld Cathedral. Return via a Chinese bridge, Gabriel's bridge, an iron age fort, along a stream, past Sir Stuart's House and back to the castle via the Old Orchard. There are large drifts of snowdrops, daffodils and flowering shrubs in season. A wollemi pine has recently been planted.
Champion Trees: *Pinus wallichiana* (Bhutan Pine) and the handsome remnants of what was the largest walnut in Scotland.

Open: 23 January - 2 March (not Friday, Saturday & Sunday), 10am - 4pm for Snowdrops and Winter Walks. Also open Sunday 23 April, 1pm - 4pm. Admission £5.00, children free. (Admission cost for all dates). Homemade teas on 23 April only.

Directions: Half-way between Perth and Dundee. From the A90 follow signs to *Rait* until small crossroad, turn right and follow signs to *Fingask.*

Opening for: All Saints Episcopal Church & Fingask Follies

Perth & Kinross

14 **GLENDOICK**
Glencarse, Perthshire PH2 7NS
Cox Family
T: 01738 860260 E: manager@glendoick.com
W: www.glendoick.com

Glendoick's gardens and garden centre with its award-winning café is the ideal spring day out in April and May. Why not visit Branklyn too, nearby in Perth. 2023 sees Glendoick Garden Centre celebrate 50 years. Glendoick boasts a unique collection of plants from three generations of Cox plant-hunting expeditions in China and the Himalaya. Enjoy one of the finest collections of rhododendrons and azaleas, magnolias and other acid-loving plants in the woodland garden and the gardens surrounding the house. Many of the rhododendron and azalea species and hybrids have been introduced from the wild or bred by the Cox family. There are fine waterfall views in the woodland gardens. The award-winning Glendoick Garden Centre has one of Scotland's best selections of plants including their world-famous rhododendrons and azaleas as well as a gift shop and café.

Open: 1 April - 31 May 10am - 4pm. Admission £5.00, children free. Also special guided talks by Ken Cox on Sundays 7/14/21 May 10am - noon. Admission £15.00 includes light refreshments, check our website for details. For garden visit group bookings contact Heather Borderie E: manager@glendoick.com. Café bookings (run separately) E: manager@garden-cafe.co.uk. Please note the woodland garden is not easily accessible to wheelchairs but some of the gardens by the house are. Toilets and refreshments are at the garden centre only. No dogs.

Directions: Follow the *brown* signs to Glendoick Garden Centre off the A90 Perth – Dundee road. The gardens are a half-mile behind the Garden Centre. After buying tickets at the Garden Centre, please drive up and park at the gardens (free parking).

Opening for: Donation to SGS

15 **HOLLYTREE LODGE**
Muckhart, Dollar FK14 7JW
Liz and Peter Wyatt
T: 07973 374687 E: elizwyatt@aol.com

A tranquil one-acre garden in the centre of the village. The garden is divided by internal hedges into different areas. Highlights include a small Japanese garden, mini orchard, naturalised spring bulbs and wildflowers, mixed herbaceous borders, rill and wildlife pond. We have an interesting collection of rhododendrons and azaleas. A variety of other unusual trees and shrubs including various acers, giving wonderful autumn colours, a handkerchief tree, Eucalyptus snow gum, *Parrotia persica*, and nothofagus, amongst others. We aim to garden organically working with nature, complementing our beekeeping interests.

Open: by arrangement 1 April - 31 October, admission £5.00, children free. Always worth a call if you are in the area outwith these dates.

Directions: Approximately 100 yards from the A91 (between Dollar and Milnathort) down the small lane directly opposite the entrance to the Inn at Muckhart.

Opening for: The Royal Air Force Benevolent Fund

Perth & Kinross

 16 MEGGINCH CASTLE
Errol PH2 7SW
Giles Herdman and Catherine Drummond-Herdman
T: 01821 642222 E: info@megginch.com
W: megginchcastle.com

After walking through the hoardes of golden daffodils, formal garden, walled garden with hens, bees and orchard with two National Collections of apples and pears, you will definitely be ready for our famous Megginch homemade teas and a piece of cake served inside this year for the first time – which in Scotland in April is a good idea!
National Plant Collection: Scottish cider apples, Scottish Heritage apples and pears.
Champion Trees: *Acer palmatum.*

Open: Sunday 16 April, noon - 4pm, admission £5.00, children free.

Directions: Ten miles from Perth and Dundee directly off the A90, Perth-bound carriageway, 600 yards after the Errol/Rait flyover, on the left hand side, 300 yards after *Beware Pedestrians Crossing* sign, or signed entrance just before the level crossing in Errol Station.

Opening for: SGS and Beneficiaries

 17 MILL OF FORNETH
Forneth, Blairgowrie PH10 6SP
Mr and Mrs Graham Wood
E: gaw@forneth-mill.co.uk

Built on the site of a former watermill on the Lunan Burn, originally laid out in the 1970s by James Aitken, the Scottish landscape designer and naturalist. The sheltered four-acre garden has a range of mature trees, including a Himalayan blue cedar, large rhododendrons, azaleas and a wide range of shrubs. The former mill lade feeds rocky waterfalls and a lily pond. Planting includes established perennials with seasonal colours, many bulbs, primulas and heathers, plus a vegetable garden on the site of an old tennis court and a new wildflower meadow.

Open: Sunday 4 June, 2pm - 5pm. Also open by arrangement 14 April - 21 April. Admission £5.00, children free.

Directions: Take the A923 Dunkeld to Blairgowrie road. Six miles east of Dunkeld turn south onto a minor road signposted *Snaigow and Clunie*. Mill of Forneth is the first gate on the left-hand side. PLEASE NOTE due to wet weather conditions there may be limited safe meadow parking on site (exceptions will be made for people with mobility problems).

Opening for: Tayside Health Fund: Haematology and Oncology Unit, Perth Royal Infirmary

Perth & Kinross

18 MUCKHART OPEN GARDENS
Coronation Hall, Pool of Muckhart, Dollar FK14 7JF
The Gardeners of Muckhart Village

A collection of gardens in and around the Pool o'Muckhart and Yetts o'Muckhart, some of which have not opened previously. For a small village Muckhart boasts an enchanting variety of large and small, formal and informal gardens displaying some of the best and most thoughtfully considered aspects of amateur gardening in this part of Scotland. From wildlife friendly gardens, magnificent trees and statues, to beautiful and constantly evolving gardens where paths meander through terraced beds and ponds, and pocket-sized cottage gardens where lettuces jostle for position amongst the bluebells. Visitors cannot fail to be inspired by the variety of gardens, and the commitment of our gardeners.

Open: Saturday/Sunday, 24/25 June, 11am - 5pm, admission £6.00, children free. (£8.00 for both days). Tickets, garden details and map are available at Muckhart Coronation Hall. Teas available from Coronation Hall between 2pm - 5pm for a small donation.

Directions: On the A91, four miles east of Dollar. Parking at Muckhart Coronation Hall, Pool of Muckhart FK14 7JF.

Opening for: Coronation Hall, Muckhart & Muckhart Primary School

19 PITCURRAN HOUSE
Abernethy PH2 9LH
The Hon Ranald and Mrs Noel-Paton
T: 01738 850933 E: patricianp@pitcurran.com

This end-of-village garden was created 18 years ago. It includes an interesting combination of trees, rare shrubs and herbaceous plants including azaleas, rhododendrons, tree peonies, trilliums and veratrum. Also a rose pergola, eucryphias and a large west-facing hydrangea border for the later summer. Above the pond there is a good collection of pink-and-white-barked birches and an embryonic arboretum.

Open: by arrangement 1 May - 1 September, admission £5.00, children free.

Directions: South-east of Perth. From the M90 (exit nine) take the A912 towards Glenfarg, go left at the roundabout onto the A913 to Abernethy. Pitcurran House is at the far eastern end of the village. Buses run through Abernethy from Perth and the surrounding districts.

Opening for: Juvenile Diabetes Research Foundation Limited

20 PRINCELAND HOUSE
Blairgowrie Road, Coupar Angus, Blairgowrie PH13 9AU
Helen and Alastair Carmichael
T: 07864 778170 E: carmichaelhf@hotmail.com

Sited on the edge of Coupar Angus, the wider grounds of Princeland House garden are currently under active renovation and replanting by Mrs Carmichael. There is a wooded area around the drive and entrance with an extended area of beautiful and different snowdrops planted in drifts among mature trees.

Open: Saturday/Sunday, 18/19 February, Saturday/Sunday, 25/26 February, Saturday/Sunday, 4/5 March and Saturday/Sunday 11/12 March, 10am - 2pm for Snowdrops and Winter Walks. Admission £5.00, children free. There will be no refreshments. Dogs on a lead only. Please call or email to book a time slot.

Perth & Kinross

Directions: From the outskirts of Coupar Angus, take the A94 Blairgowrie Road from the mini-roundabout junction with the A923, to the junction with School Road. Parking on the street is available for visitors, those with disabilities and mobility difficulties can park by the house. Entry to Princeland House is on the corner of School Road, past a lodge cottage on the left of the entrance.

Opening for: My Name'5 Doddie Foundation

 ### 21 SCONE PALACE GARDEN
Perth   PH2 6BD
The Earl & Countess of Mansfield
W: www.scone-palace.co.uk

Scone Palace will be hosting a day to celebrate the snowdrop display that grows in the gardens and grounds of this historic site. A waymarked 'Snowdrop walk' that will guide you through the Friars Den, Victorian Pinetum and down the old drive lined with an avenue of lime trees. Join the Palace gardens team as they plant up a wooded area of the grounds for a new snowdrop display led by our Head Gardener and Scotland's Garden Scheme Ambassador Brian Cunningham. Here you will learn to increase your own snowdrop display at home where lifting, splitting and transplanting will be demonstrated. As a thank you, a gift of a few snowdrops will be given to improve or start your own collection.

Open: Sunday 26 February, 10am - 3pm for Snowdrops and Winter Walks, free access but an entry donation of £5.00 is requested. A small selection of specialist snowdrops will be for sale from our gift shop with our coffee shop open for a selection of warm refreshments.

Directions: Two miles from Perth on the A93 Perth/Braemar road. Well signposted.

Opening for: SGS and Beneficiaries

 ### 22 THE ABERCAIRNY GARDEN
Abercairny House, Crieff   PH7 3NQ
T: 07483 123892 E: may.michael@abercairny.com

The Abercairny garden which was originally designed by Lewis Kennedy is in the shape of a horseshoe and set within a wall. It is edged by huge trees that include Douglas firs and *Sequoia sempervirens* and it is laid out on three terraces. The top terrace is mostly formal, with mature informal beds on either side; these beds contain roses, rhododendrons, and azaleas. The second (originally called the Bowling Green) includes rhododendrons and fruit trees. The third is made up of gardens that have been created in the last sixteen years. Here you will see, amongst many new plants, a paulownia tree, different kinds of cornus and eight magnolias. There are lots of different varieties of candelabra primulas in the primula garden. At the bottom of this garden there is a stream and Kennedy's two Swiss bridges. Look out for red squirrels.

Open: Saturday/Sunday, 20/21 May, 2pm - 5pm. Also open 1 June - 30 June, 2pm - 5pm. Admission £5.00, children free. There are no teas in June. Paths can be rough underfoot. Sensible footwear advised.

Directions: Turn south off the A85 at the New Fowlis crossroads, following signs. Turn right into the estate grounds after 1.2 miles (opposite Kintocher Farm on the left) and follow the drive for one mile past Abercairny House on the left. Car parking for the gardens is in the car park opposite the castellated stables venue.

Opening for: Siobhan's Trust

Perth & Kinross

23 THE BIELD AT BLACKRUTHVEN
Blackruthven House, Tibbermore PH1 1PY
The Bield Christian Co Ltd
T: 01738 583238 E: info@bieldatblackruthven.org.uk

The Bield is set in extensive grounds with well maintained lawns, hedges, flower meadow and specimen trees. A labyrinth is cut into the grass of the old orchard and there is a wheelchair-friendly labyrinth. Traditional walled garden with colourful, richly stocked borders and lawns, plus cut-flower garden, Healing Garden, glasshouse, trained fruit trees and organic vegetable plot. Walk through extensive woodland and visit the old curling pond. Southton Smallholding is a social enterprise ten minutes walk away, featuring vegetable plots, polytunnels and a number of animals (not staffed on the day).

Open: Saturday 3 June, 2pm - 5pm, admission £5.00, children free.

Directions: From Dundee or Edinburgh, follow signs for *Glasgow, Stirling* and *Crianlarich* which lead onto the Perth bypass. Head west on the A85 signed to *Crieff/Crianlarich* to West Huntingtower. Turn left at the crossroads to *Madderty/Tibbermore*. The entrance is left after a half-mile passing the gate lodge on your right. Parking signed to right at the steading.

Opening for: Southton Smallholding

24 THE OLD FARMHOUSE
Dunning Road, Auchterarder PH3 1DU
Jane and Nigel Gallier
T: 01764 662471 E: thegalliers@msn.com

A garden of approximately one acre with herbaceous borders, a gravel garden, vegetable garden, trained fruit trees in half-wine barrels, wild areas under-planted with bulbs, and woodland areas, with other areas still being developed. As you approach the house, look out for our kamikaze hens. The garden is not always immaculate; a well-ordered winter garden and a floriferous summer garden.

Open: by arrangement 1 May - 30 June, admission £5.00, children free.

Directions: From the A9 take the A824 and halfway between Auchterarder and Aberuthven take the B8062 at Grand Eagles and head towards Dunning. We are on the left just before the A9 bridge.

Opening for: ABF The Soldiers' Charity

25 THE POND GARDEN
The Pond, Milnathort KY13 0SD
Fay Young & Ray Perman
T: 07767 407396 E: fay@fayyoung.org
W: fayyoung.org/category/pond-cottage/

A wild woodland and wetland garden supporting birds, bees, butterflies, red squirrels, swans and other less visible wildlife. Enticing paths lead through seasonal highlights: snowdrops, daffodils, bluebells, foxgloves and ferns. Fine old beeches and oaks mark the boundary of the former Victorian estate. Since mid 1990s we have rebuilt the derelict cottage and planted a mixed species hedgerow and native trees, adding spring and autumn colour. Now exploring creative potential of 'dead hedging'. Sandstone features gather moss, and waterside benches welcome you to rest by the pond.

Perth & Kinross

Open: by arrangement 1 February - 30 June and 1 August - 31 October. Admission £5.00, children free. Open for seasonal highlights.

Directions: From Milnathort village. At the mini roundabout in the centre of the village take the north exit signed for *Path of Condie* up Wester Loan, then North Street. At the top of the hill, past the church on your left, you will cross the motorway again. Carry straight on for half-a-mile, the gate to Pond Cottage is on the right after a field opening.

Opening for: CHAS: *Children's Hospices Across Scotland*

 26 **THE STEADING AT CLUNIE**
The Steading PH10 6SG
Jean and Dave Trudgill
T: 01250 884263 E: davetrudgill@googlemail.com

The Steading is situated on the Lunan Burn midway between Lochs Clunie and Marlee. The policies include paths that extend for 800 metres along the Lunan, a small, colourful cottage garden and six acres of woodland, ponds and a wildflower meadow. The policies are open to visit in the spring when there is a profusion of primroses, wood anemones and then bluebells in the wooded areas. In the meadow, snake's head fritillary flowers first, followed by a carpet of cowslips and cuckoo flowers.

Open: Sunday 7 May, 2pm - 4pm, admission £5.00, children free. There are narrow paths, bridges and flowing water in the garden. We have friendly hens, hence no dogs.

Directions: Three miles west of Blairgowrie on the A923. About 600 metres west of the Kinloch Hotel take the track on the left, just after a mobile phone mast and a breeze-block wall.

Opening for: Save the Children UK

Braco Castle © Jodi Simpson

Renfrewshire

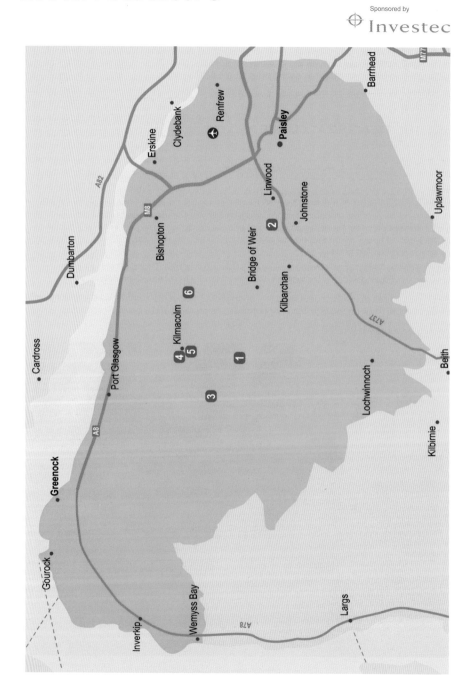

Renfrewshire

OUR VOLUNTEER ORGANISERS

District Organiser:	Alexandra MacMillan	Langside Farm, Kilmacolm, PA13 4SA E: info@scotlandsgardens.org
Area Organisers:	Helen Hunter Barbara McLean	2 Bay Street, Fairlie, North Ayrshire KA29 0AL 49 Middlepenny Road, Langbank, PA14 6XE
Treasurer:	Jean Gillan	Bogriggs Cottage, Carlung, West KA23 9PS

GARDENS OPEN ON A SPECIFIC DATE

SGS Kilmacolm Plant Sale, Outside Kilmacolm Library, Kilmacolm	Saturday, 22 April
Highwood, off Lochwinnoch Road, Kilmacolm	Sunday, 14 May
Wraes, Corseliehill Road, nr Houston	Sunday, 21 May
Carruth, Bridge of Weir	Sunday, 4 June
Craig Hepburn Memorial Garden, Stirling Drive, Linwood	Friday/Saturday 16/17 June
The Bishop's House, Kilmacolm	Sunday, 25 June

GARDENS OPEN BY ARRANGEMENT

Wraes, Corseliehill Road, nr Houston	1 May - 1 September

Wraes

Renfrewshire

1 CARRUTH
Bridge of Weir PA11 3SG
Mr and Mrs Charles Maclean

Over 20 acres of long-established rhododendrons, woodland with good bluebells, young arboretum and lawn gardens in a lovely landscaped setting. New landscaping carried out in 2020.

Open: Sunday 4 June, 2pm - 5pm, admission £5.00, children free.

Directions: Access from the B786 Kilmacolm/Lochwinnoch road. From Bridge of Weir take the Torr Road until you get to the B786. Turn right and after about 100 metres, the garden entrance is on the right. About three-and-a-half miles from Kilmacolm and five-and-a-half miles from Lochwinnoch on the B786.

Opening for: Marie Curie

2 CRAIG HEPBURN MEMORIAL GARDEN
Stirling Drive, Linwood PA3 3NB
Linwood High School
T: 01505 336146 E: gw07hindelesley@glow.sch.uk
W: facebook.com/welovegardening14/

The Craig Hepburn Memorial Garden and Outdoor Learning Centre is located in Linwood High School. Our original garden with an outdoor classroom has been expanded to include community raised beds, an orchard, greenhouse and presentation area. We work with all years in the school, reconnecting them to the natural world, whether through growing in our organic garden, encouraging biodiversity or learning about sustainability. Winners of the *Cultivation Street* competition 2020.

Open: Friday 16 June, 3:30pm - 6pm. Also open Saturday 17 June, 10am - 6pm. Admission £3.50, children free.

Directions: Exit the M8 at St James Interchange and take the A737. Take the exit for Linwood onto the A761, follow to Clippens Road and then Stirling Drive. Accessible by McGill's Buses.

Opening for: Teenage Cancer Trust

3 HIGHWOOD
off Lochwinnoch Road, Kilmacolm PA13 4TF
Dr Jill Morgan

A beautiful woodland walk around 50 acres of native bluebells, primroses and wild garlic in a delightful setting bordering the Green Water river with tumbling waterfalls. Great outdoor space for children to run and explore and splash in the burn (under supervision). A haven of tranquility only three miles from the centre of Kilmacolm. This opening is raising funds for Buildher (buildher.org) a social enterprise owned by Orkidstudio .

Open: Sunday 14 May, 2pm - 5pm, admission £5.00, children free. Stout footwear is recommended as the footpath is uneven and can be muddy in inclement weather. Dogs are welcome on a lead. Fantastic opportunity for lovers of wildflowers and photography.

Directions: Take the B786 Lochwinnoch road out of Kilmacolm and continue for approximately two miles. From Lochwinnoch take the B786 Kilmacolm road for approximately six miles. Then follow the yellow *SGS* signs.

Opening for: Orkidstudio

Renfrewshire

4 **SGS KILMACOLM PLANT SALE**
Outside Kilmacolm Library, Kilmacolm PA13 4LE
Scotland's Gardens Scheme

Spring plant sale in the middle of Kilmacolm.

Open: Saturday 22 April, 10am - noon, donations welcome.

Directions: The plant sale will be held at the Cross outside the Library and Cargill Centre in the middle of Kilmacolm. Accessible by McGill's buses.

Opening for: Pancreatic Cancer Scotland

5 **THE BISHOP'S HOUSE**
Kilmacolm PA13 4PD
Paul and Paula Yacoubian

The Bishop's House is one of six villas in Kilmacolm designed by James Salmon in 1905. It was originally named Miyanoshta but renamed when it became the official residence of the Catholic Bishops of Paisley (1948-1993). The house is now a family home and much care has been taken in preserving the house and garden, both in landscaping and planting, which remain mostly as designed by Salmon. The house sits at the top of the garden and is framed by mature beech trees. There is a burn running down the side of the property (children should be supervised).

Open: Sunday 25 June, 2pm - 5pm, admission £5.00, children free. Please note there are gravel paths.

Directions: PLEASE ACCESS THE GARDEN FROM THE GLENCAIRN ROAD ENTRANCE. Turn off the A761 in the centre of Kilmacolm onto Houston Road or Porterfield Road for access to the garden on Glencairn Road. Follow *SGS signage*. Parking on-road. McGill's buses run through Kilmacolm on the A761.

Opening for: Samaritans in Scotland

6 **WRAES**
Corseliehill Road, nr Houston PA6 7HU
Tim and Jo Mack
T: 07985 156555 E: jomack22@gmail.com

Varied seven acre rural garden with far reaching views and a variety of planting areas designed to take advantage of the natural terrain and be actively wildlife friendly. Raised formal herbaceous beds, several wildlife ponds, burnside walks, grass maze, spring garden, woodland with rhododendron collection (100 species). For those interested in growing their own food, there is a large no-dig productive area, with vegetables, fruit cage, orchard and wildflower meadow. There are lots of seating places to relax and enjoy the tranquility while the kids tackle the maze or just have a good run around! Also, delicious homemade cakes!

Open: Sunday 21 May, 2pm - 5pm. Also open by arrangement 1 May - 1 September. Admission £5.00, children free.

Directions: From Houston follow Barochan Road towards Langbank B789 for about a mile, turn left down Corseliehill Road. From Kilmacolm leave the village on Houston Road, past the golf course, turn left down Corseliehill Road for about a mile. Follow the yellow *SGS* signs.

Opening for: Breast Cancer Care

Roxburghshire

Sponsored by
⊕ Investec

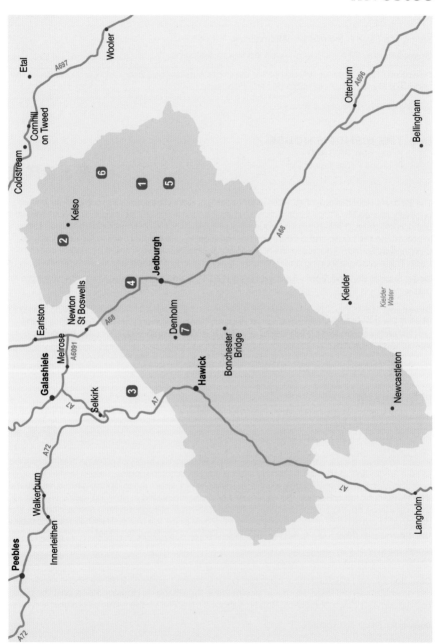

Roxburghshire

OUR VOLUNTEER ORGANISERS

District Organiser:	Penny Wright	info@scotlandsgardens.org

Area Organisers:	Christopher Bradley
	June Bradley
	Julie Golding
	Jane Robinson

District Photographer:	Malcolm Ross

Treasurer:	Vacant

GARDENS OPEN ON A SPECIFIC DATE

West Leas, Bonchester Bridge	Sunday, 4 June
Old Coach House, Hownam, Kelso	Saturday, 24 June
Old Coach House, Hownam, Kelso	Sunday, 2 July
Corbet Tower, Morebattle, near Kelso	Sunday, 2 July
West Leas, Bonchester Bridge	Sunday, 6 August

GARDENS OPEN REGULARLY

Monteviot, Jedburgh	1 April - 31 October
Floors Castle, Kelso	1 May - 30 September

GARDENS OPEN BY ARRANGEMENT – BOOK A VISIT WITH THE GARDEN OWNER

Thirlestane, Kelso	31 March - 31 October
West Leas, Bonchester Bridge	1 May - 31 October
Larch House, Clerklands, Near Lilliesleaf	1 June - 31 July

Roxburghshire

1 CORBET TOWER
Morebattle, near Kelso TD5 8AQ
Bridget Fraser

Charming Scottish Victorian garden set in parklands in the foothills of the Cheviots. The established garden includes a formal box parterre rose garden with old fashioned roses, a well-stocked, traditional walled vegetable and cutting garden, terraced lawns around the Victorian house and medieval peel tower. The gardens are approached via an attractive woodland walk with lime avenue.

Open: Sunday 2 July, 2pm - 5pm, admission £5.00, children free. Nearby Old Coach House will also be open on Sunday 2 July from 10:30am - 5pm.

Directions: From the A68 north of Jedburgh take the A698 for Kelso. At Kalemouth (Teviot Smokery) follow the B6401 to Morebattle, then the road marked Hownam to Corbet Tower.

Opening for: Cheviot Churches: Church of Scotland: Morebattle

2 FLOORS CASTLE
Kelso TD5 7SF
The Duke of Roxburghe
T: 01573 223333
W: www.floorscastle.com

The gardens are situated within the grounds of Floors Castle. Meander through to the formal Millennium Parterre and soak up the spectacular visions of colour, texture and the most delicious scents around the four herbaceous borders in one of the finest Victorian kitchen gardens in Scotland. Features include perennial gardens, fruit cage, Tapestry Garden and glasshouse access as well as the Terrace Cafe, Apple Shed Gift Shop and Deli and children's play area. Explore the grounds, which offer woodland and riverside walks from May to the end of September.

Open: 1 May - 30 September, 10am - 5pm, admission details can be found on the garden's website.

Directions: Floors Castle can be reached by following the A6089 from Edinburgh; the B6397 from Earlston; or the A698 from Coldstream. Go through Kelso, up Roxburgh Street to the Golden Gates.

Opening for: Donation to SGS

3 LARCH HOUSE
Clerklands, Near Lilliesleaf TD6 9JR
David and Julia King
T: 01835 870888 M: 07985 691775 E: nothcorner14@btinternet.com

New for 2023 the garden at Larch House is constantly evolving. Extending to over three acres and building on a layout, design and planting by the previous owners, further landscaping and renovation is ongoing. It includes a terraced area of vegetables and cut flowers edged by fruit trees, several mixed borders surrounding a lawn, a large natural wildlife pond and a newly planted bog garden. The garden leads into a mixed wood planted about six years ago where meandering paths, sometimes steep, lead to extensive views of the Cheviots. Many of the paths are gravel and may prove difficult for wheelchairs.

Open: by arrangement 1 June - 31 July, admission £5.00, children free. We welcome small groups up to approximately ten people. There may be opportunities for plant sales. Light refreshments may be available on request.

Roxburghshire

Directions: Clerklands is a small hamlet approximately two miles from Lilliesleaf. On the A7 from Selkirk, turn left and follow signs to Clerklands. After approximately three miles the house will be clearly signed. On the A7 from Hawick, turn right and follow signs to Lilliesleaf and the house will be clearly signed. Car parking is on site.

Opening for: Scotland's Gardens Scheme SCIO

4 **MONTEVIOT**
Jedburgh TD8 6UH
Marquis and Marchioness of Lothian
T: 01835 830380
W: www.monteviot.com

A series of differing gardens displaying rose and herbaceous plants surrounded by foliage plants. A water feature linked by bridges and falls passes through the Dene Garden and Water Garden. The Garden of Persistent Imagination is planted with rose and clematis beside paths which meander across a bridge and under the Moonstone Gate, past the Dali-style clock.

Open: 1 April - 31 October, noon - 5pm, admission £6.00, children free. Card payments preferred.

Directions: Turn off the A68, three miles north of Jedburgh on to the B6400. After one mile turn right.

Opening for: Donation to SGS

Monteviot

Roxburghshire

5 OLD COACH HOUSE
Hownam, Kelso TD5 8AL
Sarah and Michael Dixon
T: 01573 440277 E: sarah_hargreaves@yahoo.com

Hownam is a small hamlet under the Cheviot Hills. Opposite Old Coach House an ancient track called The Street leads over the hills into England. On a southernly facing slope, this enclosed private garden of approximately half-an-acre, is quite unusual. Stone terraces lead down to the Kale Water, accompanied by the murmuring flowing water. Steps with handrails, informal shrubs and herbaceous borders, and a wildflower meadow in various stages of development. Views across the Kale Water to rising fields and trees beyond.

Open: Saturday 24 June and Sunday 2 July, 10:30am - 5pm. Admission £5.00, children free. Homemade teas £3.00. Arts and crafts for sale. Nearby Corbet Tower will also be open on Sunday 2 July from 2 - 5pm.

Directions: Hownam is 11 miles south of Kelso and nine miles east of Jedburgh. From Morebattle (B6401) drive south for four miles to Hownam. Old Coach House is beyond the *red phone box.* There is roadside parking.

Opening for: Myeloma UK

6 THIRLESTANE
Kelso TD5 8PD
Catherine Ross and John Wylie
T: 01573 420487

Thirlestane is a large, informal garden, with some rough ground and long grass. A young, nine-acre wood has a wide mix of trees, including some specimen trees, with fine autumn colour in October. There are two ponds and a burn. An orchard has about 50 varieties of apples and other fruit trees. Beech hedges enclose prairie planting in a formal setting. There is an enclosed flower garden, raised beds for vegetables and colour-themed planting.

Open: by arrangement 31 March - 31 October, admission £5.00, children free. Please feel free to bring a picnic to enjoy in the garden. Dogs welcome.

Directions: Thirlestane is near Yetholm, not to be confused with Thirlestane, Lauder. Do not follow SatNav, it will try to take you to Lochside. From Kelso, take the B6352 towards Yetholm for about six miles. Continue past a cottage on the edge of the road. Thirlestane is next on the left, opposite the road to Lochside. From Yetholm, take the road to Kelso for about two miles. After a very sharp corner, Thirlestane is on the right.

Opening for: Alzheimer Scotland

Roxburghshire

7 WEST LEAS
Bonchester Bridge TD9 8TD
Mr and Mrs Robert Laidlaw
T: 01450 860711 E: ann@johnlaidlawandson.co.uk

The visitor to West Leas can share in an exciting and dramatic project on a grand scale, still in the making. At its core is a passion for plants, allied to a love and understanding of the land in which they are set. Collections of perennials and shrubs, many in temporary holding quarters, lighten up the landscape to magical effect. New lily pond and woodland planting added in 2019 and a new courtyard garden is under construction.

Open: Sunday 4 June, and Sunday 6 August, 2pm - 5pm. Also open by arrangement 1 May - 31 October. Admission £4.00, children free. Teas for the specific date openings will be served in Bedrule Village Hall, Bonchester Bridge, Hawick TD9 8TE.

Directions: Signposted off the Jedburgh/Bonchester Bridge Road.

Opening for: Macmillan Cancer Support: Borders Appeal

Thirlestane

Stirlingshire

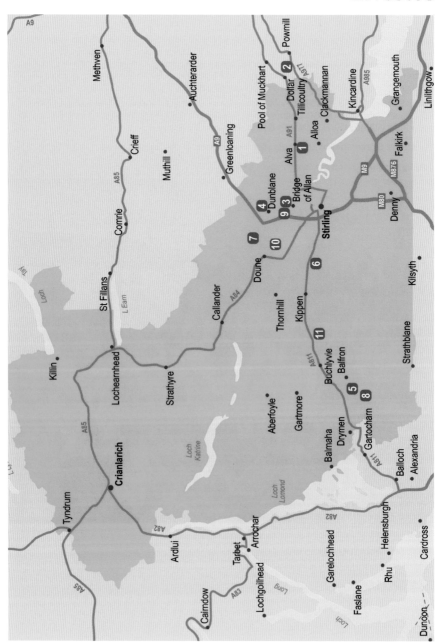

Stirlingshire

OUR VOLUNTEER ORGANISERS

District Organiser:	Willie Campbell	13 Fir Road, Doune FK16 6HU E: info@scotlandsgardens.org
District Administrator	Jo Dormer	
Area Organisers:	Sylvia Broomfield	
	Morna Knottenbelt	Gardener's Cottage Walled Garden, Ballochruin Road, Killearn G63 9QB
	Rosemary Leckie	Auchengarroch, 16 Chalton Road, Bridge of Allan, Stirling FK9 4DX
Media Officer:	Fiona Campbell	
District Photographers:	Carolyn Bell	carolynmbell@gmail.com
	Mike Bell	docmike@hotmail.co.uk
Treasurer:	Vacant	

GARDENS OPEN ON A SPECIFIC DATE

Dunblane Gardens, Dunblane	Sunday, 14 May
Bridge of Allan Gardens, Bridge of Allan	Sunday, 21 May
Shrubhill, Dunblane	Sunday, 28 May
Kilbryde Castle, Dunblane	Sunday, 4 June
Thorntree, Arnprior	Sunday, 18 June
Killearn Village Gardens, Killearn	Sunday, 30 July
60 Greenhead, Alva, Clackmannanshire	Sunday, 6 August

GARDENS OPEN REGULARLY

Gargunnock House Garden, Gargunnock	1 February - 15 March and 1 April - 30 September (Wednesdays only)

GARDENS OPEN BY ARRANGEMENT – BOOK A VISIT WITH THE GARDEN OWNER

Kilbryde Castle, Dunblane	1 February - 30 September
Thorntree, Arnprior	1 February - 31 October
Milseybank, Bridge of Allan	1 May - 31 May
Arndean, by Dollar	8 May - 4 June
Gardener's Cottage Walled Garden, Ballochruin Road, Killearn	15 June - 15 October

Stirlingshire

1 60 GREENHEAD

Alva, Clackmannanshire FK12 5HH
Lynn Cameron

A delightful hidden garden in Alva behind the primary school. Divided into 'rooms' with themes, two being Mediterranean and Oriental, there is extensive planting and clever use of pots throughout. Recycled materials are much in evidence, especially in the 'cosy' corner with a fireplace. There is a wide variety of shrubs, perennials and annuals as well as vegetables and fruit. There is a pond and a small wildlife area. There is also a 'folly' created during the lockdown of 2020. An inspiration for those trying to garden in a small space. We would ask that all children are to be accompanied.

Open: Sunday 6 August, 2pm - 5pm, admission £5.00 for adults, accompanied children free.

Directions: Signposted from the A91. Please park with consideration for other houses in the area.

Opening for: Stirling Baptist Church & CAP

2 ARNDEAN

by Dollar FK14 7NH
Johnny and Katie Stewart
T: 07940 530499 E: johnny@arndean.co.uk

Opening for more than 40 years, this is a beautiful mature garden extending to 15 acres including the woodland walk. There is a formal herbaceous part, a small vegetable garden and an orchard. In addition, there are flowering shrubs, abundant and striking rhododendrons and azaleas as well as many fine specimen trees. There is a tree house for children.

Open: by arrangement 8 May - 4 June, admission £5.00, children free.

Directions: Arndean is well signposted off the A977.

Opening for: Marie Curie

3 BRIDGE OF ALLAN GARDENS

Bridge of Allan FK9 4DX
The Gardeners of Bridge of Allan

Bridge of Allan is an attractive village north of Stirling with the River Allan flowing through it. There will be a selection of larger and smaller gardens on show, with various species of rhododendrons and azaleas, trees and shrubs, plants and flowers. Some of the gardens have water features, others have 'rooms', each with a different theme. Some gardens have a Japanese influence, others a variety of sculpture, one has quotations and poems engraved on stone, on a garden hut and bench, all with beautiful meaning. 'Second to the right and straight on till morning' – Peter Pan gives Wendy the directions to Neverland.

Open: Sunday 21 May, 1pm - 5pm, admission £6.00, children free. Tickets and maps will be available only at the Episcopal Church, Keir Street, Bridge of Allan. There will be a plant sale at the Church Garden. Teas will also be served in the Church Hall.

Directions: Gardens will be signposted from the village.

Opening for: Artlink Central Ltd & St Saviour's Episcopal Church: Bridge Of Allan

Stirlingshire

4 DUNBLANE GARDENS
Dunblane FK15 0NU
Bill Carman and Celia Aitken, Richard and Caroline Stirling-Aird,
Guy and Maud Crawford

....

Ault Wharrie Ardnablane, Dunblane FK15 0NU (Bill Carman and Celia Aitken): Ault Wharrie was formerly the Masonic Home in Dunblane. The extensive grounds have been redesigned and replanted over the last five years. These have benefitted from the shelter provided by mature trees and there are many flowering shrubs including rhododendron, camellia and magnolia. A parterre, a rockery and a large pond are all complemented by colourful herbaceous borders with a good mixture of plants including dahlias interspersed with annuals.

Kippenrait Sheriffmuir, Dunblane FK15 0LP (Richard and Caroline Stirling-Aird): Created over the last 12 years from a field, this garden has incredible views over the Carse of Stirling, east to Dumyat and the mountains in the west. It is an attractive space of two-and-a-half acres featuring spring bulbs and other spring flowering shrubs. Teas will be provided.

St Blanes House High Street, Dunblane FK15 0ER (Guy and Maud Crawford): This is a well-established, two-acre garden with a wide variety of trees, rhododendrons, azaleas and other shrubs and herbaceous perennials. There is a short walk through a wooded area. A plant sale will take place here including rhododendrons from William Campbell's collection.

Open: Sunday 14 May, 2pm - 5pm, admission £6.00, children free. A ticket available at any of the gardens will give admission to all three.

Directions: For Ault Wharrie: From the Fourways roundabout in Dunblane take the Glen Road, then the second left into Leewood Road. Continue and follow the *yellow* signs into Ardnablane. Take the first right beside a lodge and follow the directions given about parking. Overflow parking is on Leewood Road. The garden is about a 20 minute walk from Dunblane station. For Kippenrait turn up the Glen Road from Fourways roundabout in Dunblane. After three quarters of a mile, turn left signposted *Sheriffmuir*, and after about a quarter mile turn right onto the drive.

St Blanes House is almost directly opposite Dunblane Library.

Opening for: Strathcarron Hospice

Dunblane Gardens, Ault Wharrie © Morna Knottenbelt

Stirlingshire

5 GARDENER'S COTTAGE WALLED GARDEN
Ballochruin Road, Killearn G63 9QB
Morna Knottenbelt
T: 01360 551682 E: mornaknottenbelt@hotmail.com

The walled garden, acquired in 2013 by the present owners, has been planted with extensive herbaceous borders, box hedging, roses and many unusual plants. There is a White Garden, a long shrub border with primulas and gentians and a former fernery with a collection of salvias and peach and pear trees. June is a good time to visit when the roses are in bloom and borders with lupins, peonies and other perennials are in flower. By late summer, the borders have argyranthemums as well as dahlias, Michaelmas daisies, rudbeckias and blue aconitums. The Celtic Cross Garden was planted in May 2021 with a range of new plants including echinaceas, cardoons, lobelias, anthemis and lavender for mid to late summer colour. There are fine views of the Campsie Hills and the garden is surrounded by the conifers of the Designed Landscape of Carbeth.

Open: by arrangement 15 June - 15 October, admission £5.00, children free. The garden owners welcome visitors at short notice (the day before planned visits) and small numbers and individuals are welcome.

Directions: Follow Sat Nav to G63 0LF, which is Carbeth Home Farm. We are the next entrance below the farm. Turn left on to the gravel road and follow yellow *SGS* signs.

Opening for: The British Horse Society: Scotland

6 GARGUNNOCK HOUSE GARDEN
Gargunnock FK8 3AZ
The Gargunnock Trustees
T: Garden contact: William Campbell 01786 842538
E: william.campbellwj@btinternet.com

Large mature garden five miles from Stirling, with a walled garden, well-established house garden, woodland walks with species and hybrid rhododendrons, massed plantings of azaleas and wonderful specimen trees. Snowdrops in February/March are followed by over 40 varieties of daffodils and the glorious displays of azaleas and rhododendrons in May. The three-acre walled garden contains perennial borders, cut-flower beds, greenhouses, fruit orchard and newly planted arboretum of specimen trees. The Walled Garden is now used by the charity Green Routes to give gardening education to adults with learning difficulties.

Open: 1 February - 15 March, 11am - 3pm for Snowdrops and Winter Walks. Also open 1 April - 30 September (Wednesday only), 11am - 3pm. Admission £5.00, children free. There will be a plant stall at the rear of Gargunnock House. Groups would be welcome by arrangement.

Directions: Five miles west of Stirling on the A811. Car parking is at the entrance by the lodge. Honesty box is in the car park.

Opening for: Gargunnock Community Trust Ltd, Rhododendron Species Conservation Group & Green Routes Stirling

Stirlingshire

7 KILBRYDE CASTLE
Dunblane FK15 9NF
Sir James and Lady Campbell
T: 01786 824897 E: carolaandjames@googlemail.com
W: www.kilbrydecastle.com

Kilbryde Castle gardens cover some 12 acres and are situated above the Ardoch Burn and below the castle. The gardens are split into three parts: informal, woodland and wild. Natural planting (azaleas, rhododendrons, camellias and magnolias) is found in the woodland garden. There are glorious snowdrops, spring bulbs, and autumn colour provided by clematis and acers. Some new plantings for additional late summer/autumn colour were added in 2017. Visits to see the snowdrops can be made by arrangement. Following the successful event in 2022, there will again be a Plant Fair on 4 June 2023. Refreshments will also be available.

Open: by arrangement 1 February - 15 March for Snowdrops and Winter Walks. Also open Sunday 4 June, 11am - 5pm, when there will also be a **Plant Fair**. Then open by arrangement 16 March - 30 September. Admission £5.00, children free.

Directions: Three miles from Dunblane and Doune, off the A820 between Dunblane and Doune. On Scotland's Gardens Scheme open days the garden is signposted from the A820.

Opening for: Leighton Library Trust

Kilbryde Castle © Carolyn Bell

Stirlingshire

8 KILLEARN VILLAGE GARDENS
Killearn G63 9NL
The Gardeners of Killearn Village

Killearn, at the foot of the Campsie Hills with fine views of Loch Lomond, is described as one of the prettiest villages in Stirlingshire. A number of gardens both large and small will be open – some featuring a fine collection of acers plus water features, relaxed sitting areas and beautiful mixed borders. Some have been re-developed utilising raised beds or transformed through lockdown. One of the gardens has won prizes for its summer splendour.

Open: Sunday 30 July, 11am - 5pm, admission £6.00, children free. Tickets and maps will be available at the Village Hall only, where homemade teas will also be available from 11am - 4pm. A plant sale is also planned which will take place in the Village Hall car park.

Directions: Directions to Killearn Village Hall, which is in the centre of the village.
From Milngavie: Take A81 north. After Glengoyne Distillery, take right turn to Killearn.
From Stirling: Take A811 towards Glasgow. After Buchlyvie take the next turning left to Balfron. Drive through Balfron to Killearn.
X10 bus runs a service every two hours from Stirling and Glasgow.

Opening for: Strathcarron Hospice & Killearn Community Futures Company: Colourful Killearn

9 MILSEYBANK
Bridge of Allan FK9 4NB
Murray and Sheila Airth
T: 07799 036367 E: smairth@hotmail.com

Wonderful and interesting sloping garden with outstanding views, terraced for ease of access. Woodland with bluebells, rhododendrons, magnolias and camellias, and many other unusual plants, including a big variety of meconopsis. This is a true plantsman's garden with quiet corners to sit, admire and reflect. A garden to inspire you and give you ideas to take home. National Plant Collection: Meconopsis.

Open: by arrangement 1 May - 31 May, admission £5.00, children free.

Directions: Situated on the A9, one mile from junction 11, M9 and a quarter-of-a-mile from Bridge of Allan. Milseybank is at the top of the lane at Lecropt Nursery, 250 yards from the Bridge of Allan train station.

Opening for: Strathcarron Hospice

Stirlingshire

10 SHRUBHILL

Dunblane FK15 9PA
Tiff and Michaela Wright
T: 07821 693997 E: wrightrascals@gmail.com

Two acres of mixed, informal planting of some unusual rhododendrons, azaleas, specimen trees and other shrubs. Beautiful all round views particularly over the Carse of Stirling and towards Ben Ledi and Ben Lomond. Herbaceous borders, meconopsis, late spring bulbs, water feature with a wide variety of primulas. Small walled garden predominantly for fruit and a greenhouse with a well-established vine. There will be a plant sale.

Open: Sunday 28 May, 11am - 5pm, admission £5.00, children free. Parking is in a field.

Directions: Two miles from Keir roundabout on the B824 on the left, just after the *David Stirling Memorial,* follow the signs and parking advice. One mile from the A820 and on the right.

Opening for: Teapot Trust

11 THORNTREE

Arnprior FK8 3EY
Mark and Carol Seymour
T: 01786 870710 E: carolseymour666@gmail.com
W: www.thorntreebarn.co.uk

In 2023, Thorntree looks forward to welcoming visitors to their garden opening on Sunday 18 June as well by arrangement on other dates. Carol will happily walk round the garden with you or you can wander on your own. The garden continues to evolve and cotoneasters by the saltire beds have been cut back which means the four flower beds are no longer hidden behind a hedge! Also, the view past the summerhouse can be seen and the Annabelle hydrangea has popped up now that there are fewer branches above it. It is an inspiring garden to visit at any time of the year. From the garden you can see panoramic views from Ben Lomond to Doune, watching the Forth meander down the bottom of the valley. Please note: plants are always available for sale as part of the trainee experience under the WRAGS scheme.

Open: by arrangement 1 February - 15 March for Snowdrops and Winter Walks. Also open Sunday 18 June, 2pm - 5pm. And open by arrangement 16 March - 31 October. Admission £5.00, children free.

Directions: On the A811, to Arnprior, then take the Fintry Road; Thorntree is second on the right.

Opening for: Forth Driving Group RDA SCIO

Wigtownshire

Sponsored by
⊕ Investec

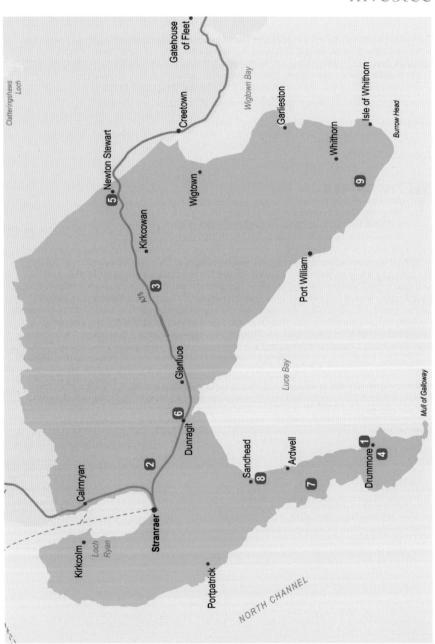

Wigtownshire

OUR VOLUNTEER ORGANISERS

District Organisers:	Ann Watson	Doonholm, Cairnryan Road, Stranraer DG9 8AT E: info@scotlandsgardens.org
Area Organisers:	Colin Belton	Amulree, 8 Mill Street, Drummore DG9 9PS
	Teri Birch	The Old Manse, Gruisey House, Sandhead DG9 9JT
	Eileen Davie	Whitehills House, Minnigaff DG8 6SL
	Mary Gladstone	Craichlaw, Kirkcowan DG8 0DQ
	Shona Greenhorn	Burbainie, Westwood Avenue, Stranraer DG9 8BT
	Annmaree Mitchell	Cottage 2, Little Float, Sandhead DG9 9LD
District Photographer:	Stuart Littlewood	Tayvallich, West Port, New Galloway DG7 3SB
Treasurer:	Marilyn Sime	1 Weir Terrace, Sandhead, Stranraer DG9 9JH

GARDENS OPEN ON A SPECIFIC DATE

Woodfall Gardens, Glasserton	Sunday, 14 May
Logan Botanic Garden, Port Logan, by Stranraer	Sunday, 21 May
Castle Kennedy and Gardens, Stranraer	Sunday, 11 June
Woodfall Gardens, Glasserton	Sunday, 18 June
Amulree, 8 Mill Street, Drummore, Stranraer	Saturday/Sunday, 15/16 July
Woodfall Gardens, Glasserton	Sunday, 23 July
Fernlea Garden, Corvisel Road, Newton Stewart	Sunday, 13 August

GARDENS OPEN REGULARLY

Glenwhan Gardens, Dunragit, by Stranraer	1 January - 31 December
Logan Botanic Garden, Port Logan, by Stranraer	4 February - 26 February (Saturdays & Sundays)
Logan Botanic Garden, Port Logan, by Stranraer	1 March - 15 November

GARDENS OPEN BY ARRANGEMENT – BOOK A VISIT WITH THE GARDEN OWNER

Amulree, 8 Mill Street, Drummore, Stranraer	1 January - 31 December
Craichlaw, Kirkcowan, Newton Stewart	1 January - 31 December
Fernlea Garden, Corvisel Road, Newton Stewart	1 April - 30 September
Damnaglaur House, Drummore, Stranraer	1 May - 30 September
The Old Manse, Sandhead, Stranraer	1 May - 30 September

Wigtownshire

1 AMULREE
8 Mill Street, Drummore, Stranraer DG9 9PS
Colin Belton and Gabrielle Reynolds
T: 0789 909 2070 E: gabygardeners@btinternet.com

Amulree is home to two complete plantaholics who probably should start taking their own advice and stop collecting quite so many plants! Starting from a blank canvas in 2017 the garden now consists of a sunny terrace with displays of half-hardy and tender plants, exuberantly planted borders separated by serpentine grass patches, a small vegetable patch, a glasshouse and a 'wild' bit. Amulree contains many unusual plants including a National Plant Collection.
National Plant Collection: *Nicotiana* species.

Open: Saturday/Sunday, 15/16 July, 10am - 4pm. Groups are welcome at other times by prior arrangement. Admission £5.00, children free.

Directions: Follow the A716 signposted *Drummore and Mull of Galloway*. At the T junction in Drummore turn right. Amulree is on the left, a few doors up from the shop. Bus route 407 from Stranraer.

Opening for: Kirkmaiden Old Kirk

2 CASTLE KENNEDY AND GARDENS
Stranraer DG9 8SJ
The Earl and Countess of Stair
T: 01581 400225
W: www.castlekennedygardens.com

Romantically situated, these famous 75 acres of landscaped gardens are located on an isthmus surrounded by two large natural lochs. At one end, the ruined Castle Kennedy overlooks a beautiful herbaceous walled garden with Lochinch Castle at the other end. With over 300 years of planting, there is an impressive collection of rare trees, rhododendrons, exotic shrubs and many spectacular Champion Trees. The stunning snowdrop walks, daffodils, spring flowers, rhododendron and magnolia displays and herbaceous borders make this a 'must visit' garden throughout the year.
Champion Trees: 95 in total; including 12 British, 30 Scottish, 44 for Dumfries and Galloway and 9 trees described as 'otherwise remarkable'.

Open: Sunday 11 June, 10am - 5pm, admission details can be found on the garden's website. Also open through the season, check the garden's website for details.

Directions: On the A75, five miles east of Stranraer. The nearest train station is in Stranraer. On a local bus route.

Opening for: Home-Start Wigtownshire

3 CRAICHLAW
Kirkcowan, Newton Stewart DG8 0DQ
Mr and Mrs Andrew Gladstone
T: 01671 830208 E: craichlaw@aol.com

Formal garden with herbaceous borders around the house. Set in extensive grounds with lawns, lochs and woodland. A path around the main loch leads to a water garden returning past a recently planted arboretum in the old walled garden. The best times to visit the garden are early February for snowdrops, May to mid-June for the water garden and rhododendrons, and mid-June to August for herbaceous borders.

Wigtownshire

Open: by arrangement 1 January - 31 December, admission £5.00. We have Snowdrops and Winter Walks from February to mid-March

Directions: Take the B733 for Kirkcowan, off the A75 at the Halfway House eight miles west of Newton Stewart and Craichlaw House is the first turning on the right.

Opening for: SGS and Beneficiaries

Craichlaw

4 DAMNAGLAUR HOUSE

Drummore, Stranraer DG9 9QN
Frances Collins
T: 01776 840636/ 07884 435353 E: chunky.collins@btinternet.com

Since moving into Damnaglaur House in 1991, its owners have totally transformed the garden, putting in a series of 'semi-terraces' and, following the planting of wind-defeating shrubs, they were able to introduce many special herbaceous plants and trees. Just short of half-an-acre, the garden has slowly evolved into one which feels substantially larger because of its design; the gravel paths weave their way through many hidden corners to come upon countless gems. The views from the garden are stunning, down to Drummore, across Luce Bay and in the far distance, to the Galloway Hills. An archway, arbour and pergola give extra height for the planting. Seating around the garden gives visitors a chance to sit and enjoy their surroundings, especially close to the pond with its numerous fish and trickling waterfall. Various areas have been replanted over the past few years, with a small 'seaside' garden being introduced.

Open: by arrangement 1 May – 30 September, admission £6.00, which includes light refreshments, children free. Plants for sale, by donation.

Directions: From Drummore, follow signs to the *Mull of Galloway* for a mile on the B7041 to junction with B7065; Damnaglaur is on the right.

Opening for: British Red Cross: Yemen appeal

Wigtownshire

5 FERNLEA GARDEN
Corvisel Road, Newton Stewart DG8 6LW
Mrs Jenny Gustafson
T: 07909 951 885/ 01671 638273 E: jennygustafson2@hotmail.com

A secluded town garden of a third-of-an-acre, it was created in 2006 to complement a new house. There are many rare and unusual trees and shrubs. Two herbaceous borders, one with hot colours and the other pastels. A Chinese-inspired corner, small pond, fruit trees including a Galloway pippin apple and soft fruit. The upper part of the garden is hidden behind a tall beech hedge, where there is a summer house and adjacent woodland planting.

Open: Sunday 13 August, 2pm - 5pm. Also open by arrangement 1 April - 30 September. Admission £5.00, children free. We welcome enquiries from individuals and small groups for our By Arrangement openings.

Directions: Turn right at the roundabout on the A75 if coming from Dumfries direction. Go left at the cattle market (opposite the Crown Hotel) and it is the first through road on the right.

Opening for: *The Woodland Trust Scotland*

6 GLENWHAN GARDENS
Dunragit, by Stranraer DG9 8PH
Tessa Knott
T: 07787 990702
W: www.glenwhangardens.co.uk

Described as one of the most beautiful gardens in Scotland, Glenwhan Gardens is situated at 300 feet and overlooks Luce Bay and the Mull of Galloway, with clear views to the Isle of Man. Forty years ago there was wild moorland, but now, following considerable dedication and vision, you can see glorious collections of plants from around the world. There is colour in all seasons and the winding paths, well-placed seats and varied sculptures, set around small lakes, add to the tranquil atmosphere. There is a 17-acre moorland wildflower walk, the chance to see red squirrels and a well-marked Tree Trail.

Open: 1 January - 31 December, 2pm - 5pm, admission by donation. Admission to gardens at the entrance.

Directions: Seven miles east of Stranraer, one mile off the A75 at Dunragit (follow brown *VisitScotland* and *yellow SGS arrows*).

Opening for: *SGS and Beneficiaries*

7 LOGAN BOTANIC GARDEN
Port Logan, by Stranraer DG9 9ND
A Regional Garden of the Royal Botanic Garden Edinburgh
T: 01776 860231 E: logan@rbge.org.uk
W: www.rbge.org.uk/logan

Logan Botanic Garden lies at the south-western tip of Scotland, unrivalled as 'Scotland's Most Exotic Garden'. Warmed by the Gulf Stream, a remarkable collection of southern hemisphere plants flourish, making this a plantsman's paradise. Logan enjoys an almost subtropical climate where the Garden's avenues and borders feature a spectacular and colourful array of half-hardy perennials. The Garden is warmed by the Gulf Stream which enables plants from Australia, New Zealand, South and Central America and Southern Africa to thrive. Voted 'Best Garden in the UK' 2021, Logan promises a delightful day out for all'.

Wigtownshire

National Plant Collection: *Gunnera, Leptospermum, Griselinia, Clianthus* and *Sutherlandia.*
Champion Trees: *Polylepis* and *Eucalyptus.*
Open: Sunday 21 May, 10am - 5pm. Also open 4 February - 26 February (Saturday & Sunday), 10am - 4pm for Snowdrops and Winter Walks and 1 March - 15 November, 10am - 5pm. Admission details can be found on the garden's website.

Directions: Ten miles south of Stranraer on the A716 then two-and-a-half miles from Ardwell village.

Opening for: Board Of Trustees Of The Royal Botanic Garden Edinburgh

---

 THE OLD MANSE
Sandhead, Stranraer DG9 9JT
Mrs Teri Birch
T: 01776 830455 E: birchteri@gmail.com

....

Recently designed, landscaped and replanted by the current owners who are keen to develop the garden to its full potential. Comprising about half-an-acre, the garden is surrounded by stone walls and has a burn running through it. Recent projects include a formal parterre, a rose garden, herbaceous borders and rockeries. The planting is creative and thoughtful, using grasses, bulbs, annuals, herbaceous perennials and alpines to make full use of the temperate climate enjoyed in this location. Current projects include developing a shady woodland area.

Open: by arrangement 1 May - 30 September, admission £6.00, children free.

Directions: From Stranraer take the A716 south following signs for *Drummore*; past Sandhead, look for a tourist sign for *Kirkmadrine Stones and Clachanmore* and turn immediately right. The Old Manse is on the corner on the right (known locally as *Doctors' Corner*). A bus service is available from Stranraer and stops at Doctors' Corner.

Opening for: Board Of Trustees Of The Royal Botanic Garden Edinburgh

---

 WOODFALL GARDENS
Glasserton DG8 8LY
Ross and Liz Muir
E: woodfallgardens@btinternet.com
W: www.woodfall-gardens.co.uk

....

This lovely three-acre 18th-century triple walled garden has been thoughtfully restored to provide year-round interest. It contains many mature trees and shrubs, including some less common species, herbaceous borders and shrub roses which surround the foundations of original greenhouses, grass borders, a parterre, extensive beds of fruit and vegetables, a herb garden and a small woodland walk. This unusual garden is well worth a visit.

Open: Sunday 14 May, Sunday 18 June and Sunday 23 July, 10:30am - 4:30pm. Admission £5.00, children free. Please check the garden's website for further openings.

Directions: Two miles south-west of Whithorn at junction off A746 and A747 (directly behind Glasserton Church).

Opening for: Whithorn Primary School

GARDEN PHOTO BOOKS

Your Garden...

Professionally photographed across the seasons

Featured in a stunning coffee-table book

Ideal Gift!

SCAN ME

RAY COX
PHOTOGRAPHY

07762 067 255
www.rcoxgardenphotos.co.uk

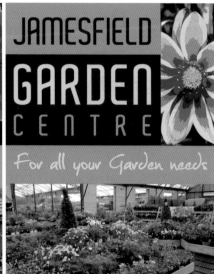

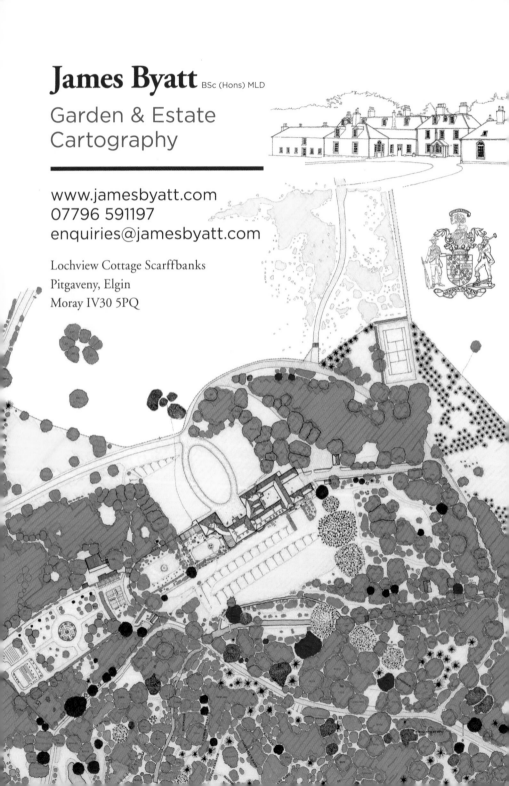

James Byatt BSc (Hons) MLD

Garden & Estate Cartography

www.jamesbyatt.com
07796 591197
enquiries@jamesbyatt.com

Lochview Cottage Scarffbanks
Pitgaveny, Elgin
Moray IV30 5PQ

Gardens open on a specific date

FEBRUARY

Tuesday 7 February
East Lothian   Shepherd House, Inveresk, Musselburgh

Thursday 9 February
East Lothian   Shepherd House, Inveresk, Musselburgh

Tuesday 14 February
East Lothian   Shepherd House, Inveresk, Musselburgh

Wednesday 15 February
Peeblesshire & Tweeddale   Kirkton Manor House, Peebles

Thursday 16 February
East Lothian   Shepherd House, Inveresk, Musselburgh

Saturday 18 February
East Lothian   Shepherd House, Inveresk, Musselburgh
Perth & Kinross   Princeland House, Blairgowrie Road, Coupar Angus, Blairgowrie

Sunday 19 February
Dumfriesshire   Craig, Langholm
Dunbartonshire   NEW Stuckenduff, Shore Road, Shandon
East Lothian   Shepherd House, Inveresk, Musselburgh
Kirkcudbrightshire   Danevale Park, Crossmichael
Perth & Kinross   Cloan, by Auchterarder
Perth & Kinross   Princeland House, Blairgowrie Road, Coupar Angus, Blairgowrie

Tuesday 21 February
East Lothian   Shepherd House, Inveresk, Musselburgh

Wednesday 22 February
Peeblesshire & Tweeddale   Kirkton Manor House, Peebles

Thursday 23 February
East Lothian   Shepherd House, Inveresk, Musselburgh

Saturday 25 February
Angus & Dundee   NEW Kinblethmont House, by Arbroath, Angus
Fife   NEW Dunimarle Castle, Balgownie West, Culross
Fife   Lindores House, by Newburgh
Fife   Millfield Garden, Millfield House, Falkland, Fife
Perth & Kinross   Princeland House, Blairgowrie Road, Coupar Angus, Blairgowrie

Sunday 26 February
Angus & Dundee   NEW Kinblethmont House, by Arbroath, Angus
Fife   NEW Dunimarle Castle, Balgownie West, Culross
Fife   Millfield Garden, Millfield House, Falkland, Fife
Perth & Kinross   NEW Scone Palace Garden, Perth
Perth & Kinross   Princeland House, Blairgowrie Road, Coupar Angus, Blairgowrie

Tuesday 28 February
East Lothian   Shepherd House, Inveresk, Musselburgh

MARCH

Wednesday 1 March
Peeblesshire & Tweeddale   Kirkton Manor House, Peebles

Thursday 2 March
East Lothian   Shepherd House, Inveresk, Musselburgh

Saturday 4 March
Perth & Kinross   Princeland House, Blairgowrie Road, Coupar Angus, Blairgowrie

Sunday 5 March
Kincardine & Deeside   Ecclesgreig Castle, St Cyrus
Lanarkshire   Cleghorn, Stable House, Cleghorn Farm, Lanark
Peeblesshire & Tweeddale   Kailzie Gardens, Kailzie Gardens
Perth & Kinross   Princeland House, Blairgowrie Road, Coupar Angus, Blairgowrie

Wednesday 8 March
Peeblesshire & Tweeddale   Kirkton Manor House, Peebles

Thursday 9 March
Angus & Dundee   Lawton House, Inverkeilor, by Arbroath

Friday 10 March
Angus & Dundee   Lawton House, Inverkeilor, by Arbroath

Saturday 11 March
Angus & Dundee   Lawton House, Inverkeilor, by Arbroath
Perth & Kinross   Princeland House, Blairgowrie Road, Coupar Angus, Blairgowrie

Sunday 12 March
Angus & Dundee   Lawton House, Inverkeilor, by Arbroath
Perth & Kinross   Princeland House, Blairgowrie Road, Coupar Angus, Blairgowrie

Wednesday 15 March
Peeblesshire & Tweeddale   Kirkton Manor House, Peebles

Saturday 18 March
Dumfriesshire   NEW Tinnisburn Plants, Upper Millsteads, Canonbie

Sunday 19 March
Dumfriesshire   NEW Tinnisburn Plants, Upper Millsteads, Canonbie

Wednesday 22 March
Peeblesshire & Tweeddale   Kirkton Manor House, Peebles

Sunday 26 March
East Lothian   Winton Castle, Pencaitland
Kirkcudbrightshire   The Limes, Kirkcudbright

Wednesday 29 March
East Lothian   Humbie Dean, Humbie
Peeblesshire & Tweeddale   Kirkton Manor House, Peebles

APRIL

Wednesday 5 April
Peeblesshire & Tweeddale   Kirkton Manor House, Peebles

Saturday 8 April

Fife — NEW St Andrews Botanic Garden Spring Fair, Canongate, Fife

Sunday 9 April

Aberdeenshire — Auchmacoy, Ellon

Wednesday 12 April

East Lothian — Humbie Dean, Humbie

Peeblesshire & Tweeddale — Kirkton Manor House, Peebles

Saturday 15 April

Angus & Dundee — 10 Menzieshill Road, Dundee

Caithness, Sutherland, Orkney & Shetland — NEW 16 Mulla, Voe, Shetland

Fife — Cambo Spring Plant & Garden Market, Kingsbarns

Fife — Willowhill, Forgan, Newport-on-Tay

Inverness, Ross, Cromarty & Skye — Dundonnell House, Little Loch Broom, Wester Ross

Sunday 16 April

Aberdeenshire — Westhall Castle, Oyne, Inverurie

Angus & Dundee — 10 Menzieshill Road, Dundee

Caithness, Sutherland, Orkney & Shetland — NEW 16 Mulla, Voe, Shetland

Fife — Willowhill, Forgan, Newport-on-Tay

Kirkcudbrightshire — 3 Millhall, Shore Road, Kirkcudbright

Perth & Kinross — Megginch Castle, Errol

Monday 17 April

Fife — Willowhill, Forgan, Newport-on-Tay

Tuesday 18 April

East Lothian — Shepherd House, Inveresk, Musselburgh

Wednesday 19 April

Peeblesshire & Tweeddale — Kirkton Manor House, Peebles

Thursday 20 April

Angus & Dundee — Inchmill Cottage, Glenprosen, near Kirriemuir

East Lothian — Shepherd House, Inveresk, Musselburgh

Saturday 22 April

Angus & Dundee — 17a Menzieshill Road, Dundee

Renfrewshire — SGS Kilmacolm Plant Sale, Outside Kilmacolm Library, Kilmacolm

Sunday 23 April

Angus & Dundee — 17a Menzieshill Road, Dundee

Angus & Dundee — Forfar Open Garden, 36 Lochside Road, Forfar

Perth & Kinross — Fingask Castle, Rait

Tuesday 25 April

East Lothian — Shepherd House, Inveresk, Musselburgh

Wednesday 26 April

East Lothian — Humbie Dean, Humbie

Peeblesshire & Tweeddale — Kirkton Manor House, Peebles

Thursday 27 April

East Lothian — Shepherd House, Inveresk, Musselburgh

Saturday 29 April

East Lothian	A Blackbird Sings, 20 Kings Park, Longniddry
Edinburgh, Midlothian & West Lothian	41 Hermitage Gardens, Edinburgh

Sunday 30 April

Ayrshire & Arran	Blair Castle & Estate, Dalry, Ayrshire
Fife	South Flisk, Blebo Craigs, Cupar
Fife	Teasses Gardens, near Ceres

MAY

Monday 1 May

Kirkcudbrightshire	Threave Garden, Castle Douglas

Tuesday 2 May

East Lothian	Shepherd House, Inveresk, Musselburgh

Wednesday 3 May

Edinburgh, Midlothian & West Lothian	Newliston, Kirkliston
Peeblesshire & Tweeddale	Kirkton Manor House, Peebles

Thursday 4 May

East Lothian	Shepherd House, Inveresk, Musselburgh
Edinburgh, Midlothian & West Lothian	Newliston, Kirkliston

Friday 5 May

Edinburgh, Midlothian & West Lothian	Newliston, Kirkliston

Saturday 6 May

Angus & Dundee	17a Menzieshill Road, Dundee
Argyll & Lochaber	Knock Newhouse, Lochgair
Edinburgh, Midlothian & West Lothian	Dr Neil's Garden, Duddingston Village
Edinburgh, Midlothian & West Lothian	Newliston, Kirkliston

Sunday 7 May

Angus & Dundee	17a Menzieshill Road, Dundee
Angus & Dundee	Kirkton Cottage, Aberlemno
Argyll & Lochaber	Knock Newhouse, Lochgair
Dumfriesshire	NEW Dalswinton House with Gardens Cottage, Dalswinton
East Lothian	Tyninghame House and The Walled Garden, Dunbar
Edinburgh, Midlothian & West Lothian	Dr Neil's Garden, Duddingston Village
Edinburgh, Midlothian & West Lothian	Greentree, 18 Green Hill Park, Edinburgh
Edinburgh, Midlothian & West Lothian	Newliston, Kirkliston
Fife	Greenhead Farmhouse, Greenhead of Arnot, Leslie
Kirkcudbrightshire	Cally Gardens, Cally Avenue, Gatehouse of Fleet
Perth & Kinross	Glendoick, Glencarse, Perthshire
Perth & Kinross	The Steading at Clunie, The Steading

Tuesday 9 May

East Lothian	Shepherd House, Inveresk, Musselburgh

Wednesday 10 May

Edinburgh, Midlothian & West Lothian	Newliston, Kirkliston
Peeblesshire & Tweeddale	Kirkton Manor House, Peebles

Thursday 11 May

Argyll & Lochaber	NEW Baravalla Garden, by West Loch Tarbert, Argyll
East Lothian	Shepherd House, Inveresk, Musselburgh
Edinburgh, Midlothian & West Lothian	Newliston, Kirkliston

Friday 12 May

Edinburgh, Midlothian & West Lothian	Newliston, Kirkliston

Saturday 13 May

Angus & Dundee	10 Menzieshill Road, Dundee
Argyll & Lochaber	Achamore Gardens, Isle of Gigha
Argyll & Lochaber	Kames Bay, Kilmelford
Ayrshire & Arran	Kirkfauld, 5 Kirkton Road, Kilmarnock
Dumfriesshire	Portrack, The Garden of Cosmic Speculation, Holywood
East Lothian	Shepherd House, Inveresk, Musselburgh
Edinburgh, Midlothian & West Lothian	Newliston, Kirkliston
Edinburgh, Midlothian & West Lothian	Redcroft, 23 Murrayfield Road, Edinburgh
Fife	NEW The Garden with the Dragon, 2, Upper Wellheads, Limekilns
Fife	Willowhill, Forgan, Newport-on-Tay

Sunday 14 May

Angus & Dundee	10 Menzieshill Road, Dundee
Angus & Dundee	Dalfruin, Kirktonhill Road, Kirriemuir
Argyll & Lochaber	Kames Bay, Kilmelford
Argyll & Lochaber	Strachur Flower & Woodland Gardens, Strachur
Ayrshire & Arran	Kirkfauld, 5 Kirkton Road, Kilmarnock
Berwickshire	Broomhill Villa, 4 Edinburgh Road, Greenlaw
Caithness, Sutherland, Orkney & Shetland	Old Granary Quoy, The Quoy of Houton, Orphir, Orkney
Caithness, Sutherland, Orkney & Shetland	The Quoy of Houton, Orphir, Orkney
Dumfriesshire	Portrack, The Garden of Cosmic Speculation, Holywood
Dunbartonshire	18 Duchess Park with Westburn, Helensburgh
East Lothian	Shepherd House, Inveresk, Musselburgh
Edinburgh, Midlothian & West Lothian	14 East Brighton Crescent, Portobello, Edinburgh
Edinburgh, Midlothian & West Lothian	5 Greenbank Crescent, Edinburgh
Edinburgh, Midlothian & West Lothian	Newliston, Kirkliston
Edinburgh, Midlothian & West Lothian	Redcroft, 23 Murrayfield Road, Edinburgh
Fife	Willowhill, Forgan, Newport-on-Tay
Kirkcudbrightshire	Arbigland House, Kirkbean, Dumfries
Perth & Kinross	Cloan, by Auchterarder
Perth & Kinross	Glendoick, Glencarse, Perthshire
Renfrewshire	Highwood, off Lochwinnoch Road, Kilmacolm
Stirlingshire	Dunblane Gardens, Dunblane
Wigtownshire	Woodfall Gardens, Glasserton

Monday 15 May

Fife	Willowhill, Forgan, Newport-on-Tay

Tuesday 16 May

East Lothian	Shepherd House, Inveresk, Musselburgh
Fife	NEW Kenlygreen House, Boarhills, St Andrews

Wednesday 17 May

East Lothian	Humbie Dean, Humbie
Edinburgh, Midlothian & West Lothian	Newliston, Kirkliston
Peeblesshire & Tweeddale	Kirkton Manor House, Peebles

Thursday 18 May

Angus & Dundee	Inchmill Cottage, Glenprosen, near Kirriemuir
East Lothian	Shepherd House, Inveresk, Musselburgh
Edinburgh, Midlothian & West Lothian	Newliston, Kirkliston

Friday 19 May

Edinburgh, Midlothian & West Lothian	Newliston, Kirkliston

Saturday 20 May

Ayrshire & Arran	NEW Burnhouse, Cemetery Road, Galston
Edinburgh, Midlothian & West Lothian	Newliston, Kirkliston
Fife	NEW The Garden with the Dragon, 2, Upper Wellheads, Limekilns
Moray & Nairn	NEW Easter Laggan, Dulnain Bridge, Grantown-on-Spey
Perth & Kinross	NEW The Abercairny Garden, Abercairny House, Crieff

Sunday 21 May

Angus & Dundee	NEW Braidestone Farm, Meigle, Blairgowrie
Argyll & Lochaber	Fasnacloich, Appin
Argyll & Lochaber	Strachur Flower & Woodland Gardens, Strachur
Ayrshire & Arran	NEW Burnhouse, Cemetery Road, Galston
Caithness, Sutherland, Orkney & Shetland	NEW Linfirlea, Pipersquoy Road, Kirkwall
Dunbartonshire	Ross Priory, Gartocharn
Edinburgh, Midlothian & West Lothian	Moray Place and Bank Gardens, Edinburgh
Edinburgh, Midlothian & West Lothian	Newliston, Kirkliston
Fife	Balcarres, Colinsburgh
Fife	Kirklands, Saline
Fife	The Tower, 1 Northview Terrace, Wormit
Kincardine & Deeside	Inchmarlo Retirement Village Garden, Inchmarlo, Banchory
Kirkcudbrightshire	Brooklands, Crocketford
Kirkcudbrightshire	The Limes, Kirkcudbright
Perth & Kinross	NEW The Abercairny Garden, Abercairny House, Crieff
Perth & Kinross	Glendoick, Glencarse, Perthshire
Renfrewshire	Wraes, Corseliehill Road, nr Houston
Stirlingshire	Bridge of Allan Gardens, Bridge of Allan
Wigtownshire	Logan Botanic Garden, Port Logan, by Stranraer

Tuesday 23 May

East Lothian	Shepherd House, Inveresk, Musselburgh

Wednesday 24 May

Edinburgh, Midlothian & West Lothian	Newliston, Kirkliston
Peeblesshire & Tweeddale	Kirkton Manor House, Peebles

Thursday 25 May

East Lothian	Shepherd House, Inveresk, Musselburgh
Edinburgh, Midlothian & West Lothian	Newliston, Kirkliston

Friday 26 May

Edinburgh, Midlothian & West Lothian	Newliston, Kirkliston

Saturday 27 May

Angus & Dundee	Balhary Walled Garden, Balhary, Alyth, Blairgowrie
Angus & Dundee	Westgate and Windyridge, 10 & 12 Glamis Drive, Dundee
Argyll & Lochaber	Inveryne Woodland Garden, Kilfinan, Tighnabruaich
Ayrshire & Arran	The Wildings, Bankwood, Galston
East Lothian	A Blackbird Sings, 20 Kings Park, Longniddry
Edinburgh, Midlothian & West Lothian	Newliston, Kirkliston
Fife	NEW 20 Brucehaven Crescent, Limekilns
Fife	NEW The Garden with the Dragon, 2, Upper Wellheads, Limekilns

Sunday 28 May

Angus & Dundee	Forfar Open Garden, 36 Lochside Road, Forfar
Angus & Dundee	Westgate and Windyridge, 10 & 12 Glamis Drive, Dundee
Argyll & Lochaber	Inveryne Woodland Garden, Kilfinan, Tighnabruaich
Argyll & Lochaber	Knock Newhouse, Lochgair
Dumfriesshire	Craigieburn House, by Moffat
Edinburgh, Midlothian & West Lothian	Newliston, Kirkliston

Sunday 28 May - continued

Fife	NEW 20 Brucehaven Crescent, Limekilns
Fife	Earlshall Castle, Leuchars
Fife	Lindores House, by Newburgh
Fife	South Flisk, Blebo Craigs, Cupar
Glasgow & District	Kilsyth Gardens, Allanfauld Road
Kincardine & Deeside	Finzean House, Finzean, Banchory
Kirkcudbrightshire	Corsock House, Corsock, Castle Douglas
Peeblesshire & Tweeddale	Haystoun, Peebles
Peeblesshire & Tweeddale	Quercus Garden Plants, Whitmuir Farm, West Linton
Stirlingshire	Shrubhill, Dunblane

Tuesday 30 May

East Lothian	Shepherd House, Inveresk, Musselburgh

Wednesday 31 May

Edinburgh, Midlothian & West Lothian	Newliston, Kirkliston
Peeblesshire & Tweeddale	Kirkton Manor House, Peebles

JUNE

Thursday 1 June

East Lothian	Shepherd House, Inveresk, Musselburgh
Edinburgh, Midlothian & West Lothian	Newliston, Kirkliston
Inverness, Ross, Cromarty & Skye	Dundonnell House, Little Loch Broom, Wester Ross

Friday 2 June

Edinburgh, Midlothian & West Lothian	Newliston, Kirkliston

Saturday 3 June

Angus & Dundee	NEW 6 Minto Place, Dundee
Ayrshire & Arran	Kirkmuir Cottage, Stewarton
Edinburgh, Midlothian & West Lothian	Newliston, Kirkliston
Perth & Kinross	Cloan, by Auchterarder
Perth & Kinross	The Bield at Blackruthven, Blackruthven House, Tibbermore

Sunday 4 June

Angus & Dundee	NEW 6 Minto Place, Dundee
Ayrshire & Arran	Kirkmuir Cottage, Stewarton
Dumfriesshire	NEW Langholm Gardens Day Trail, Langholm
Dumfriesshire	Capenoch, Penpont, Thornhill
Dunbartonshire	Geilston Garden, Main Road, Cardross
East Lothian	Stobshiel House, Humbie
Edinburgh, Midlothian & West Lothian	Dean Gardens, Edinburgh
Edinburgh, Midlothian & West Lothian	Hunter's Tryst, 95 Oxgangs Road, Edinburgh
Edinburgh, Midlothian & West Lothian	Newliston, Kirkliston
Kincardine & Deeside	Glensaugh, Glensaugh Lodge, Fettercairn, Laurencekirk
Lanarkshire	Biggar Open Gardens, High Street Biggar
Moray & Nairn	NEW Glenernie, Glenernie House, Dunphail, Moray
Peeblesshire & Tweeddale	Stobo Japanese Water Garden, Stobo Farm, Stobo
Perth & Kinross	Cloan, by Auchterarder
Perth & Kinross	Mill of Forneth, Forneth, Blairgowrie
Renfrewshire	Carruth, Bridge of Weir
Roxburghshire	West Leas, Bonchester Bridge
Stirlingshire	Kilbryde Castle, Dunblane

Tuesday 6 June

East Lothian	Shepherd House, Inveresk, Musselburgh

Wednesday 7 June

East Lothian	Humbie Dean, Humbie
Peeblesshire & Tweeddale	NEW Beechwood, Broughton, Peeblesshire
Peeblesshire & Tweeddale	Kirkton Manor House, Peebles
Peeblesshire & Tweeddale	Laidlawstiel House, Clovenfords, Galashiels
Peeblesshire & Tweeddale	The Potting Shed, Broughton Place, Broughton, Biggar

Thursday 8 June

East Lothian	Shepherd House, Inveresk, Musselburgh
Peeblesshire & Tweeddale	Laidlawstiel House, Clovenfords, Galashiels

Friday 9 June

Aberdeenshire	NEW Two Gardens in Banchory Devenick, Banchory Devenick

Saturday 10 June

Aberdeenshire	NEW Two Gardens in Banchory Devenick, Banchory Devenick
Angus & Dundee	NEW Letham Grange Gardens & Ashbrook Nursery Tours
Moray & Nairn	NEW Carestown Steading, Deskford, Buckie

Sunday 11 June

Aberdeenshire	NEW Two Gardens in Banchory Devenick, Banchory Devenick
Angus & Dundee	NEW Inverbrothock School Sensory Garden and Forest Garden
Argyll & Lochaber	Ardchattan Priory, North Connel
Argyll & Lochaber	Ardverikie with Aberarder, Kinloch Laggan, Newtonmore
Dumfriesshire	Bonerick House, Irongray , Dumfries
Dumfriesshire	Leap Cottage, West Cluden, Dumfries
Fife	NEW Kincardine's Gardens – Great and Small
Kincardine & Deeside	NEW Arbuthnott House Gardens, Arbuthnott House, Laurencekirk
Kirkcudbrightshire	Seabank, The Merse, Rockcliffe
Lanarkshire	Meadowhead, Dolphinton, West Linton
Peeblesshire & Tweeddale	Lamancha Community Hub Plant Sale, Old Moffat Road, Lamancha
Perth & Kinross	36 Muirfield, Perth
Wigtownshire	Castle Kennedy and Gardens, Stranraer

Tuesday 13 June

East Lothian	Shepherd House, Inveresk, Musselburgh

Wednesday 14 June

Fife	Gilston House, by Largoward, Leven
Peeblesshire & Tweeddale	NEW Beechwood, Broughton, Peeblesshire
Peeblesshire & Tweeddale	Kirkton Manor House, Peebles
Peeblesshire & Tweeddale	The Potting Shed, Broughton Place, Broughton, Biggar

Thursday 15 June

Angus & Dundee	Inchmill Cottage, Glenprosen, near Kirriemuir
East Lothian	Shepherd House, Inveresk, Musselburgh

Friday 16 June

East Lothian	NEW Bowerhouse, Dunbar
Perth & Kinross	Delvine, Murthly
Renfrewshire	Craig Hepburn Memorial Garden, Stirling Drive, Linwood

Saturday 17 June

Angus & Dundee	Cotton of Craig, Kilry, Blairgowrie
Angus & Dundee	Estir Bogside, Alyth
Angus & Dundee	St Bride's Cottage, South Kingennie, Broughty Ferry
East Lothian	NEW Bowerhouse, Dunbar
East Lothian	Camptoun House, Camptoun, East Lothian
Edinburgh, Midlothian & West Lothian	Eskbank Village Gardens, 23 Lasswade Road, Eskbank

Saturday 17 June – continued

Fife	Willowhill, Forgan, Newport-on-Tay
Renfrewshire	Craig Hepburn Memorial Garden, Stirling Drive, Linwood

Sunday 18 June

Angus & Dundee	Brechin Gardens in Summer, Locations across Brechin
Angus & Dundee	St Bride's Cottage, South Kingennie, Broughty Ferry
Ayrshire & Arran	Barrmill Community Garden, Barrmill Park and Gardens
Berwickshire	Duns Open Gardens , Volunteer Hall, Langtongate, Duns
Caithness, Sutherland, Orkney & Shetland	NEW 19 Burnside, Kirkwall, Orkney
Dumfriesshire	Dunesslin, Dunscore
East Lothian	Camptoun House, Camptoun, East Lothian
Edinburgh, Midlothian & West Lothian	Claremont, Redmill
Edinburgh, Midlothian & West Lothian	Meadow Place, 19 Meadow Place
Edinburgh, Midlothian & West Lothian	Rivaldsgreen House, 48 Friars Brae, Linlithgow
Glasgow & District	The Gardens of Milton of Campsie, Milton of Campsie
Inverness, Ross, Cromarty & Skye	Old Allangrange, Munlochy
Peeblesshire & Tweeddale	Carolside, Earlston
Stirlingshire	Thorntree, Arnprior
Wigtownshire	Woodfall Gardens, Glasserton

Monday 19 June

Fife	Willowhill, Forgan, Newport-on-Tay

Tuesday 20 June

East Lothian	Shepherd House, Inveresk, Musselburgh

Wednesday 21 June

East Lothian	Humbie Dean, Humbie
Peeblesshire & Tweeddale	NEW Beechwood, Broughton, Peeblesshire
Peeblesshire & Tweeddale	Kirkton Manor House, Peebles
Peeblesshire & Tweeddale	The Potting Shed, Broughton Place, Broughton, Biggar

Thursday 22 June

East Lothian	Shepherd House, Inveresk, Musselburgh

Saturday 24 June

Angus & Dundee	Balhary Walled Garden, Balhary, Alyth, Blairgowrie
Angus & Dundee	Kirkton Cottage, Aberlemno
East Lothian	A Blackbird Sings, 20 Kings Park, Longniddry
East Lothian	Belhaven House, Edinburgh Road, Belhaven, Dunbar
Perth & Kinross	Muckhart Open Gardens, Coronation Hall, Pool of Muckhart
Roxburghshire	NEW Old Coach House, Hownam, Kelso

Sunday 25 June

Aberdeenshire	Heatherwick Farm, Kintore, Inverurie
Angus & Dundee	NEW Braidestone Farm and The Doocot, by Meigle
Berwickshire	Ruthven House, Coldstream
Caithness, Sutherland, Orkney & Shetland	NEW Finya, Grimeston Road, Harray, Orkney
Caithness, Sutherland, Orkney & Shetland	NEW Westlea, Cromarty Square, St Margaret's Hope, Orkney
Dumfriesshire	Cowhill Tower, Holywood
East Lothian	NEW The Gardens at Archerfield Walled Garden, Archerfield Estate, Dirleton, North Berwick.
East Lothian	Tyninghame House and The Walled Garden, Dunbar
Edinburgh, Midlothian & West Lothian	Stockbridge Gardens,
Fife	Earlshall Castle, Leuchars
Fife	Newburgh – Hidden Gardens, Newburgh
Fife	The Tower, 1 Northview Terrace, Wormit
Inverness, Ross, Cromarty & Skye	House of Aigas and Field Centre, by Beauly
Moray & Nairn	Gordonstoun, Duffus, near Elgin

Moray & Nairn	Haugh Garden, College of Roseisle
Peeblesshire & Tweeddale	Gattonside Village Gardens, Gattonside
Perth & Kinross	Muckhart Open Gardens, Coronation Hall, Pool of Muckhart, Dollar
Renfrewshire	NEW The Bishop's House, Kilmacolm

Tuesday 27 June

East Lothian	Shepherd House, Inveresk, Musselburgh
Lanarkshire	Little Sparta, Stonypath, Dunsyre

Wednesday 28 June

Peeblesshire & Tweeddale	NEW Beechwood, Broughton, Peeblesshire
Peeblesshire & Tweeddale	Kirkton Manor House, Peebles
Peeblesshire & Tweeddale	The Potting Shed, Broughton Place, Broughton, Biggar

Thursday 29 June

East Lothian	Shepherd House, Inveresk, Musselburgh

Friday 30 June

East Lothian	Gullane House, Sandy Loan, Gullane

JULY
. . . .

Saturday 1 July

Angus & Dundee	Angus Plant Sale, Logie Walled Garden, Kirriemuir
Ayrshire & Arran	Underwood Lodge, Craigie, Kilmarnock, South Ayrshire
Caithness, Sutherland, Orkney & Shetland	NEW 16 Mulla, Voe, Shetland
East Lothian	NEW Papple Steading, Papple, Haddington
East Lothian	Eastfield and Redcliff Gardens, Whittingehame
East Lothian	Gullane House, Sandy Loan, Gullane
Moray & Nairn	Cuthberts Brae, 84 Seatown, Buckie
Perth & Kinross	Blair Castle Gardens, Blair Atholl

Sunday 2 July

Aberdeenshire	Bruckhills Croft, Rothienorman, Inverurie
Ayrshire & Arran	Barnweil Garden, Craigie, near Kilmarnock
Caithness, Sutherland, Orkney & Shetland	NEW 16 Mulla, Voe, Shetland
Caithness, Sutherland, Orkney & Shetland	NEW Westlea, Cromarty Square, St Margaret's Hope, Orkney
East Lothian	NEW Papple Steading, Papple, Haddington
East Lothian	Eastfield and Redcliff Gardens, Whittingehame
Edinburgh, Midlothian & West Lothian	Riccarton Mains House, Currie
Glasgow & District	Horatio's Garden, Queen Elizabeth University Hospital
Kirkcudbrightshire	Southwick House, Southwick
Moray & Nairn	Cuthberts Brae, 84 Seatown, Buckie
Peeblesshire & Tweeddale	Glen House, Glen Estate, Innerleithen
Roxburghshire	NEW Old Coach House, Hownam, Kelso
Roxburghshire	Corbet Tower, Morebattle, near Kelso

Tuesday 4 July

Ayrshire & Arran	Dougarie, Isle of Arran
East Lothian	Shepherd House, Inveresk, Musselburgh
Lanarkshire	Little Sparta, Stonypath, Dunsyre

Wednesday 5 July

Peeblesshire & Tweeddale	Kirkton Manor House, Peebles
Peeblesshire & Tweeddale	Portmore, Eddleston
Peeblesshire & Tweeddale	The Potting Shed, Broughton Place, Broughton, Biggar

Thursday 6 July

East Lothian	Shepherd House, Inveresk, Musselburgh

Saturday 8 July

Aberdeenshire	Parkvilla, 47 Schoolhill, Ellon
Angus & Dundee	Hospitalfield Gardens, Hospitalfield House, Westway, Arbroath
Ayrshire & Arran	The Wildings, Bankwood, Galston
Edinburgh, Midlothian & West Lothian	NEW Suntrap Garden, 43 Gogarbank Edinburgh
Fife	Crail: Gardens in the Burgh, Crail

Sunday 9 July

Aberdeenshire	Garden House, 5 Woodlands Gardens, Cults, Aberdeen
Aberdeenshire	Parkvilla, 47 Schoolhill, Ellon
Angus & Dundee	Dunninald Castle, Montrose
Caithness, Sutherland, Orkney & Shetland	NEW Kierfield House, Kierfield House, Sandwick, Orkney
Caithness, Sutherland, Orkney & Shetland	Old Granary Quoy, The Quoy of Houton, Orphir, Orkney
Caithness, Sutherland, Orkney & Shetland	The Quoy of Houton, Orphir, Orkney
Dumfriesshire	Whiteside, Dunscore
East Lothian	Gifford Village and Broadwoodside, Gifford
Edinburgh, Midlothian & West Lothian	NEW Falcon Bowling & Tennis Club, Edinburgh
Edinburgh, Midlothian & West Lothian	NEW Suntrap Garden, 43 Gogarbank Edinburgh
Fife	Crail: Gardens in the Burgh, Crail
Glasgow & District	Strathbungo Garden, March Street, Glasgow
Inverness, Ross, Cromarty & Skye	7 Braes of Conon, Conon Bridge
Kincardine & Deeside	Douneside House, Tarland
Moray & Nairn	Glebe House, Main Street, Urquhart

Tuesday 11 July

East Lothian	Shepherd House, Inveresk, Musselburgh

Wednesday 12 July

Peeblesshire & Tweeddale	Kirkton Manor House, Peebles
Peeblesshire & Tweeddale	Portmore, Eddleston

Thursday 13 July

East Lothian	Shepherd House, Inveresk, Musselburgh

Friday 14 July

Fife	Lucklaw House, Logie, Cupar

Saturday 15 July

Angus & Dundee	Montrose Gardens, Locations across Montrose
Ayrshire & Arran	NEW The Pines, Southwood Road, Troon
Ayrshire & Arran	Whitewin House, Golf Course Road, Girvan
Caithness, Sutherland, Orkney & Shetland	Amat, Amat Lodge, Ardgay
Wigtownshire	Amulree, 8 Mill Street, Drummore, Stranraer

Sunday 16 July

Angus & Dundee	Montrose Gardens, Locations across Montrose
Ayrshire & Arran	NEW The Pines, Southwood Road, Troon
Ayrshire & Arran	Whitewin House, Golf Course Road, Girvan
Berwickshire	NEW The Moorhouse, Duns
Caithness, Sutherland, Orkney & Shetland	NEW 19 Burnside, Kirkwall, Orkney
Caithness, Sutherland, Orkney & Shetland	NEW Annie's Place, Old Manse, Palace Village, Birsay, Orkney
Caithness, Sutherland, Orkney & Shetland	NEW Finya, Grimeston Road, Harray, Orkney
Caithness, Sutherland, Orkney & Shetland	NEW Kierfield House, Kierfield House, Sandwick
Caithness, Sutherland, Orkney & Shetland	NEW Linfirlea, Pipersquoy Road, Kirkwall
Caithness, Sutherland, Orkney & Shetland	NEW Round House, Berstane Road, Kirkwall, Orkney
Caithness, Sutherland, Orkney & Shetland	Amat, Amat Lodge, Ardgay
Edinburgh, Midlothian & West Lothian	NEW Maggie's Edinburgh, Western General Hospital, Crewe Road, Edinburgh
Edinburgh, Midlothian & West Lothian	Claremont, Redmill
Inverness, Ross, Cromarty & Skye	2 Durnamuck, Little Loch Broom, Wester Ross

Inverness, Ross, Cromarty & Skye	Kiltarlity Gardens, Kiltarlity,
Kincardine & Deeside	NEW Hopewell, Tarland
Kirkcudbrightshire	Dalbeattie Community Allotments Association, Port Road, Dalbeattie
Peeblesshire & Tweeddale	Carolside, Earlston
Wigtownshire	Amulree, 8 Mill Street, Drummore, Stranraer

Tuesday 18 July

East Lothian	Shepherd House, Inveresk, Musselburgh

Wednesday 19 July

East Lothian	Humbie Dean, Humbie
Peeblesshire & Tweeddale	Portmore, Eddleston

Thursday 20 July

Angus & Dundee	Inchmill Cottage, Glenprosen, near Kirriemuir
East Lothian	Shepherd House, Inveresk, Musselburgh

Friday 21 July

Aberdeenshire	NEW Two Gardens in Banchory Devenick, Banchory Devenick

Saturday 22 July

Aberdeenshire	NEW Two Gardens in Banchory Devenick, Banchory Devenick
Ayrshire & Arran	Whitewin House, Golf Course Road, Girvan
Caithness, Sutherland, Orkney & Shetland	42 Astle, Dornoch
Caithness, Sutherland, Orkney & Shetland	Skelbo House, Skelbo, Dornoch
Fife	Willowhill, Forgan, Newport-on-Tay
Moray & Nairn	NEW A Trio of Gardens near Rafford, Rafford, Forres

Sunday 23 July

Aberdeenshire	NEW Two Gardens in Banchory Devenick, Banchory Devenick
Ayrshire & Arran	Whitewin House, Golf Course Road, Girvan
Berwickshire	Marlfield, Coldstream
Caithness, Sutherland, Orkney & Shetland	42 Astle, Dornoch
Caithness, Sutherland, Orkney & Shetland	Skelbo House, Skelbo, Dornoch
Edinburgh, Midlothian & West Lothian	14 East Brighton Crescent, Portobello, Edinburgh
Edinburgh, Midlothian & West Lothian	Craigentinny Telferton Allotments, Telferton Road, Edinburgh
Inverness, Ross, Cromarty & Skye	Ar Dachaigh, Redhill Farm, Allanfearn, Inverness
Kirkcudbrightshire	Crofts, Kirkpatrick Durham, Castle Douglas
Peeblesshire & Tweeddale	Kailzie Gardens, Kailzie Gardens
Wigtownshire	Woodfall Gardens, Glasserton

Monday 24 July

Fife	Willowhill, Forgan, Newport-on-Tay

Tuesday 25 July

East Lothian	Shepherd House, Inveresk, Musselburgh

Wednesday 26 July

Peeblesshire & Tweeddale	Portmore, Eddleston

Thursday 27 July

East Lothian	Shepherd House, Inveresk, Musselburgh

Saturday 29 July

Angus & Dundee	Balhary Walled Garden, Balhary, Alyth, Blairgowrie
Angus & Dundee	Kirkton Cottage, Aberlemno
Ayrshire & Arran	NEW Dalhowan Farm, Dalhowan Farm, Crosshill, Maybole
Ayrshire & Arran	Whitewin House, Golf Course Road, Girvan
Caithness, Sutherland, Orkney & Shetland	NEW 11 Lyron, Rendall, Orkney

Saturday 29 July – continued

East Lothian	A Blackbird Sings, 20 Kings Park, Longniddry
Fife	Willowhill, Forgan, Newport-on-Tay
Inverness, Ross, Cromarty & Skye	Dundonnell House, Little Loch Broom, Wester Ross

Sunday 30 July

Angus & Dundee	NEW Edzell Village Gardens, Edzell
Ayrshire & Arran	Whitewin House, Golf Course Road, Girvan
Caithness, Sutherland, Orkney & Shetland	NEW Annie's Place, Old Manse, Palace Village, Birsay, Orkney
Caithness, Sutherland, Orkney & Shetland	NEW Castlehill B&B, Evie, Orkney
Caithness, Sutherland, Orkney & Shetland	Langwell, Berriedale, Caithness
Dumfriesshire	Craigieburn House with Waterside Garden, By Moffat
East Lothian	NEW West Bank, West Bank House, Macmerry, Tranent
Inverness, Ross, Cromarty & Skye	House of Aigas and Field Centre, by Beauly
Kirkcudbrightshire	Kings Grange House, Castle Douglas
Lanarkshire	The Walled Garden, Shieldhill, Quothquan, Biggar
Moray & Nairn	Haugh Garden, College of Roseisle
Peeblesshire & Tweeddale	West Linton Village Gardens, West Linton
Stirlingshire	NEW Killearn Village Gardens, Killearn

Monday 31 July

Fife	Willowhill, Forgan, Newport-on-Tay

AUGUST

Wednesday 2 August

Peeblesshire & Tweeddale	Portmore, Eddleston

Saturday 5 August

Angus & Dundee	Torwood, Milton of Ogilvie, Glenogilvy, Glamis by Forfar
Ayrshire & Arran	Whitewin House, Golf Course Road, Girvan
Caithness, Sutherland, Orkney & Shetland	NEW 11 Lyron, Rendall, Orkney
East Lothian	Greywalls, Gullane
Edinburgh, Midlothian & West Lothian	39 Nantwich Drive, Edinburgh
Fife	Willowhill, Forgan, Newport-on-Tay

Sunday 6 August

Angus & Dundee	Torwood, Milton of Ogilvie, Glenogilvy, Glamis by Forfar
Ayrshire & Arran	Whitewin House, Golf Course Road, Girvan
Dumfriesshire	Dalswinton Mill, Dalswinton
Edinburgh, Midlothian & West Lothian	39 Nantwich Drive, Edinburgh
Edinburgh, Midlothian & West Lothian	Claremont, Redmill
Kincardine & Deeside	Glenbervie House, Drumlithie, Stonehaven
Perth & Kinross	Drummond Castle Gardens, Muthill, Crieff
Roxburghshire	West Leas, Bonchester Bridge
Stirlingshire	60 Greenhead, Alva, Clackmannanshire

Monday 7 August

Fife	Willowhill, Forgan, Newport-on-Tay

Wednesday 9 August

Peeblesshire & Tweeddale	Portmore, Eddleston

Saturday 12 August

Aberdeenshire	Tarland Community Garden, Tarland, Aboyne
Ayrshire & Arran	Netherthird Community Garden, Craigens Road, Netherthird
Ayrshire & Arran	Whitewin House, Golf Course Road, Girvan
Fife	Willowhill, Forgan, Newport-on-Tay

Sunday 13 August

Ayrshire & Arran	Whitewin House, Golf Course Road, Girvan
Caithness, Sutherland, Orkney & Shetland	NEW Linfirlea, Pipersquoy Road, Kirkwall, Orkney
Dumfriesshire	Shawhead, 7 Vendace Drive, Lochmaben
Inverness, Ross, Cromarty & Skye	Old Allangrange, Munlochy
Kirkcudbrightshire	Cally Gardens, Cally Avenue, Gatehouse of Fleet
Perth & Kinross	Cloan, by Auchterarder
Wigtownshire	Fernlea Garden, Corvisel Road, Newton Stewart

Monday 14 August

Fife	Willowhill, Forgan, Newport-on-Tay

Wednesday 16 August

East Lothian	Humbie Dean, Humbie
Peeblesshire & Tweeddale	Portmore, Eddleston

Thursday 17 August

Angus & Dundee	Inchmill Cottage, Glenprosen, near Kirriemuir

Saturday 19 August

Ayrshire & Arran	Whitewin House, Golf Course Road, Girvan
Fife	Willowhill, Forgan, Newport-on-Tay
Inverness, Ross, Cromarty & Skye	2 Durnamuck, Little Loch Broom, Wester Ross

Sunday 20 August

Ayrshire & Arran	Whitewin House, Golf Course Road, Girvan
Caithness, Sutherland, Orkney & Shetland	NEW Annie's Place, Old Manse, Palace Village, Birsay, Orkney
Caithness, Sutherland, Orkney & Shetland	The Garden at the Auld Post Office B&B, Spittal-by-Mybster, Caithness
Peeblesshire & Tweeddale	NEW Macbiehill Gardens, The Walled Garden, Macbiehill
Peeblesshire & Tweeddale	Quercus Garden Plants, Whitmuir Farm, West Linton

Monday 21 August

Fife	Willowhill, Forgan, Newport-on-Tay

Wednesday 23 August

Peeblesshire & Tweeddale	Portmore, Eddleston

Saturday 26 August

Angus & Dundee	Balhary Walled Garden, Balhary, Alyth, Blairgowrie
East Lothian	A Blackbird Sings, 20 Kings Park, Longniddry
Fife	Willowhill, Forgan, Newport-on-Tay

Sunday 27 August

Kincardine & Deeside	Glensaugh, Glensaugh Lodge, Fettercairn, Laurencekirk

Tuesday 29 August

Lanarkshire	Little Sparta, Stonypath, Dunsyre

Wednesday 30 August

Peeblesshire & Tweeddale	Portmore, Eddleston

SEPTEMBER

Saturday 2 September

Dunbartonshire	James Street Community Garden Plant Sale, Helensburgh

Sunday 3 September

Kirkcudbrightshire   3 Millhall, Shore Road, Kirkcudbright

Peeblesshire & Tweeddale   NEW Garvald West Linton Gardens, West Linton

Tuesday 5 September

Lanarkshire   Little Sparta, Stonypath, Dunsyre

Sunday 17 September

Fife   Greenhead Farmhouse, Greenhead of Arnot, Leslie

Thursday 21 September

Angus & Dundee   Inchmill Cottage, Glenprosen, near Kirriemuir

Saturday 30 September

Angus & Dundee   Balhary Walled Garden, Balhary, Alyth, Blairgowrie

OCTOBER
. . . .

Sunday 1 October

Argyll & Lochaber   Benmore Botanic Garden, Benmore, Dunoon

Sunday 8 October

Fife   SGS Autumn Plant Sale at St Andrews Botanic Garden, St Andrews

Peeblesshire & Tweeddale   Dawyck Botanic Garden, Stobo

Saturday 21 October

Angus & Dundee   Westgate, 12 Glamis Drive, Dundee

Sunday 22 October

Angus & Dundee   Westgate, 12 Glamis Drive, Dundee

Index of Gardens

PRE-ORDER YOUR SCOTLAND'S GARDENS SCHEME GUIDEBOOK FOR 2024!

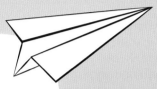

PLEASE SEND ME _____ COPY / COPIES OF THE SGS GUIDEBOOK FOR 2024, PRE-ORDER PRICE £7.50 PLUS £3.00 UK P&P AS SOON AS IT IS AVAILABLE.

I ENCLOSE A CHEQUE / POSTAL ORDER MADE PAYABLE TO SCOTLAND'S GARDENS SCHEME.

NAME

ADDRESS

POSTCODE

Scotland's GARDENS Scheme
OPEN FOR CHARITY

SCOTLAND'S GARDENS SCHEME,
23 CASTLE STREET, EDINBURGH
EH2 3DN

COPIES OF OUR GUIDEBOOK MAY ALSO BE PURCHASED ON OUR WEBSITE: SCOTLANDSGARDENS.ORG

Will you make a small £5.00 donation today?

By donating to Scotland's Gardens Scheme you will make an instant difference because it will help us to continue and improve our volunteer support and develop our garden opening programme for all to enjoy.
Please donate on our website: scotlandsgardens.org/donate/ or scan the QR code below.

image © Evie Shaffer, Pexels